CW00385819

MYTHS AND LEGENDS OF ANCIENT GREECE AND ROME

E. M. Berens

COLLINS
CLASSICS

William Collins
An imprint of HarperCollinsPublishers
1 London Bridge Street
London
SE1 9GF

WilliamCollinsBooks.com

This William Collins paperback edition published in Great Britain in 2016

4

A catalogue record for this book
is available from the British Library

ISBN 978–0–00–818055–3

Typeset in Kalix 11/14 pt by Palimpsest Book Production Limited,
Falkirk, Stirlingshire

Printed and bound in Great Britain by
CPI Group (UK) Ltd, Croydon CR0 4YY

MIX
Paper from
responsible sources
FSC® C007454

FSC™ is a non-profit international organisation established to promote
the responsible management of the world's forests. Products carrying the
FSC label are independently certified to assure consumers that they come
from forests that are managed to meet the social, economic and
ecological needs of present and future generations,
and other controlled sources.

Find out more about HarperCollins and the environment at
www.harpercollins.co.uk/green

Life & Times section © HarperCollinsPublishers Ltd
Silvia Crompton asserts her moral rights as author of the Life & Times section
Classic Literature: Words and Phrases adapted from
Collins English Dictionary

All rights reserved. No part of this publication may be
reproduced, stored in a retrieval system, or transmitted,
in any form or by any means, electronic, mechanical,
photocopying, recording or otherwise, without the
prior permission of the publishers.

This book is sold subject to the condition that it shall not,
by way of trade or otherwise, be lent, re-sold, hired out or otherwise
circulated without the publisher's prior consent in any form of
binding or cover other than that in which it is published and
without a similar condition including this condition being
imposed on the subsequent purchaser.

History of William Collins

In 1819, millworker William Collins from Glasgow, Scotland, set up a company for printing and publishing pamphlets, sermons, hymn books and prayer books. That company was Collins and was to mark the birth of HarperCollins Publishers as we know it today. The long tradition of Collins dictionary publishing can be traced back to the first dictionary William co-published in 1825, *Greek and English Lexicon*. Indeed, from 1840 onwards, he began to produce illustrated dictionaries and even obtained a licence to print and publish the Bible.

Soon after, William published the first Collins novel; however, it was the time of the Long Depression, where harvests were poor, prices were high, potato crops had failed and violence was erupting in Europe. As a result, many factories across the country were forced to close down and William chose to retire in 1846, partly due to the hardships he was facing.

Aged 30, William's son, William II, took over the business. A keen humanitarian with a warm heart and a generous spirit, William II was truly "Victorian" in his outlook. He introduced new, up-to-date steam presses and published affordable editions of Shakespeare's works and *The Pilgrim's Progress*, making them available to the masses for the first time.

A new demand for educational books meant that success came with the publication of travel books, scientific books, encyclopedias and dictionaries. This demand to be educated led to the later publication of atlases, and Collins also held the monopoly on scripture writing at the time.

In the 1860s Collins began to expand and diversify

and the idea of "books for the millions" was developed, although the phrase wasn't coined until 1907. Affordable editions of classical literature were published, and in 1903 Collins introduced 10 titles in their Collins Handy Illustrated Pocket Novels. These proved so popular that a few years later this had increased to an output of 50 volumes, selling nearly half a million in their year of publication. In the same year, The Everyman's Library was also instituted, with the idea of publishing an affordable library of the most important classical works, biographies, religious and philosophical treatments, plays, poems, travel and adventure. This series eclipsed all competition at the time, and the introduction of paperback books in the 1950s helped to open that market and marked a high point in the industry.

HarperCollins is and has always been a champion of the classics, and the current Collins Classics series follows in this tradition – publishing classical literature that is affordable and available to all. Beautifully packaged, highly collectible, and intended to be reread and enjoyed at every opportunity.

MYTHS AND LEGENDS OF ANCIENT GREECE AND ROME

Preface.

The want of an interesting work on Greek and Roman mythology, suitable for the requirements of both boys and girls, has long been recognized by the principals of our advanced schools. The study of the classics themselves, even where the attainments of the pupil have rendered this feasible, has not been found altogether successful in giving to the student a clear and succinct idea of the religious beliefs of the ancients, and it has been suggested that a work which would so deal with the subject as to render it at once interesting and instructive would be hailed as a valuable introduction to the study of classic authors, and would be found to assist materially the labours of both master and pupil.

In endeavouring to supply this want I have sought to place before the reader a lifelike picture of the deities of classical times as they were conceived and worshipped by the ancients themselves, and thereby to awaken in the minds of young students a desire to become more intimately acquainted with the noble productions of classical antiquity.

It has been my aim to render the Legends, which form the second portion of the work, a picture, as it were, of old Greek life; its customs, its superstitions, and its princely hospitalities, for which reason they are given at somewhat greater length than is usual in works of the kind.

In a chapter devoted to the purpose some interesting particulars have been collected respecting the public worship of the ancient Greeks and Romans (more especially of the former), to which is subjoined an account of their principal festivals.

I may add that no pains have been spared in order that, without passing over details the omission of which would have marred the completeness of the work, not a single passage should be found which could possibly offend the most scrupulous delicacy; and also that I have purposely treated the subject with that reverence which I consider due to every religious system, however erroneous.

It is hardly necessary to dwell upon the importance of the study of Mythology: our poems, our novels, and even our daily journals teem with classical allusions; nor can a visit to our art galleries and museums be fully enjoyed without something more than a mere superficial knowledge of a subject which has in all ages inspired painters, sculptors, and poets. It therefore only remains for me to express a hope that my little work may prove useful, not only to teachers and scholars, but also to a large class of general readers, who, in whiling away a leisure hour, may derive some pleasure and profit from its perusal.

E. M. BERENS.
1880.

CONTENTS.

PART I.—MYTHS.

Introduction   3

FIRST DYNASTY.
ORIGIN OF THE WORLD—
URANUS AND GÆA (Cœlus and Terra)   7

SECOND DYNASTY.
CRONUS (Saturn)   11
RHEA (Ops)   14
DIVISION OF THE WORLD   15
THEORIES AS TO THE ORIGIN OF MAN   17

THIRD DYNASTY.
OLYMPIAN DIVINITIES—
ZEUS (Jupiter)   22
HERA (Juno)   34
PALLAS-ATHENE (Minerva)   38

THEMIS   42
HESTIA (Vesta)   43
DEMETER (Ceres)   45
APHRODITE (Venus)   52
HELIOS (Sol)   55
EOS (Aurora)   61
PHŒBUS-APOLLO   62
HECATE   78
SELENE (Luna)   79
ARTEMIS (Diana)   80
HEPHÆSTUS (Vulcan)   90
POSEIDON (Neptune)   93

SEA DIVINITIES—
OCEANUS   100
NEREUS   100
PROTEUS   101
TRITON AND THE TRITONS   101
GLAUCUS   102
THETIS   102
THAUMAS, PHORCYS, AND CETO   103
LEUCOTHEA   104
THE SIRENS   104
ARES (Mars)   104
NIKE (Victoria)   109
HERMES (Mercury)   110

DIONYSUS (Bacchus or Liber)   116
AÏDES (Pluto)   122
PLUTUS   128

MINOR DIVINITIES—

THE HARPIES,   129
ERINYES, EUMENIDES (Furiæ, Diræ),   130
MOIRÆ OR FATES (Parcæ),   131
NEMESIS,   132
NIGHT AND HER CHILDREN—
   NYX (Nox),   134
   THANATOS (Mors), HYPNUS (Somnus),   134
   MORPHEUS,   135
THE GORGONS,   136
GRÆÆ,   137
SPHINX,   138
TYCHE (Fortuna) and ANANKE (Necessitas),   139
KER,   140
ATE,   141
MOMUS,   141
EROS (Cupid, Amor) and PSYCHE,   142
HYMEN,   146
IRIS,   147
HEBE (Juventas),   147
GANYMEDES,   148
THE MUSES,   148

PEGASUS,	151
THE HESPERIDES,	152
CHARITES OR GRACES,	153
HORÆ (Seasons),	154
THE NYMPHS,	155
WATER NYMPHS,	155
DRYADES, OR TREE NYMPHS,	158
NYMPHS OF THE VALLEYS AND MOUNTAINS,	158
THE WINDS,	160
PAN (Faunus),	161
THE SATYRS,	164
PRIAPUS,	165
ASCLEPIAS (Æsculapius),	166

ROMAN DIVINITIES—
JANUS,	168
FLORA,	170
ROBIGUS,	170
POMONA,	171
VERTUMNUS,	171
PALES,	171
PICUS,	172
PICUMNUS AND PILUMNUS,	172
SILVANUS,	172
TERMINUS,	173
CONSUS,	173

LIBITINA,   174
LAVERNA,   174
COMUS,   174
CAMENÆ,   174
GENII,   175
MANES,   176
PENATES,   177

PUBLIC WORSHIP OF THE ANCIENT GREEKS
AND ROMANS—
TEMPLES,   178
STATUES,   180
ALTARS,   181
PRIESTS,   181
SACRIFICES,   182
ORACLES,   184
SOOTHSAYERS (Augurs),   185
FESTIVALS,   186

GREEK FESTIVALS—
ELEUSINIAN MYSTERIES,   187
THESMOPHORIA,   188
DIONYSIA,   188
PANATHENÆA,   189
DAPHNEPHORIA,   190

ROMAN FESTIVALS—

SATURNALIA,   191
CEREALIA,   192
VESTALIA,   192

PART II.—LEGENDS.

CADMUS,   195
PERSEUS,   197
ION,   202
DÆDALUS AND ICARUS,   204
THE ARGONAUTS,   205
PELOPS,   224
HERACLES,   226
BELLEROPHON,   248
THESEUS,   250
ŒDIPUS,   260
THE SEVEN AGAINST THEBES,   263
THE EPIGONI,   267
ALCMÆON AND THE NECKLACE,   268
THE HERACLIDÆ,   271
THE SIEGE OF TROY,   275
RETURN OF THE GREEKS FROM TROY,   295

NOTES   315
CLASSIC LITERATURE: WORDS AND PHRASES   319

PART I.
—MYTHS.

INTRODUCTION.

Before entering upon the many strange beliefs of the ancient Greeks, and the extraordinary number of gods they worshipped, we must first consider what kind of beings these divinities were.

In appearance, the gods were supposed to resemble mortals, whom, however, they far surpassed in beauty, grandeur, and strength; they were also more commanding in stature, height being considered by the Greeks an attribute of beauty in man or woman. They resembled human beings in their feelings and habits, intermarrying and having children, and requiring daily nourishment to recruit their strength, and refreshing sleep to restore their energies. Their blood, a bright ethereal fluid called Ichor, never engendered disease, and, when shed, had the power of producing new life.

The Greeks believed that the mental qualifications of their gods were of a much higher order than those of men, but nevertheless, as we shall see, they were not considered to be exempt from human passions, and we frequently behold them actuated by revenge, deceit, and jealousy. They, however, always punish the evil-doer, and visit with dire calamities any impious mortal who dares to neglect their worship or despise their rites. We often hear of them visiting mankind and partaking of their hospitality, and not unfrequently both gods

3

and goddesses become attached to mortals, with whom they unite themselves, the offspring of these unions being called heroes or demi-gods, who were usually renowned for their great strength and courage. But although there were so many points of resemblance between gods and men, there remained the one great characteristic distinction, viz., that the gods enjoyed immortality. Still, they were not invulnerable, and we often hear of them being wounded, and suffering in consequence such exquisite torture that they have earnestly prayed to be deprived of their privilege of immortality.

The gods knew no limitation of time or space, being able to transport themselves to incredible distances with the speed of thought. They possessed the power of rendering themselves invisible at will, and could assume the forms of men or animals as it suited their convenience. They could also transform human beings into trees, stones, animals, &c., either as a punishment for their misdeeds, or as a means of protecting the individual, thus transformed, from impending danger. Their robes were like those worn by mortals, but were perfect in form and much finer in texture. Their weapons also resembled those used by mankind; we hear of spears, shields, helmets, bows and arrows, &c., being employed by the gods. Each deity possessed a beautiful chariot, which, drawn by horses or other animals of celestial breed, conveyed them rapidly over land and sea according to their pleasure. Most of these divinities lived on the summit of Mount Olympus, each possessing his or her individual habitation, and all meeting together on festive occasions in the council-chamber of the gods, where their banquets were enlivened by the sweet strains of Apollo's lyre, whilst the beautiful voices of the Muses poured forth their rich melodies to his harmonious accompaniment. Magnificent temples were erected to their honour, where they were worshipped with the greatest solemnity; rich gifts were presented to them, and animals, and indeed sometimes human beings, were sacrificed on their altars.

In the study of Grecian mythology we meet with some

curious, and what may at first sight appear unaccountable notions. Thus we hear of terrible giants hurling rocks, upheaving mountains, and raising earthquakes which engulf whole armies; these ideas, however, may be accounted for by the awful convulsions of nature, which were in operation in pre-historic times. Again, the daily recurring phenomena, which to us, who know them to be the result of certain well-ascertained laws of nature, are so familiar as to excite no remark, were, to the early Greeks, matter of grave speculation, and not unfrequently of alarm. For instance, when they heard the awful roar of thunder, and saw vivid flashes of lightning, accompanied by black clouds and torrents of rain, they believed that the great god of heaven was angry, and they trembled at his wrath. If the calm and tranquil sea became suddenly agitated, and the crested billows rose mountains high, dashing furiously against the rocks, and threatening destruction to all within their reach, the sea-god was supposed to be in a furious rage. When they beheld the sky glowing with the hues of coming day they thought that the goddess of the dawn, with rosy fingers, was drawing aside the dark veil of night, to allow her brother, the sun-god, to enter upon his brilliant career. Thus personifying all the powers of nature, this very imaginative and highly poetical nation beheld a divinity in every tree that grew, in every stream that flowed, in the bright beams of the glorious sun, and the clear, cold rays of the silvery moon; for them the whole universe lived and breathed, peopled by a thousand forms of grace and beauty.

The most important of these divinities may have been something more than the mere creations of an active and poetical imagination. They were possibly human beings who had so distinguished themselves in life by their preeminence over their fellow-mortals that after death they were deified by the people among whom they lived, and the poets touched with their magic wand the details of lives, which, in more prosaic times, would simply have been recorded as illustrious.

It is highly probable that the reputed actions of these

deified beings were commemorated by bards, who, travelling from one state to another, celebrated their praise in song; it therefore becomes exceedingly difficult, nay almost impossible, to separate bare facts from the exaggerations which never fail to accompany oral traditions.

In order to exemplify this, let us suppose that Orpheus, the son of Apollo, so renowned for his extraordinary musical powers, had existed at the present day. We should no doubt have ranked him among the greatest of our musicians, and honoured him as such; but the Greeks, with their vivid imagination and poetic licence, exaggerated his remarkable gifts, and attributed to his music supernatural influence over animate and inanimate nature. Thus we hear of wild beasts tamed, of mighty rivers arrested in their course, and of mountains being moved by the sweet tones of his voice. The theory here advanced may possibly prove useful in the future, in suggesting to the reader the probable basis of many of the extraordinary accounts we meet with in the study of classical mythology.

And now a few words will be necessary concerning the religious beliefs of the Romans. When the Greeks first settled in Italy they found in the country they colonized a mythology belonging to the Celtic inhabitants, which, according to the Greek custom of paying reverence to all gods, known or unknown, they readily adopted, selecting and appropriating those divinities which had the greatest affinity to their own, and thus they formed a religious belief which naturally bore the impress of its ancient Greek source. As the primitive Celts, however, were a less civilized people than the Greeks, their mythology was of a more barbarous character, and this circumstance, combined with the fact that the Romans were not gifted with the vivid imagination of their Greek neighbours, leaves its mark on the Roman mythology, which is far less fertile in fanciful conceits, and deficient in all those fairy-like stories and wonderfully poetic ideas which so strongly characterize that of the Greeks.

FIRST DYNASTY.

ORIGIN OF THE WORLD—

URANUS AND GÆA. (CŒLUS AND TERRA.)

The ancient Greeks had several different theories with regard to the origin of the world, but the generally accepted notion was that before this world came into existence, there was in its place a confused mass of shapeless elements called Chaos. These elements becoming at length consolidated (by what means does not appear), resolved themselves into two widely different substances, the lighter portion of which, soaring on high, formed the sky or firmament, and constituted itself into a vast, overarching vault, which protected the firm and solid mass beneath.

Thus came into being the two first great primeval deities of the Greeks, Uranus and Ge or Gæa.

Uranus, the more refined deity, represented the light and air of heaven, possessing the distinguishing qualities of light, heat, purity, and omnipresence, whilst Gæa, the firm, flat,[1] life-sustaining earth, was worshipped as the great all-nourishing mother. Her many titles refer to her more or less in this character, and she appears to have been universally revered among the Greeks, there being scarcely a city in Greece which did not contain a temple erected in her honour;

indeed Gæa was held in such veneration that her name was always invoked whenever the gods took a solemn oath, made an emphatic declaration, or implored assistance.

Uranus, the heaven, was believed to have united himself in marriage with Gæa, the earth; and a moment's reflection will show what a truly poetical, and also what a logical idea this was; for, taken in a figurative sense, this union actually does exist. The smiles of heaven produce the flowers of earth, whereas his long-continued frowns exercise so depressing an influence upon his loving partner, that she no longer decks herself in bright and festive robes, but responds with ready sympathy to his melancholy mood.

The first-born child of Uranus and Gæa was Oceanus,[2] the ocean stream, that vast expanse of ever-flowing water which encircled the earth. Here we meet with another logical though fanciful conclusion, which a very slight knowledge of the workings of nature proves to have been just and true. The ocean is formed from the rains which descend from heaven and the streams which flow from earth. By making Oceanus therefore the offspring of Uranus and Gæa, the ancients, if we take this notion in its literal sense, merely assert that the ocean is produced by the combined influence of heaven and earth, whilst at the same time their fervid and poetical imagination led them to see in this, as in all manifestations of the powers of nature, an actual, tangible divinity.

But Uranus, the heaven, the embodiment of light, heat, and the breath of life, produced offspring who were of a much less material nature than his son Oceanus. These other children of his were supposed to occupy the intermediate space which divided him from Gæa. Nearest to Uranus, and just beneath him, came Aether (Ether), a bright creation representing that highly rarified atmosphere which immortals alone could breathe. Then followed Aër (Air), which was in close proximity to Gæa, and represented, as its name implies, the grosser atmosphere surrounding the earth which mortals could freely breathe, and without which they would perish. Aether and Aër were separated from each other by divinities called Nephelae. These were their restless and wandering sisters, who existed in the form of clouds, ever floating between Aether and Aër. Gæa also produced the mountains, and Pontus (the sea). She united herself with the latter, and their offspring were the sea-deities Nereus, Thaumas, Phorcys, Ceto, and Eurybia.

Co-existent with Uranus and Gæa were two mighty powers who were also the offspring of Chaos. These were Erebus (Darkness) and Nyx (Night), who formed a striking contrast to the cheerful light of heaven and the bright smiles of earth. Erebus reigned in that mysterious world below where no ray of sunshine, no gleam of daylight, nor vestige of health-giving terrestrial life ever appeared. Nyx, the sister of Erebus, represented Night, and was worshipped by the ancients with the greatest solemnity.

Uranus was also supposed to have been united to Nyx, but only in his capacity as god of light, he being considered the source and fountain of all light, and their children were Eos (Aurora), the Dawn, and Hemera, the Daylight. Nyx again, on her side was also doubly united, having been married at some indefinite period to Erebus.

In addition to those children of heaven and earth already enumerated, Uranus and Gæa produced two distinctly different races of beings called Giants and Titans. The Giants personified brute strength alone, but the Titans united to their great physical power intellectual qualifications variously developed. There were three Giants, Briareus, Cottus, and Gyges, who each possessed a hundred hands and fifty heads, and were known collectively by the name of the Hecatoncheires, which signified hundred-handed. These mighty Giants could shake the universe and produce earthquakes; it is therefore evident that they represented those active subterranean forces to which allusion has been made in the opening chapter. The

Titans were twelve in number; their names were: Oceanus, Ceos, Crios, Hyperion, Iapetus, Cronus, Theia, Rhea, Themis, Mnemosyne, Phœbe, and Tethys.

Now Uranus, the chaste light of heaven, the essence of all that is bright and pleasing, held in abhorrence his crude, rough, and turbulent offspring, the Giants, and moreover feared that their great power might eventually prove hurtful to himself. He therefore hurled them into Tartarus, that portion of the lower world which served as the subterranean dungeon of the gods. In order to avenge the oppression of her children, the Giants, Gæa instigated a conspiracy on the part of the Titans against Uranus, which was carried to a successful issue by her son Cronus. He wounded his father, and from the blood of the wound which fell upon the earth sprang a race of monstrous beings also called Giants. Assisted by his brother-Titans, Cronus succeeded in dethroning his father, who, enraged at his defeat, cursed his rebellious son, and foretold to him a similar fate. Cronus now became invested with supreme power, and assigned to his brothers offices of distinction, subordinate only to himself. Subsequently, however, when, secure of his position, he no longer needed their assistance, he basely repaid their former services with treachery, made war upon his brothers and faithful allies, and, assisted by the Giants, completely defeated them, sending such as resisted his all-conquering arm down into the lowest depths of Tartarus.

SECOND DYNASTY.

CRONUS (Saturn).

Cronus was the god of time in its sense of eternal duration. He married Rhea, daughter of Uranus and Gæa, a very important divinity, to whom a special chapter will be devoted hereafter. Their children were, three sons: Aïdes (Pluto), Poseidon (Neptune), Zeus (Jupiter), and three daughters: Hestia (Vesta), Demeter (Ceres), and Hera (Juno). Cronus, having an uneasy conscience, was afraid that his children might one day rise up against his authority, and thus verify the prediction of his father Uranus. In order, therefore, to render the prophecy impossible of fulfilment, Cronus swallowed each child as soon as it was born,[3] greatly to the sorrow and indignation of his wife Rhea. When it came to Zeus, the sixth and last, Rhea resolved to try and save this one child at least, to love and cherish, and appealed to her parents, Uranus and Gæa, for counsel and assistance. By their advice she wrapped a stone in baby-clothes, and Cronus, in eager haste, swallowed it, without noticing the deception. The child thus saved, eventually, as we shall see, dethroned his father Cronus, became supreme god in his stead, and was universally venerated as the great national god of the Greeks.

Anxious to preserve the secret of his existence from

Cronus, Rhea sent the infant Zeus secretly to Crete, where he was nourished, protected, and educated. A sacred goat, called Amalthea, supplied the place of his mother, by providing him with milk; nymphs, called Melissae, fed him with honey, and eagles and doves brought him nectar and ambrosia.[4] He was kept concealed in a cave in the heart of Mount Ida, and the Curetes, or priests of Rhea, by beating their shields together, kept up a constant noise at the entrance, which drowned the cries of the child and frightened away all intruders. Under the watchful care of the Nymphs the infant Zeus throve rapidly, developing great physical powers, combined with extraordinary wisdom and intelligence. Grown to manhood, he determined to compel his father to restore his brothers and sisters to the light of day, and is said to have been assisted in this difficult task by the goddess Metis, who artfully persuaded Cronus to drink a potion, which caused him to give back the children he had swallowed. The stone which had counterfeited Zeus was placed at Delphi, where it was long exhibited as a sacred relic.

Cronus was so enraged at being circumvented that war between the father and son became inevitable. The rival forces ranged themselves on two separate high mountains in Thessaly; Zeus, with his brothers and sisters, took his stand on Mount Olympus, where he was joined by Oceanus, and others of the Titans, who had forsaken Cronus on account of his oppressions. Cronus and his brother-Titans took possession of Mount Othrys, and prepared for battle. The struggle was long and fierce, and at length Zeus, finding that he was no nearer victory than before, bethought himself of the existence of the imprisoned Giants, and knowing that they would be able to render him most powerful assistance, he hastened to liberate them. He also called to his aid the Cyclops (sons of Poseidon and Amphitrite),[5] who had only one eye each in the middle of their foreheads, and were called Brontes (Thunder), Steropes (Lightning), and Pyracmon (Fire-anvil). They promptly responded to his summons for help, and brought with them tremendous thunderbolts which the Hecatoncheires, with their hundred hands, hurled down upon the enemy, at the same time raising mighty earthquakes, which swallowed up and destroyed all who opposed them. Aided by these new and powerful allies, Zeus now made a furious onslaught on his enemies, and so tremendous was the encounter that all nature is said to have throbbed in accord with this mighty effort of the celestial deities. The sea rose mountains high, and its angry billows hissed and foamed; the earth shook to its foundations, the heavens sent forth rolling thunder, and flash after flash of death-bringing lightning, whilst a blinding mist enveloped Cronus and his allies.

And now the fortunes of war began to turn, and victory smiled on Zeus. Cronus and his army were completely overthrown, his brothers despatched to the gloomy depths of the lower world, and Cronus himself was banished from his kingdom and deprived for ever of the supreme power, which now became vested in his son Zeus. This war was called the Titanomachia, and is most graphically described by the old classic poets.

With the defeat of Cronus and his banishment from his dominions, his career as a ruling Greek divinity entirely ceases. But being, like all the gods, immortal, he was supposed to be still in existence, though possessing no longer either influence or authority, his place being filled to a certain extent by his descendant and successor, Zeus.

Cronus is often represented as an old man leaning on a scythe, with an hour-glass in his hand. The hour-glass symbolizes the fast-fleeting moments as they succeed each other unceasingly; the scythe is emblematical of time, which mows down all before it.

SATURN.

The Romans, according to their custom of identifying their deities with those of the Greek gods whose attributes were similar to their own, declared Cronus to be identical with their old agricultural divinity Saturn. They believed that after his defeat in the Titanomachia and his banishment from his dominions by Zeus, he took refuge with Janus, king of Italy, who received the exiled deity with great kindness, and even shared his throne with him. Their united reign became so thoroughly peaceful and happy, and was distinguished by such uninterrupted prosperity, that it was called the Golden Age.

Saturn is usually represented bearing a sickle in the one hand and a wheat-sheaf in the other.

A temple was erected to him at the foot of the Capitoline Hill, in which were deposited the public treasury and the laws of the state.

RHEA (Ops).

Rhea, the wife of Cronus, and mother of Zeus and the other great gods of Olympus, personified the earth, and was regarded as the Great Mother and unceasing producer of all plant-life. She was also believed to exercise unbounded sway over the animal creation, more especially over the lion, the noble king of beasts. Rhea is generally represented wearing a crown of turrets or towers and seated on a throne, with lions crouching at her feet. She is sometimes depicted sitting in a chariot, drawn by lions.

The principal seat of her worship, which was always of a very riotous character, was at Crete. At her festivals, which took place at night, the wildest music of flutes, cymbals, and drums resounded, whilst joyful shouts and cries, accompanied by dancing and loud stamping of feet, filled the air.

This divinity was introduced into Crete by its first colonists from Phrygia, in Asia Minor, in which country she was worshipped under the name of Cybele. The people of Crete adored her as the Great Mother, more especially in her signification as the sustainer of the vegetable world. Seeing, however, that year by year, as winter appears, all her glory vanishes, her flowers fade, and her trees become leafless, they poetically expressed this process of nature under the figure of a lost love. She was said to have been tenderly attached to a youth of remarkable beauty, named Atys, who, to her grief and indignation, proved faithless to her. He was about to unite himself to a nymph called Sagaris, when, in the midst of the wedding feast, the rage of the incensed goddess suddenly burst forth upon all present. A panic seized the assembled guests, and Atys, becoming afflicted with temporary madness, fled to the mountains and destroyed himself. Cybele, moved with sorrow and regret, instituted a yearly mourning for his loss, when her priests, the Corybantes, with their usual noisy accompaniments, marched into the mountains to seek the lost youth. Having discovered him[6] they gave full vent to their ecstatic delight by indulging in the most violent gesticulations, dancing, shouting, and, at the same time, wounding and gashing themselves in a frightful manner.

OPS.

In Rome the Greek Rhea was identified with Ops, the goddess of plenty, the wife of Saturn, who had a variety of appellations. She was called Magna-Mater, Mater-Deorum, Berecynthia-Idea, and also Dindymene. This latter title she acquired from three high mountains in Phrygia, whence she was brought to Rome as Cybele during the second Punic war, B.C. 205, in obedience to an injunction contained in the Sybilline books. She was represented as a matron crowned with towers, seated in a chariot drawn by lions.

DIVISION OF THE WORLD.

We will now return to Zeus and his brothers, who, having gained a complete victory over their enemies, began to consider how the world, which they had conquered, should

15

be divided between them. At last it was settled by lot that Zeus should reign supreme in Heaven, whilst Aïdes governed the Lower World, and Poseidon had full command over the Sea, but the supremacy of Zeus was recognized in all three kingdoms, in heaven, on earth (in which of course the sea was included), and under the earth. Zeus held his court on the top of Mount Olympus, whose summit was beyond the clouds; the dominions of Aïdes were the gloomy unknown regions below the earth; and Poseidon reigned over the sea. It will be seen that the realm of each of these gods was enveloped in mystery. Olympus was shrouded in mists, Hades was wrapt in gloomy darkness, and the sea was, and indeed still is, a source of wonder and deep interest. Hence we see that what to other nations were merely strange phenomena, served this poetical and imaginative people as a foundation upon which to build the wonderful stories of their mythology.

The division of the world being now satisfactorily arranged, it would seem that all things ought to have gone on smoothly, but such was not the case. Trouble arose in an unlooked-for quarter. The Giants, those hideous monsters (some with legs formed of serpents) who had sprung from the earth and the blood of Uranus, declared war against the triumphant deities of Olympus, and a struggle ensued, which, in consequence of Gæa having made these children of hers invincible as long as they kept their feet on the ground, was wearisome and protracted. Their mother's precaution, however, was rendered unavailing by pieces of rock being hurled upon them, which threw them down, and their feet being no longer placed firmly on their mother-earth, they were overcome, and this tedious war (which was called the Gigantomachia) at last came to an end. Among the most daring of these earth-born giants were Enceladus, Rhœtus, and the valiant Mimas, who, with youthful fire and energy, hurled against heaven great masses of rock and burning oak-trees, and defied the lightnings of Zeus. One of the most powerful monsters who opposed Zeus in this war was called Typhon or Typhœus. He was the youngest son of Tartarus and Gæa, and had a hundred heads, with eyes which struck terror to the beholders, and awe-inspiring voices frightful to hear. This dreadful monster resolved to conquer both gods and men, but his plans were at length defeated by Zeus, who, after a violent encounter, succeeded in destroying him with a thunderbolt, but not before he had so terrified the gods that they had fled for refuge to Egypt, where they metamorphosed themselves into different animals and thus escaped.

THEORIES AS TO THE ORIGIN OF MAN.

Just as there were several theories concerning the origin of the world, so there were various accounts of the creation of man.

The first natural belief of the Greek people was that man had sprung from the earth. They saw the tender plants and flowers force their way through the ground in the early spring of the year after the frost of winter had disappeared, and so they naturally concluded that man must also have issued from the earth in a similar manner. Like the wild plants and flowers, he was supposed to have had no cultivation, and resembled in his habits the untamed beasts of the field, having no habitation except that which nature had provided in the holes of the rocks, and in the dense forests whose overarching boughs protected him from the inclemency of the weather.

In the course of time these primitive human beings became tamed and civilized by the gods and heroes, who taught them to work in metals, to build houses, and other useful arts of civilization. But the human race became in the course of time so degenerate that the gods resolved to destroy all mankind by means of a flood; Deucalion (son of Prometheus) and his wife Pyrrha, being, on account of their piety, the only mortals saved.

By the command of his father, Deucalion built a ship, in which he and his wife took refuge during the deluge, which lasted for nine days. When the waters abated the ship rested on Mount Othrys in Thessaly, or according to some on Mount Parnassus. Deucalion and his wife now consulted the oracle of Themis as to how the human race might be restored. The answer was, that they were to cover their heads, and throw the bones of their mother behind them. For some time they were perplexed as to the meaning of the oracular command, but at length both agreed that by the bones of their mother were meant the stones of the earth. They accordingly took up stones from the mountain side and cast them over their shoulders. From those thrown by Deucalion there sprang up men, and from those thrown by Pyrrha, women.

After the lapse of time the theory of Autochthony (from *autos*, self, and *chthon*, earth) was laid aside. When this belief existed there were no religious teachers whatever; but in course of time temples were raised in honour of the different gods, and priests appointed to offer sacrifices to them and conduct their worship. These priests were looked upon as authorities in all religious matters, and the doctrine they taught was, that man had been created by the gods, and that there had been several successive ages of men, which were called the Golden, Silver, Brazen, and Iron Ages.

Life in the Golden Age was one unceasing round of ever-recurring pleasures unmarred by sorrow or care. The favoured mortals living at this happy time led pure and joyous lives, thinking no evil, and doing no wrong. The earth brought forth fruits and flowers without toil or labour in plentiful luxuriance, and war was unknown. This delightful and god-like existence lasted for hundreds of years, and when at length life on earth was ended, death laid his hand so gently upon them that they passed painlessly away in a happy dream, and continued their existence as ministering spirits in Hades, watching over and protecting those they had loved and left behind on earth. The men of the Silver Age[7] were a long time growing up, and during their childhood, which lasted a hundred years, they suffered from ill-health and extreme debility. When they at last became men they lived but a short time, for they would not abstain from mutual injury, nor pay the service due to the gods, and were therefore banished to Hades. There, unlike the beings of the Golden Age, they exercised no beneficent supervision over the dear ones left behind, but wandered about as restless spirits, always sighing for the lost pleasures they had enjoyed in life.

The men of the Brazen Age were quite a different race of beings, being as strong and powerful as those of the Silver Age were weak and enervated. Everything which surrounded them was of brass; their arms, their tools, their dwellings, and all that they made. Their characters seem to have resembled the metal in which they delighted; their minds and hearts were hard, obdurate, and cruel. They led a life of strife and contention, introduced into the world, which had hitherto known nothing but peace and tranquillity, the scourge of war, and were in fact only happy when fighting and quarrelling with each other. Hitherto Themis, the goddess of Justice, had been living among mankind, but becoming disheartened at their evil doings, she abandoned the earth, and winged her flight back to heaven. At last the gods became so tired of their evil deeds and continual dissensions, that they removed them from the face of the earth, and sent them down to Hades to share the fate of their predecessors.

We now come to the men of the Iron Age. The earth, no longer teeming with fruitfulness, only yielded her increase after much toil and labour. The goddess of Justice having abandoned mankind, no influence remained sufficiently powerful to preserve them from every kind of wickedness and sin. This condition grew worse as time went on, until at last Zeus in his anger let loose the water-courses from above, and drowned every individual of this evil race, except Deucalion and Pyrrha.

The theory of Hesiod,[8] the oldest of all the Greek poets, was that the Titan Prometheus, the son of Iapetus, had formed man out of clay, and that Athene had breathed a soul into him. Full of love for the beings he had called into existence, Prometheus determined to elevate their minds and improve their condition in every way; he therefore taught them astronomy, mathematics, the alphabet, how to cure diseases, and the art of divination. He created this race in such great numbers that the gods began to see the necessity of instituting certain fixed laws with regard to the sacrifices due to them, and the worship to which they considered themselves entitled from mankind in return for the protection which they accorded them. An assembly was therefore convened at Mecone in order to settle these points. It was decided that Prometheus, as the advocate of man, should slay an ox, which should be divided into two equal parts, and that the gods should select one portion which should henceforth, in all future sacrifices, be set apart for them. Prometheus so divided the ox that one part consisted of the bones (which formed of course the least valuable portion of the animal), artfully concealed by the white fat; whilst the other contained all the edible parts, which he covered with the skin, and on the top of all he laid the stomach.

Zeus, pretending to be deceived, chose the heap of bones, but he saw through the stratagem, and was so angry at the deception practised on him by Prometheus that he avenged himself by refusing to mortals the gift of fire. Prometheus, however, resolved to brave the anger of the great ruler of Olympus, and to obtain from heaven the vital spark so necessary for the further progress and comfort of the human race. He accordingly contrived to steal some sparks from the chariot of the sun, which he conveyed to earth hidden in a hollow tube. Furious at being again outwitted, Zeus determined to be revenged first on mankind, and then on Prometheus. To punish the former he commanded Hephæstus (Vulcan) to mould a beautiful woman out of clay, and determined that through her instrumentality trouble and misery should be brought into the world.

The gods were so charmed with the graceful and artistic creation of Hephæstus, that they all determined to endow her with some special gift. Hermes (Mercury) bestowed on her a smooth persuasive tongue, Aphrodite gave her beauty and the art of pleasing; the Graces made her fascinating, and Athene (Minerva) gifted her with the possession of feminine accomplishments. She was called Pandora, which means all-gifted, having received every attribute necessary to make her charming and irresistible. Thus beautifully formed and endowed, this exquisite creature, attired by the Graces, and crowned with flowers by the Seasons, was conducted to the house of Epimetheus[9] by Hermes the messenger of the gods. Now Epimetheus had been warned by his brother not to accept any gift whatever from the gods; but he was so fascinated by the beautiful being who suddenly appeared before him, that he welcomed her to his home, and made her his wife. It was not long, however, before he had cause to regret his weakness.

He had in his possession a jar of rare workmanship, containing all the blessings reserved by the gods for mankind, which he had been expressly forbidden to open. But woman's proverbial curiosity could not withstand so great a temptation, and Pandora determined to solve the mystery at any cost. Watching her opportunity she raised the lid, and immediately all the blessings which the gods had thus reserved for mankind took wing and flew away. But all was not lost. Just as Hope (which lay at the bottom) was about to escape, Pandora hastily closed the lid of the jar, and thus preserved to man that never-failing solace which helps him to bear with courage the many ills which assail him.[10]

Having punished mankind, Zeus determined to execute vengeance on Prometheus. He accordingly chained him to a rock in Mount Caucasus, and sent an eagle every day to gnaw away his liver, which grew again every night ready for fresh torments. For thirty years Prometheus endured this fearful punishment; but at length Zeus relented, and permitted his son Heracles (Hercules) to kill the eagle, and the sufferer was released.

THIRD DYNASTY.

OLYMPIAN DIVINITIES—

ZEUS[11] (JUPITER).

Zeus, the great presiding deity of the universe, the ruler of heaven and earth, was regarded by the Greeks, first, as the god of all aërial phenomena; secondly, as the personification of the laws of nature; thirdly, as lord of state-life; and fourthly, as the father of gods and men.

As the god of aërial phenomena he could, by shaking his ægis,[12] produce storms, tempests, and intense darkness. At his command the mighty thunder rolls, the lightning flashes, and the clouds open and pour forth their refreshing streams to fructify the earth.

As the personification of the operations of nature, he represents those grand laws of unchanging and harmonious order, by which not only the physical but also the moral world is governed. Hence he is the god of regulated time as marked by the changing seasons, and by the regular succession of day and night, in contradistinction to his father Cronus, who represents time absolutely, *i.e.* eternity.

As the lord of state-life, he is the founder of kingly power, the upholder of all institutions connected with the state, and the special friend and patron of princes, whom he guards and assists with his advice and counsel. He protects the assembly of the people, and, in fact, watches over the welfare of the whole community.

As the father of the gods, Zeus sees that each deity performs his or her individual duty, punishes their misdeeds, settles their disputes, and acts towards them on all occasions as their all-knowing counsellor and mighty friend.

As the father of men, he takes a paternal interest in the actions and well-being of mortals. He watches over them with tender solicitude, rewarding truth, charity, and uprightness, but severely punishing perjury, cruelty, and want of hospitality. Even the poorest and most forlorn wanderer finds in him a powerful advocate, for he, by a wise and merciful dispensation, ordains that the mighty ones of the earth should succour their distressed and needy brethren.

The Greeks believed that the home of this their mighty and all-powerful deity was on the top of Mount Olympus, that high and lofty mountain between Thessaly and Macedon, whose summit, wrapt in clouds and mist, was hidden from mortal view. It was supposed that this mysterious region, which even a bird could not reach, extended beyond the clouds right into Aether, the realm of the immortal gods. The poets describe this ethereal atmosphere as bright, glistening, and refreshing, exercising a peculiar, gladdening influence over the minds and hearts of those privileged beings permitted to share its delights. Here youth never ages, and the passing years leave no traces on its favoured inhabitants. On the cloud-capped summit of Olympus was the palace of Zeus and Hera, of burnished gold, chased silver, and gleaming ivory. Lower down were the homes of the other gods, which, though less commanding in position and size, were yet similar to that of Zeus in design and workmanship, all being the work of the divine artist Hephæstus. Below these were other palaces of silver, ebony, ivory, or burnished brass, where the Heroes, or Demi-gods, resided.

As the worship of Zeus formed so important a feature in

the religion of the Greeks, his statues were necessarily both numerous and magnificent. He is usually represented as a man of noble and imposing mien, his countenance expressing all the lofty majesty of the omnipotent ruler of the universe, combined with the gracious, yet serious, benignity of the father and friend of mankind. He may be recognized by his rich flowing beard, and the thick masses of hair, which rise straight from the high and intellectual forehead and fall to his shoulders in clustering locks. The nose is large and finely formed, and the slightly-opened lips impart an air of sympathetic kindliness which invites confidence. He is always accompanied by an eagle, which either surmounts his sceptre, or sits at his feet; he generally bears in his uplifted hand a sheaf of thunder-bolts, just ready to be hurled, whilst in the other he holds the lightning. The head is frequently encircled with a wreath of oak-leaves.

The most celebrated statue of the Olympian Zeus was that by the famous Athenian sculptor Phidias, which was forty feet high, and stood in the temple of Zeus at Olympia. It was formed of ivory and gold, and was such a masterpiece of art, that it was reckoned among the seven wonders of the world. It represented the god, seated on a throne, holding in his right hand a life-sized image of Nike (the goddess of Victory), and in his left a royal sceptre, surmounted by an eagle. It is said that the great sculptor had concentrated all the marvellous powers of his genius on this sublime conception, and earnestly entreated Zeus to give him a decided proof that his labours were approved. An answer to his prayer came through the open roof of the temple in the shape of a flash of lightning, which Phidias interpreted as a sign that the god of heaven was pleased with his work.

Zeus was first worshipped at Dodona in Epirus, where, at the foot of Mount Tomarus, on the woody shore of Lake Joanina, was his famous oracle, the most ancient in Greece. Here the voice of the eternal and invisible god was supposed to be heard in the rustling leaves of a giant oak, announcing to mankind the will of heaven and the destiny of mortals; these revelations being interpreted to the people by the priests of Zeus, who were called Selli. Recent excavations which have been made at this spot have brought to light the ruins of the ancient temple of Zeus, and also, among other interesting relics, some plates of lead, on which are engraved inquiries which were evidently made by certain individuals who consulted the oracle. These little leaden plates speak to us, as it were, in a curiously homely manner of a by-gone time in the buried past. One person inquires what god he should apply to for health and fortune; another asks for advice concerning his child; and a third, evidently a shepherd, promises a gift to the oracle should a speculation in sheep turn out successfully. Had these little memorials been of gold instead of lead, they would doubtless have shared the fate of the numerous treasures which adorned this and other temples, in the universal pillage which took place when Greece fell into the hands of barbarians.

Though Dodona was the most ancient of his shrines, the great national seat of the worship of Zeus was at Olympia in Elis, where there was a magnificent temple dedicated to him, containing the famous colossal statue by Phidias above described. Crowds of devout worshippers flocked to this world-renowned fane from all parts of Greece, not only to pay homage to their supreme deity, but also to join in the celebrated games which were held there at intervals of four years. The Olympic games were such a thoroughly national institution, that even Greeks who had left their native country made a point of returning on these occasions, if possible, in order to contend with their fellow-countrymen in the various athletic sports which took place at these festivals.

It will be seen on reflection that in a country like Greece, which contained so many petty states, often at variance with each other, these national gatherings must have been most valuable as a means of uniting the Greeks in one great bond of brotherhood. On these festive occasions the whole nation met together, forgetting for the moment all past differences, and uniting in the enjoyment of the same festivities.

It will doubtless have been remarked that in the representations of Zeus he is always accompanied by an eagle. This royal bird was sacred to him, probably from the fact of its being the only creature capable of gazing at the sun without being dazzled, which may have suggested the idea that it was able to contemplate the splendour of divine majesty unshrinkingly.

The oak-tree, and also the summits of mountains, were sacred to Zeus. His sacrifices consisted of white bulls, cows, and goats.

Zeus had seven immortal wives, whose names were Metis, Themis, Eurynome, Demeter, Mnemosyne, Leto, and Hera.

METIS, his first wife, was one of the Oceanides or sea-nymphs. She was the personification of prudence and wisdom, a convincing proof of which she displayed in her successful administration of the potion which caused Cronus to yield up his children. She was endowed with the gift of prophecy, and foretold to Zeus that one of their children would gain ascendency over him. In order, therefore, to avert the possibility of the prediction being fulfilled he swallowed her before any children were born to them. Feeling afterwards violent pains in his head, he sent for Hephæstus, and ordered him to open it with an axe. His command was obeyed, and out sprang, with a loud and martial shout, a beautiful being, clad in armour from head to foot. This was Athene (Minerva), goddess of Armed Resistance and Wisdom.

THEMIS was the goddess of Justice, Law, and Order.

EURYNOME was one of the Oceanides, and the mother of the Charites or Graces.

DEMETER,[13] the daughter of Cronus and Rhea, was the goddess of Agriculture.

MNEMOSYNE, the daughter of Uranus and Gæa, was the goddess of Memory and the mother of the nine Muses.

LETO (Latona) was the daughter of Cœus and Phœbe. She was gifted with wonderful beauty, and was tenderly loved by Zeus, but her lot was far from being a happy one, for Hera, being extremely jealous of her, persecuted her with inveterate cruelty, and sent the dreadful serpent Python[14] to terrify and torment her wherever she went. But Zeus, who had observed with the deepest compassion her weary wanderings and agonized fears, resolved to create for her some place of refuge, however humble, where she might feel herself safe from the venomous attacks of the serpent. He therefore brought her to Delos, a floating island in the Ægean Sea, which he made stationary by attaching it with chains of adamant to the bottom of the sea. Here she gave birth to her twin-children, Apollo and Artemis (Diana), two of the most beautiful of the immortals.

According to some versions of the story of Leto, Zeus transformed her into a quail, in order that she might thus elude the vigilance of Hera, and she is said to have resumed her true form when she arrived at the island of Delos.

HERA, being the principal wife of Zeus and queen of heaven, a detailed account will be given of her in a special chapter.

In the union of Zeus with most of his immortal wives we shall find that an allegorical meaning is conveyed. His marriage with Metis, who is said to have surpassed both gods and men in knowledge, represents supreme power allied to wisdom and prudence. His union with Themis typifies the bond which exists between divine majesty and justice, law, and order. Eurynome, as the mother of the Charites or Graces, supplied the refining and harmonizing influences of grace and beauty, whilst the marriage of Zeus with Mnemosyne typifies the union of genius with memory.

In addition to the seven immortal wives of Zeus, he was also allied to a number of mortal maidens whom he visited under various disguises, as it was supposed that if he revealed himself in his true form as king of heaven the splendour of his glory would cause instant destruction to mortals. The mortal consorts of Zeus have been such a favourite theme with poets, painters, and sculptors, that it is necessary to give some account of their individual history. Those best known are Antiope, Leda, Europa, Callisto, Alcmene, Semele, Io, and Danae.

ANTIOPE, to whom Zeus appeared under the form of a satyr, was the daughter of Nicteus, king of Thebes. To escape the anger of her father she fled to Sicyon, where king Epopeus, enraptured with her wonderful beauty, made her his wife without asking her father's consent. This so enraged Nicteus that he declared war against Epopeus, in order to compel him to restore Antiope. At his death, which took place before he could succeed in his purpose, Nicteus left his kingdom to his brother Lycus, commanding him, at the same time, to carry on the war, and execute his vengeance. Lycus invaded Sicyon, defeated and killed Epopeus, and brought back Antiope as a prisoner. On the way to Thebes she gave birth to her twin-sons, Amphion and Zethus, who, by the orders of Lycus, were at once exposed on Mount Cithaeron, and would have perished but for the kindness of a shepherd, who took pity on them and preserved their lives. Antiope was, for many years, held captive by her uncle Lycus, and compelled to suffer the utmost cruelty at the hands of his wife Dirce. But one day her bonds were miraculously loosened, and she flew for shelter and protection to the humble dwelling of her sons on Mount Cithaeron. During the long period of their mother's captivity the babes had grown into sturdy youths, and, as they listened angrily to the story of her wrongs, they became all impatience to avenge them. Setting off at once to Thebes they succeeded in possessing themselves of the town, and after slaying the cruel Lycus they bound Dirce by the hair to the horns of a wild bull, which dragged her hither and thither until she expired. Her mangled body was cast into the fount near Thebes, which still bears her name. Amphion became king of Thebes in his uncle's stead. He was a friend of the Muses, and devoted to music and poetry. His brother, Zethus, was famous for his skill in archery, and was passionately fond of the chase. It is said that when Amphion wished to inclose the town of Thebes with walls and towers, he had but to play a sweet melody on the lyre, given to him by Hermes, and the huge stones began to move, and obediently fitted themselves together.

The punishment of Dirce at the hands of Amphion and Zethus forms the subject of the world-renowned marble group in the museum at Naples, known by the name of the Farnese Bull.

In sculpture Amphion is always represented with a lyre; Zethus with a club.

LEDA, whose affections Zeus won under the form of a swan, was the daughter of Thestius, king of Ætolia. Her twin-sons, Castor and (Polydeuces or) Pollux,[15] were renowned for their tender attachment to each other. They were also famous for their physical accomplishments, Castor being the most expert charioteer of his day, and Pollux the first of pugilists. Their names appear both among the hunters of the Calydonian boar-hunt and the heroes of the Argonautic expedition. The brothers became attached to the daughters of Leucippus, prince of the Messenians, who had been betrothed by their father to Idas and Lynceus, sons of Aphareus. Having persuaded Leucippus to break his promise, the twins carried off the maidens as their brides. Idas and Lynceus, naturally furious at this proceeding, challenged the Dioscuri to mortal combat, in which Castor perished by the hand of Idas, and Lynceus by that of Pollux. Zeus wished to confer the gift of immortality upon Pollux, but he refused to accept it unless allowed to share it with Castor. Zeus gave the desired permission, and the faithful brothers were both allowed to live, but only on alternate days. The Dioscuri received divine honours throughout Greece, and were worshipped with special reverence at Sparta.

EUROPA was the beautiful daughter of Agenor, king of Phœnicia. She was one day gathering flowers with her companions in a meadow near the sea-shore, when Zeus, charmed with her great beauty, and wishing to win her love, transformed himself into a beautiful white bull, and trotted quietly up to the princess, so as not to alarm her. Surprised at the gentleness of the animal, and admiring its beauty, as it lay placidly on the grass, she caressed it, crowned it with flowers, and, at last, playfully seated herself on its back. Hardly had she done so than the disguised god bounded away with his lovely burden, and swam across the sea with her to the island of Crete.

Europa was the mother of Minos, Aeacus, and Rhadamanthus. Minos, who became king of Crete, was celebrated for his justice and moderation, and after death he was created one of the judges of the lower world, which office he held in conjunction with his brothers.

CALLISTO, the daughter of Lycaon, king of Arcadia, was a huntress in the train of Artemis, devoted to the pleasures of the chase, who had made a vow never to marry; but Zeus, under the form of the huntress-goddess, succeeded in obtaining her affections. Hera, being extremely jealous of her, changed her into a bear, and caused Artemis (who failed to recognize her attendant under this form) to hunt her in the chase, and put an end to her existence. After her death she was placed by Zeus among the stars as a constellation, under the name of Arctos, or the bear.

ALCMENE, the daughter of Electryon, king of Mycenae, was betrothed to her cousin Amphytrion; but, during his absence on a perilous undertaking, Zeus assumed his form, and obtained her affections. Heracles (whose world-renowned exploits will be related among the legends) was the son of Alcmene and Zeus.

SEMELE, a beautiful princess, the daughter of Cadmus, king of Phœnicia, was greatly beloved by Zeus. Like the unfortunate Callisto, she was hated by Hera with jealous malignity, and the haughty queen of heaven determined to effect her destruction. Disguising herself, therefore, as Berœ, Semele's faithful old nurse, she artfully persuaded her to insist upon Zeus visiting her, as he appeared to Hera, in all his power and glory, well knowing that this would cause her instant death. Semele, suspecting no treachery, followed the advice of her supposed nurse; and the next time Zeus came to her, she earnestly entreated him to grant the favour she was about to ask. Zeus swore by the Styx (which was to the gods an irrevocable oath) to accede to her request whatsoever it might be. Semele, therefore, secure of gaining her petition, begged of Zeus to appear to her in all the glory of his divine power and majesty. As he had sworn to grant whatever she asked of him, he was compelled to comply with her wish; he therefore revealed himself as the mighty lord of the universe, accompanied by thunder and lightning, and she was instantly consumed in the flames.

IO, daughter of Inachus, king of Argos, was a priestess of Hera. She was very beautiful, and Zeus, who was much attached to her, transformed her into a white cow, in order to defeat the jealous intrigues of Hera, who, however, was not to be deceived. Aware of the stratagem, she contrived to obtain the animal from Zeus, and placed her under the watchful care of a man called Argus-Panoptes, who fastened her to an olive-tree in the grove of Hera. He had a hundred eyes, of which, when asleep, he never closed more than two at a time; being thus always on the watch, Hera found him extremely useful in keeping guard over Io. Hermes, however, by the command of Zeus, succeeded in putting all his eyes to sleep with the sound of his magic lyre, and then, taking advantage of his helpless condition, slew him. The story goes, that in commemoration of the services which Argus had rendered her, Hera placed his eyes on the tail of a peacock, as a lasting memorial of her gratitude. Ever fertile in resource, Hera now sent a gadfly to worry and torment the unfortunate Io incessantly, and she wandered all over the world in hopes of escaping from her tormentor. At length she reached Egypt, where she found rest and freedom from the persecutions of her enemy. On the banks of the Nile she resumed her original form and gave birth to a son called Epaphus, who afterwards became king of Egypt, and built the famous city of Memphis.

DANAE.—Zeus appeared to Danae under the form of a shower of gold. (Further details concerning her will be found in the legend of Perseus.)

The Greeks supposed that the divine ruler of the Universe occasionally assumed a human form, and descended from his celestial abode, in order to visit mankind and observe their proceedings, his aim being generally either to punish the guilty, or to reward the deserving.

On one occasion Zeus, accompanied by Hermes, made a journey through Phrygia, seeking hospitality and shelter wherever they went. But nowhere did they receive a kindly welcome till they came to the humble cottage of an old man and his wife called Philemon and Baucis, who entertained them with the greatest kindness, setting before them what frugal fare their humble means permitted, and bidding them welcome with unaffected cordiality. Observing in the course of their simple repast that the wine bowl was miraculously replenished, the aged couple became convinced of the divine nature of their guests. The gods now informed them that on account of its wickedness their native place was doomed to destruction, and told them to climb the neighbouring hill with them, which overlooked the village where they dwelt. What was their dismay on beholding at their feet, in place of the spot where they had passed so many happy years together, nothing but a watery plain, the only house to be seen being their own little cottage, which suddenly changed itself into a temple before their eyes. Zeus now asked the worthy pair to name any wish they particularly desired and it should be granted. They accordingly begged that they might serve the gods in the temple below, and end life together.

Their wish was granted, for, after spending the remainder of their lives in the worship of the gods, they both died at the same instant, and were transformed by Zeus into trees, remaining for ever side by side.

Upon another occasion Zeus, wishing to ascertain for himself the truth of the reports concerning the atrocious wickedness of mankind, made a journey through Arcadia. Being recognized by the Arcadians as king of heaven, he was received by them with becoming respect and veneration; but Lycaon, their king, who had rendered himself infamous by the gross impiety of himself and his sons, doubted the divinity of Zeus, ridiculed his people for being so easily duped, and, according to his custom of killing all strangers who ventured to trust his hospitality, resolved to murder him. Before executing this wicked design, however, he decided to put Zeus to the test, and having killed a boy for the purpose, placed before him a dish containing human flesh. But Zeus was not to be deceived. He beheld the revolting dish with horror and loathing, and angrily upsetting the table upon which it was placed, turned Lycaon into a wolf, and destroyed all his fifty sons by lightning, except Nyctimus, who was saved by the intervention of Gæa.

JUPITER.

The Roman Jupiter, who is so frequently confounded with the Greek Zeus, is identical with him only as being the head of the Olympic gods, and the presiding deity over Life, Light, and Aërial Phenomena. Jupiter is lord of life in its widest and most comprehensive signification, having absolute power over life and death, in which respect he differed from the Greek Zeus, who was to a certain extent controlled by the all-potent sway of the Moiræ or Fates. Zeus, as we have seen, often condescends to visit mankind, either as a mortal, or under various disguises, whereas Jupiter always remains essentially the supreme god of heaven, and never appears upon earth.

The most celebrated temple of Jupiter was that on the Capitoline Hill in the city of Rome, where he was worshipped under the names of Jupiter-Optimus-Maximus, Capitolinus, and Tarpeius.

The Romans represented him seated on a throne of ivory, holding in his right hand a sheaf of thunderbolts, and in his left a sceptre, whilst an eagle stands beside his throne.

HERA (JUNO).

Hera, the eldest daughter of Cronus and Rhea, was born at Samos, or, according to some accounts, at Argos, and was reared by the sea-divinities Oceanus and Tethys, who were models of conjugal fidelity.[16] She was the principal wife of Zeus, and, as queen of heaven, participated in the honours paid to him, but her dominion only extended over the air (the lower aërial regions). Hera appears to be the sublime embodiment of strict matronly virtue, and is on that account the protectress of purity and married women. Faultless herself in her fidelity as a wife, she is essentially the type of the sanctity of the marriage tie, and holds in abhorrence any violation of its obligations. So strongly was she imbued with this hatred of any immorality, that, finding herself so often called upon to punish the failings of both gods and men in this respect, she became jealous, harsh, and vindictive. Her exalted position as the wife of the supreme deity, combined with her extreme beauty, caused her to become exceedingly vain, and she consequently resented with great severity any infringement on her rights as queen of heaven, or any apparent slight on her personal appearance.

The following story will signally illustrate how ready she was to resent any slight offered to her.

At the marriage of the sea-nymph Thetis with a mortal called Peleus, all the gods and goddesses were present, except Eris (the goddess of Discord). Indignant at not being invited, she determined to cause dissension in the assembly, and for this purpose threw into the midst of the guests a golden apple with the inscription on it "For the Fairest." Now, as all the goddesses were extremely beautiful, each claimed the apple; but at length, the rest having relinquished their pretensions, the number of candidates was reduced to three, Hera, Athene, and Aphrodite, who agreed to appeal to Paris for a settlement of this delicate question, he being noted for the wisdom he had displayed in his judgment upon several occasions. Paris was the son of Priam, king of Troy, who, ignorant of his noble birth, was at this time feeding his flocks on Mount Ida, in Phrygia. Hermes, as messenger of the gods, conducted the three rival beauties to the young shepherd, and with breathless anxiety they awaited his decision. Each fair candidate endeavoured to secure his favour by the most tempting offers. Hera promised him extensive dominions; Athene, martial fame and glory; and Aphrodite, the loveliest woman in the world. But whether he really considered Aphrodite the fairest of the three, or preferred a beautiful wife to fame and power, we cannot tell; all we know is that to her he awarded the golden apple, and she became ever after universally acknowledged as the goddess of beauty. Hera, having fully expected that Paris would give her the preference, was so indignant that she never forgave him, and not only persecuted him, but all the family of Priam, whose dreadful sufferings and misfortunes during the Trojan war were attributed to her influence. In fact, she carried her animosity to such an extent that it was often the cause of domestic disagreements between herself and Zeus, who espoused the cause of the Trojans.

Among the many stories of these frequent quarrels there is one connected with Heracles, the favourite son of Zeus, which is as follows:—Hera having raised a storm at sea in order to drive him out of his course, Zeus became so angry that he hung her in the clouds by a golden chain, and attached heavy anvils to her feet. Her son Hephæstus tried to release his mother from her humiliating position, for which Zeus threw him out of heaven, and his leg was broken by the fall.

Hera, being deeply offended with Zeus, determined to separate herself from him for ever, and she accordingly left him and took up her abode in Eubœa. Surprised and grieved at this unlooked-for desertion, Zeus resolved to leave no means untried to win her back again. In this emergency he consulted Cithaeron, king of Platea, who was famed for his great wisdom and subtlety. Cithaeron advised him to dress up an image in bridal attire and place it in a chariot, announcing that this was Platea, his future wife. The artifice succeeded. Hera, incensed at the idea of a rival, flew to meet the procession in great anger, and seizing the supposed bride, she furiously attacked her and dragged off her nuptial attire. Her delight on discovering the deception was so great that a reconciliation took place, and, committing the image to the flames, with joyful laughter she seated herself in its place and returned to Olympus.

Hera was the mother of Ares (Mars), Hephæstus, Hebe, and Eileithyia. Ares was the god of War; Hephæstus, of Fire; Hebe, of Youth; and Eileithyia presided over the birth of mortals.

Hera dearly loved Greece, and indeed always watched

over and protected Greek interests, her beloved and favourite cities being Argos, Samos, Sparta, and Mycenæ.

Her principal temples were at Argos and Samos. From a remote period she was greatly venerated at Olympia, and her temple there, which stood in the Altis or sacred grove, was five hundred years older than that of Zeus on the same spot. Some interesting excavations which are now going on there have brought to light the remains of the ancient edifice, which contains among other treasures of antiquity several beautiful statues, the work of the famous sculptors of ancient Greece. At first this temple was built of wood, then of stone, and the one lately discovered was formed of conglomerate of shells.

In the Altis races were run by young maidens in honour of Hera, and the fleetest of foot received in token of her victory an olive-wreath and a piece of the flesh of the sacrifices. These races, like the Olympic Games, were celebrated at intervals of four years, and were called Heræ. A beautiful robe, woven by sixteen women chosen from the sixteen cities of Elis, was always offered to Hera on these occasions, and choral songs and sacred dances formed part of the ceremonies.

Hera is usually represented seated on a throne, holding a pomegranate in one hand and a sceptre surmounted by a cuckoo in the other. She appears as a calm, dignified matron of majestic beauty, robed in a tunic and mantle, her forehead is broad and intellectual, her eyes large and fully opened, and her arms dazzlingly white and finely moulded.

The finest statue of this divinity was that by Polycletus at Argos.

Her attributes are the diadem, veil, sceptre, and peacock.

The first day of every month a ewe-lamb and sow were sacrificed to Hera. The hawk, goose, and more particularly the peacock[17] were sacred to her. Flocks of these beautiful birds generally surround her throne and draw her chariot, Iris, the Rainbow, being seated behind her.

Her favourite flowers were the dittany, poppy, and lily.

JUNO.

Juno, the Roman divinity supposed to be identical with the Greek Hera, differed from her in the most salient points, for whereas Hera invariably appears as the haughty, unbending queen of heaven, Juno, on the other hand, is revered and beloved as the type of a matron and housewife. She was worshipped in Rome under various titles, most of which point to her vocation as the protectress of married women. Juno was believed to watch over and guard the life of every woman from her birth to her death. The principal temples dedicated to her were in Rome, one being erected on the Aventine, and the other on the Capitoline Hill. She had also a temple on the Arx, in which she was worshipped as Juno Moneta, or the warning goddess. Adjacent to this shrine was the public mint. [18] On the 1st of March a grand annual festival, called the Matronalia, was celebrated in her honour by all the married women of Rome, and this religious institution was accompanied with much solemnity.[19]

PALLAS-ATHENE (MINERVA).

Pallas-Athene, goddess of Wisdom and Armed Resistance, was a purely Greek divinity; that is to say, no other nation possessed a corresponding conception. She was supposed, as already related, to have issued from the head of Zeus himself, clad in armour from head to foot. The miraculous advent of this maiden goddess is beautifully described by Homer in one of his hymns: snow-capped Olympus shook to its foundation; the glad earth re-echoed her martial shout; the billowy sea became agitated; and Helios, the sun-god, arrested his fiery steeds in their headlong course to welcome this wonderful emanation from the godhead. Athene was at once admitted into the assembly of the gods, and henceforth took her place as the most faithful and sagacious of all her father's counsellors. This brave, dauntless maiden, so exactly the essence of all that is noble in the character of "the father of gods and men," remained throughout chaste in word and deed, and kind at heart, without exhibiting any of those failings which somewhat mar the nobler features in the character of Zeus. This direct emanation from his own self, justly his favourite child, his better and purer counterpart, received from him several important prerogatives. She was permitted to hurl the thunderbolts, to prolong the life of man, and to bestow the gift of prophecy; in fact Athene was the only divinity whose authority was equal to that of Zeus himself, and when he had ceased to visit the earth in person she was empowered by him to act as his deputy. It was her especial duty to protect the state and all peaceful associations of mankind, which she possessed the power of defending when occasion required. She encouraged the maintenance of law and order, and defended the right on all occasions, for which reason, in the Trojan war she espouses the cause of the Greeks and exerts all her influence on their behalf. The Areopagus, a court of justice where religious causes and murders were tried, was believed to have been instituted by her, and when both sides happened to have an equal number of votes she gave the casting-vote in favour of the accused. She was the patroness of learning, science, and art, more particularly where these contributed directly towards the welfare of nations. She presided over all inventions connected with agriculture, invented the plough, and taught mankind how to use oxen for farming purposes. She also instructed mankind in the use of numbers, trumpets, chariots, &c., and presided over the building of the Argo,[20] thereby encouraging the useful art of navigation. She also taught the Greeks how to build the wooden horse by means of which the destruction of Troy was effected.

The safety of cities depended on her care, for which reason her temples were generally built on the citadels, and she was supposed to watch over the defence of the walls, fortifications, harbours, &c. A divinity who so faithfully guarded the best interests of the state, by not only protecting it from the attacks of enemies, but also by developing its chief resources of wealth and prosperity, was worthily chosen as the presiding deity of the state, and in this character as an essentially political goddess she was called Athene-Polias.

The fact of Athene having been born clad in armour, which merely signified that her virtue and purity were unassailable, has given rise to the erroneous supposition that she was the presiding goddess of war; but a deeper study of her character in all its bearings proves that, in contradistinction to her brother Ares, the god of war, who loved strife for its own sake, she only takes up arms to protect the innocent and deserving against tyrannical oppression. It is true that in the Iliad we frequently see her on the battlefield fighting valiantly, and protecting her favourite heroes; but this is always at the command of Zeus, who even supplies her with arms for the purpose, as it is supposed that she possessed none of her own. A marked feature in the representations of this deity is the ægis, that wonderful shield given to her by her father as a further means of defence, which, when in danger, she swung so swiftly round and round that it kept at a distance all antagonistic influences; hence her name Pallas, from *pallo*, I swing. In the centre of this shield, which was covered with dragon's scales, bordered with serpents, and which she sometimes wore as a breastplate, was the awe-inspiring head of the Medusa, which had the effect of turning to stone all beholders.

In addition to the many functions which she exercised in connection with the state, Athene presided over the two chief departments of feminine industry, spinning and weaving. In the latter art she herself displayed unrivalled ability and exquisite taste. She wove her own robe and that of Hera, which last she is said to have embroidered very richly; she also gave Jason a cloak wrought by herself, when he set forth in quest of the Golden Fleece. Being on one occasion challenged to a contest in this accomplishment by a mortal maiden named Arachne, whom she had instructed in the art of weaving, she accepted the challenge and was completely vanquished by her pupil. Angry at her defeat, she struck the unfortunate maiden on the forehead with the shuttle which she held in her hand; and Arachne, being of a sensitive nature, was so hurt by this indignity that she hung herself in despair, and was changed by Athene into a spider. This goddess is said to have invented the flute,[21] upon which she played with considerable talent, until one day, being laughed at by the assembled gods and goddesses for the contortions which her countenance assumed during these musical efforts, she hastily ran to a fountain in order to convince herself whether she deserved their ridicule. Finding to her intense disgust that such was indeed the fact, she threw the flute away, and never raised it to her lips again.

Athene is usually represented fully draped; she has a serious and thoughtful aspect, as though replete with earnestness and wisdom; the beautiful oval contour of her countenance is adorned by the luxuriance of her wealth of hair, which is drawn back from the temples and hangs down in careless grace; she looks the embodiment of strength, grandeur, and majesty; whilst her broad shoulders and small hips give her a slightly masculine appearance.

When represented as the war-goddess she appears clad in armour, with a helmet on her head, from which waves a large plume; she carries the ægis on her arm, and in her hand a golden staff, which possessed the property of endowing her chosen favourites with youth and dignity.

Athene was universally worshipped throughout Greece, but was regarded with special veneration by the Athenians, she being the guardian deity of Athens. Her most celebrated temple was the Parthenon, which stood on the Acropolis at Athens, and contained her world-renowned statue by Phidias, which ranks second only to that of Zeus by the same great artist. This colossal statue was 39 feet high, and was composed of ivory and gold; its majestic beauty formed the chief attraction of the temple. It represented her standing erect, bearing her spear and shield; in her hand she held an image of Nike, and at her feet there lay a serpent.

The tree sacred to her was the olive, which she herself produced in a contest with Poseidon. The olive-tree thus called into existence was preserved in the temple of Erectheus, on the Acropolis, and is said to have possessed such marvellous vitality, that when the Persians burned it after sacking the town it immediately burst forth into new shoots.

The principal festival held in honour of this divinity was the Panathenæa.

The owl, cock, and serpent were the animals sacred to her, and her sacrifices were rams, bulls, and cows.

MINERVA.

The Minerva of the Romans was identified with the Pallas-Athene of the Greeks. Like her she presides over learning and all useful arts, and is the patroness of the feminine accomplishments of sewing, spinning, weaving, &c. Schools were under her especial care, and schoolboys, therefore, had holidays during her festivals (the Greater Quinquatria), when they always brought a gift to their master, called the Minerval.

It is worthy of notice that the only three divinities worshipped in the Capitol were Jupiter, Juno, and Minerva, and in their joint honour the Ludi Maximi or great games were held.

THEMIS.

Themis, who has already been alluded to as the wife of Zeus, was the daughter of Cronus and Rhea, and personified those divine laws of justice and order by means of which the well-being and morality of communities are regulated. She presided over the assemblies of the people and the laws of hospitality. To her was intrusted the office of convoking the assembly of the gods, and she was also mistress of ritual and ceremony.

On account of her great wisdom Zeus himself frequently sought her counsel and acted upon her advice. Themis was a prophetic divinity, and had an oracle near the river Cephissus in Bœotia.

She is usually represented as being in the full maturity of womanhood, of fair aspect, and wearing a flowing garment, which drapes her noble, majestic form; in her right hand she holds the sword of justice, and in her left the scales, which indicate the impartiality with which every cause is carefully weighed by her, her eyes being bandaged so that the personality of the individual should carry no weight with respect to the verdict.

This divinity is sometimes identified with Tyche, sometimes with Ananke.

Themis, like so many other Greek divinities, takes the place of a more ancient deity of the same name who was a daughter of Uranus and Gæa. This elder Themis inherited from her mother the gift of prophecy, and when she became merged into her younger representative she transmitted to her this prophetic power.

HESTIA (Vesta).

Hestia was the daughter of Cronus and Rhea. She was the goddess of Fire in its first application to the wants of mankind, hence she was essentially the presiding deity of the domestic hearth and the guardian spirit of man, and it was her pure and benign influence which was supposed to protect the sanctity of domestic life.

Now in these early ages the hearth was regarded as the most important and most sacred portion of the dwelling, probably because the protection of the fire was an important consideration, for if once permitted to become extinct, re-ignition was attended with extreme difficulty. In fact, the hearth was held so sacred that it constituted the sanctum of the family, for which reason it was always erected in the centre of every house. It was a few feet in height and was built of stone; the fire was placed on the top of it, and served the double purpose of preparing the daily meals, and consuming the family sacrifices. Round this domestic hearth or altar were gathered the various members of the family, the head of the house occupying the place of honour nearest the hearth. Here prayers were said and sacrifices offered, and here also every kind and loving feeling was fostered, which even extended to the hunted and guilty stranger, who, if he once succeeded in touching this sacred altar, was safe from pursuit and punishment, and was henceforth placed under the protection of the family. Any crime committed within the sacred precincts of the domestic hearth was invariably visited by death.

In Grecian cities there was a common hall, called the Prytaneum, in which the members of the government had their meals at the expense of the state, and here too was the Hestia, or public hearth, with its fire, by means of which those meals were prepared. It was customary for emigrants to take with them a portion of this sacred fire, which they jealously guarded and brought with them to their new home, where it served as a connecting link between the young Greek colony and the mother country. Hestia is generally represented standing, and in accordance with the dignity and sanctity of her character, always appears fully draped. Her countenance is distinguished by a serene gravity of expression.

VESTA.

Vesta occupies a distinguished place among the earlier divinities of the Romans. Her temple in Rome, containing as it were the hearthstone of the nation, stood close beside the palace of Numa Pompilius.

On her altar burned the never-ceasing fire, which was tended by her priestesses, the Vestal Virgins.[22]

The temple of Vesta was circular in form, and contained that sacred and highly prized treasure the Palladium of Troy.[23]

The great festival in honour of Vesta, called the Vestalia, was celebrated on the 9th of June.

DEMETER (Ceres).

Demeter (from *Ge-meter*, earth-mother) was the daughter of Cronus and Rhea.[24] She represented that portion of Gæa (the whole solid earth) which we call the earth's crust, and which produces all vegetation. As goddess of agriculture, field-fruits, plenty, and productiveness, she was the sustainer of material life, and was therefore a divinity of great importance. When ancient Gæa lost, with Uranus, her position as a ruling divinity, she abdicated her sway in favour of her daughter Rhea, who henceforth inherited the powers which her mother had previously possessed, receiving in her place the honour and worship of mankind. In a very old poem Gæa is accordingly described as retiring to a cavern in the bowels of the earth, where she sits in the lap of her daughter, slumbering, moaning, and nodding for ever and ever.

It is necessary to keep clearly in view the distinctive difference between the three great earth-goddesses Gæa, Rhea, and Demeter. Gæa represents the earth as a whole, with its mighty subterranean forces; Rhea is that productive power which causes vegetation to spring forth, thus sustaining men and animals; Demeter, by presiding over agriculture, directs and utilizes Rhea's productive powers. But in later times, when Rhea, like other ancient divinities, loses her importance as a ruling deity, Demeter assumes all her functions and attributes, and then becomes the goddess of the life-producing and life-maintaining earth-crust. We must bear in mind the fact that man in his primitive state knew neither how to sow nor how to till the ground; when, therefore, he had exhausted the pastures which surrounded him he was compelled to seek others which were as yet unreaped; thus, roaming constantly from one place to another, settled habitations, and consequently civilizing influences, were impossible. Demeter, however, by introducing a knowledge of agriculture, put an end, at once and for ever, to that nomadic life which was now no longer necessary.

The favour of Demeter was believed to bring mankind rich harvests and fruitful crops, whereas her displeasure caused blight, drought, and famine. The island of Sicily was supposed to be under her especial protection, and there she was regarded with particular veneration, the Sicilians naturally attributing the wonderful fertility of their country to the partiality of the goddess.

Demeter is usually represented as a woman of noble bearing and majestic appearance, tall, matronly, and dignified, with beautiful golden hair, which falls in rippling curls over her stately shoulders, the yellow locks being emblematical of the ripened ears of corn. Sometimes she appears seated in a chariot drawn by winged dragons, at others she stands erect, her figure drawn up to its full height, and always fully draped; she bears a sheaf of wheat-ears in one hand and a lighted torch in the other. The wheat-ears are not unfrequently replaced by a bunch of poppies, with which her brows are also garlanded, though sometimes she merely wears a simple riband in her hair.

Demeter, as the wife of Zeus, became the mother of Persephone (Proserpine), to whom she was so tenderly attached that her whole life was bound up in her, and she knew no happiness except in her society. One day, however, whilst Persephone was gathering flowers in a meadow, attended by the ocean-nymphs, she saw to her surprise a beautiful narcissus, from the stem of which sprang forth a hundred blossoms. Drawing near to examine this lovely flower, whose exquisite scent perfumed the air, she stooped down to gather it, suspecting no evil, when a yawning abyss opened at her feet, and Aïdes, the grim ruler of the lower world, appeared from its depths, seated in his dazzling chariot drawn by four black horses. Regardless of her tears and the shrieks of her female attendants, Aïdes seized the terrified maiden, and bore her away to the gloomy realms over which he reigned in melancholy grandeur. Helios, the all-seeing sun-god, and Hecate, a mysterious and very ancient divinity, alone heard her cries for aid, but were powerless to help her. When Demeter became conscious of her loss her grief was intense, and she refused to be comforted. She knew not where to seek for her child, but feeling that repose and inaction were impossible, she set out on her weary search, taking with her two torches which she lighted in the flames of Mount Etna to guide her on her way. For nine long days and nights she wandered on, inquiring of every one she met for tidings of her child. But all was in vain! Neither gods nor men could give her the comfort which her soul so hungered for. At last, on the tenth day, the disconsolate mother met Hecate, who informed her that she had heard her daughter's cries, but knew not who it was that had borne her away. By Hecate's advice Demeter consulted Helios, whose all-seeing eye nothing escapes, and from him she learnt that it was Zeus himself who had permitted Aïdes to seize Persephone, and transport her to the lower world in order that she might become his wife. Indignant with Zeus for having given his sanction to the abduction of his daughter, and filled with the bitterest sorrow, she abandoned her home in Olympus, and refused all heavenly food. Disguising herself as an old woman, she descended upon earth, and commenced a weary pilgrimage among mankind. One evening she arrived at a place called Eleusis, in Attica, and sat down to rest herself near a well beneath the shade of an olive-tree. The youthful daughters of Celeus, the king of the country, came with their pails of brass to draw water from this well, and seeing that the tired wayfarer appeared faint and dispirited, they spoke kindly to her, asking who she was, and whence she came. Demeter replied that she had made her escape from pirates, who had captured her, and added that she would feel grateful for a home with any worthy family, whom she would be willing to serve in a menial capacity. The princesses, on hearing this, begged Demeter to have a moment's patience while they returned home and consulted their mother, Metaneira. They soon brought the joyful intelligence that she was desirous of securing her services as nurse to her infant son Demophoon, or Triptolemus. When Demeter arrived at the house a radiant light suddenly illumined her, which circumstance so overawed Metaneira that she treated the unknown stranger with the greatest respect, and hospitably offered her food and drink. But Demeter, still grief-worn and dejected, refused her friendly offers, and held herself apart from the social board. At length, however, the maid-servant Iambe succeeded, by means of playful jests and merriment, in somewhat dispelling the grief of the sorrowing mother, causing her at times to smile in spite of herself, and even inducing her to partake of a mixture of barley-meal, mint, and water, which was prepared according to the directions of the goddess herself. Time passed on, and the young child throve amazingly under the care of his kind and judicious nurse, who, however, gave him no food, but anointed him daily with ambrosia, and every night laid him secretly in the fire in order to render him immortal and exempt from old age. But, unfortunately, this benevolent design on the part of Demeter was frustrated by Metaneira herself, whose curiosity, one night, impelled her to watch the proceedings of the mysterious being who nursed her child. When to her horror she beheld her son placed in the flames, she shrieked aloud. Demeter, incensed at this untimely interruption, instantly withdrew the child, and throwing him on the ground, revealed herself in her true character. The bent and aged form had vanished, and in its place there stood a bright and beauteous being, whose golden locks streamed over her shoulders in richest luxuriance, her whole aspect bespeaking dignity and majesty. She told the awe-struck Metaneira that she was the goddess Demeter, and had intended to make her son immortal, but that her fatal curiosity had rendered this impossible, adding, however, that the child, having slept in her arms, and been nursed on her lap, should ever command the respect and esteem of mankind. She then desired that a temple and altar should be erected to her on a neighbouring hill by the people of Eleusis, promising that she herself would direct them how to perform the sacred rites and ceremonies, which should be observed in her honour. With these words she took her departure never to return.

Obedient to her commands, Celeus called together a meeting of his people, and built the temple on the spot which the goddess had indicated. It was soon completed, and Demeter took up her abode in it, but her heart was still sad for the loss of her daughter, and the whole world felt the influence of her grief and dejection. This was indeed a terrible year for mankind. Demeter no longer smiled on the earth she was wont to bless, and though the husbandman sowed the grain, and the groaning oxen ploughed the fields, no harvest rewarded their labour. All was barren, dreary desolation. The world was threatened with famine, and the gods with the loss of their accustomed honours and sacrifices; it became evident, therefore, to Zeus himself that some measures must be adopted to appease the anger of the goddess. He accordingly despatched Iris and many of the other gods and goddesses to implore Demeter to return to Olympus; but all their prayers were fruitless. The incensed goddess swore that until her daughter was restored to her she would not allow the grain to spring forth from the earth. At length Zeus sent Hermes, his faithful messenger, to the lower world with a petition to Aïdes, urgently entreating him to restore Persephone to the arms of her disconsolate mother. When he arrived in the gloomy realms of Aïdes, Hermes found him seated on a throne with the beautiful Persephone beside him, sorrowfully bewailing her unhappy fate. On learning his errand, Aïdes consented to resign Persephone, who joyfully prepared to follow the messenger of the gods to the abode of life and light. Before taking leave of her husband, he presented to her a few seeds of pomegranate, which in her excitement she thoughtlessly swallowed, and this simple act, as the sequel will show, materially affected her whole future life. The meeting between mother and child was one of unmixed rapture, and for the moment all the past was forgotten. The loving mother's happiness would now have been complete had not Aïdes asserted his rights. These were, that if any immortal had tasted food in his realms they were bound to remain there for ever. Of course the ruler of the lower world had to prove this assertion. This, however, he found no difficulty in doing, as Ascalaphus, the son of Acheron and Orphne, was his witness to the fact.[25] Zeus, pitying the disappointment of Demeter at finding her hopes thus blighted, succeeded in effecting a compromise by inducing his brother Aïdes to allow Persephone to spend six months of the year with the gods above, whilst during the other six she was to be the joyless companion of her grim lord below. Accompanied by her daughter, the beautiful Persephone, Demeter now resumed her long-abandoned dwelling in Olympus; the sympathetic earth responded gaily to her bright smiles, the corn at once sprang forth from the ground in fullest plenty, the trees, which late were sered and bare, now donned their brightest emerald robes, and the flowers, so long imprisoned in the hard, dry soil, filled the whole air with their fragrant perfume. Thus ends this charming story, which was a favourite theme with all the classic authors.

It is very possible that the poets who first created this graceful myth merely intended it as an allegory to illustrate the change of seasons; in the course of time, however, a literal meaning became attached to this and similar poetical fancies, and thus the people of Greece came to regard as an article of religious belief what, in the first instance, was nothing more than a poetic simile.

In the temple erected to Demeter at Eleusis, the famous Eleusinian Mysteries were instituted by the goddess herself. It is exceedingly difficult, as in the case of all secret societies, to discover anything with certainty concerning these sacred rites. The most plausible supposition is that the doctrines taught by the priests to the favoured few whom they initiated, were religious truths which were deemed unfit for the uninstructed mind of the multitude. For instance, it is supposed that the myth of Demeter and Persephone was explained by the teachers of the Mysteries to signify the temporary loss which mother earth sustains every year when the icy breath of winter robs her of her flowers and fruits and grain.

It is believed that in later times a still deeper meaning was conveyed by this beautiful myth, viz., the doctrine of the immortality of the soul. The grain, which, as it were, remains dead for a time in the dark earth, only to rise one day dressed in a newer and lovelier garb, was supposed to symbolize the soul, which, after death, frees itself from corruption, to live again under a better and purer form.

When Demeter instituted the Eleusinian Mysteries, Celeus and his family were the first to be initiated, Celeus himself being appointed high-priest. His son Triptolemus and his daughters, who acted as priestesses, assisted him in the duties of his sacred office. The Mysteries were celebrated by the Athenians every five years, and were, for a long time, their exclusive privilege. They took place by torchlight, and were conducted with the greatest solemnity.

In order to spread abroad the blessings which agriculture confers, Demeter presented Triptolemus with her chariot drawn by winged dragons, and, giving him some grains of corn, desired him to journey through the world, teaching mankind the arts of agriculture and husbandry.

Demeter exercised great severity towards those who incurred her displeasure. We find examples of this in the stories of Stellio and Eresicthon. Stellio was a youth who ridiculed the goddess for the eagerness with which she was eating a bowl of porridge, when weary and faint in the vain search for her daughter. Resolved that he should never again have an opportunity of thus offending, she angrily threw into his face the remainder of the food, and changed him into a spotted lizard.

Eresicthon, son of Triopas, had drawn upon himself the anger of Demeter by cutting down her sacred groves, for which she punished him with a constant and insatiable hunger. He sold all his possessions in order to satisfy his cravings, and was forced at last to devour his own limbs. His daughter Metra, who was devotedly attached to him, possessed the power of transforming herself into a variety of different animals. By this means she contrived to support her father, who sold her again and again each time she assumed a different form, and thus he dragged on a pitiful existence.

CERES.

The Roman Ceres is actually the Greek Demeter under another name, her attributes, worship, festivals, &c., being precisely identical.

The Romans were indebted to Sicily for this divinity, her worship having been introduced by the Greek colonists who settled there.

The Cerealia, or festivals in honour of Ceres, commenced on the 12th of April, and lasted several days.

APHRODITE (VENUS).

Aphrodite (from *aphros*, sea-foam, and *dite*, issued), the daughter of Zeus and a sea-nymph called Dione, was the goddess of Love and Beauty.

Dione, being a sea-nymph, gave birth to her daughter beneath the waves; but the child of the heaven-inhabiting Zeus was forced to ascend from the ocean-depths and mount to the snow-capped summits of Olympus, in order to breathe that ethereal and most refined atmosphere which pertains to the celestial gods.

Aphrodite was the mother of Eros (Cupid), the god of Love, also of Æneas, the great Trojan hero and the head of that Greek colony which settled in Italy, and from which arose the city of Rome. As a mother Aphrodite claims our sympathy for the tenderness she exhibits towards her children. Homer tells us in his Iliad, how, when Æneas was wounded in battle, she came to his assistance, regardless of personal danger, and was herself severely wounded in attempting to save his life.

Aphrodite was tenderly attached to a lovely youth, called Adonis, whose exquisite beauty has become proverbial. He was a motherless babe, and Aphrodite, taking pity on him, placed him in a chest and intrusted him to the care of Persephone, who became so fond of the beautiful youth that she refused to part with him. Zeus, being appealed to by the rival foster-mothers, decided that Adonis should spend four months of every year with Persephone, four with Aphrodite, whilst during the remaining four months he should be left to his own devices. He became, however, so attached to Aphrodite that he voluntarily devoted to her the time at his own disposal. Adonis was killed, during the chase, by a wild boar, to the great grief of Aphrodite, who bemoaned his loss so persistently that Aïdes, moved with pity, permitted him to pass six months of every year with her, whilst the remaining half of the year was spent by him in the lower world.

Aphrodite possessed a magic girdle (the famous *cestus*) which she frequently lent to unhappy maidens suffering from the pangs of unrequited love, as it was endowed with the power of inspiring affection for the wearer, whom it invested with every attribute of grace, beauty, and fascination.

Her usual attendants are the Charites or Graces (Euphrosyne, Aglaia, and Thalia), who are represented undraped and intertwined in a loving embrace.

In Hesiod's *Theogony* she is supposed to belong to the more ancient divinities, and, whilst those of later date are represented as having descended one from another, and all more or less from Zeus, Aphrodite has a variously-accounted-for, yet independent origin.

The most poetical version of her birth is that when Uranus was wounded by his son Cronus, his blood mingled with the foam of the sea, whereupon the bubbling waters at once assumed a rosy tint, and from their depths arose, in all the surpassing glory of her loveliness, Aphrodite, goddess of love and beauty! Shaking her long, fair tresses, the water-drops rolled down into the beautiful sea-shell in which she stood, and became transformed into pure glistening pearls. Wafted by the soft and balmy breezes, she floated on to Cythera, and was thence transported to the island of Cyprus. Lightly she stepped on shore, and under the gentle pressure of her delicate foot the dry and rigid sand became transformed into a verdant meadow, where every varied shade of colour and every sweet odour charmed the senses. The whole island of Cyprus became clothed with verdure, and greeted this fairest of all created beings with a glad smile of friendly welcome. Here she was received by the Seasons, who decked her with garments of immortal fabric, encircling her fair brow with a wreath of purest gold, whilst from her ears depended costly rings, and a glittering chain embraced her swan-like throat. And now, arrayed in all the panoply of her irresistible charms, the nymphs escort her to the dazzling halls of Olympus, where she is received with ecstatic enthusiasm by the admiring gods and goddesses. The gods all vied with each other in aspiring to the honour of her hand, but Hephæstus became the envied possessor of this lovely being, who, however, proved as faithless as she was beautiful, and caused her husband much unhappiness, owing to the preference she showed at various times for some of the other gods and also for mortal men.

The celebrated Venus of Milo, now in the Louvre, is an exquisite statue of this divinity. The head is beautifully formed; the rich waves of hair descend on her rather low but broad forehead and are caught up gracefully in a small knot at the back of the head; the expression of the face is most bewitching, and bespeaks the perfect joyousness of a happy nature combined with the dignity of a goddess; the drapery falls in careless folds from the waist downwards, and her whole attitude is the embodiment of all that is graceful and lovely in womanhood. She is of medium height, and the form is perfect in its symmetry and faultless proportions.

Aphrodite is also frequently represented in the act of confining her dripping locks in a knot, whilst her attendant nymphs envelop her in a gauzy veil.

The animals sacred to her were the dove, swan, swallow, and sparrow. Her favourite plants were the myrtle, apple-tree, rose, and poppy.

The worship of Aphrodite is supposed to have been introduced into Greece from Central Asia. There is no doubt that she was originally identical with the famous Astarté, the Ashtoreth of the Bible, against whose idolatrous worship and infamous rites the prophets of old hurled forth their sublime and powerful anathemas.

VENUS.

The Venus of the Romans was identified with the Aphrodite of the Greeks. The worship of this divinity was only established in Rome in comparatively later times. Annual festivals, called Veneralia, were held in her honour, and the month of April, when flowers and plants spring forth afresh, was sacred to her. She was worshipped as Venus Cloacina (or the Purifier), and as Venus Myrtea (or the myrtle goddess), an epithet derived from the myrtle, the emblem of Love.

HELIOS (Sol).

The worship of Helios was introduced into Greece from Asia. According to the earliest conceptions of the Greeks he was not only the sun-god, but also the personification of life and all life-giving power, for light is well known to be an indispensable condition of all healthy terrestrial life. The worship of the sun was originally very widely spread, not only among the early Greeks themselves, but also among other primitive nations. To us the sun is simply the orb of light, which, high above our heads, performs each day the functions assigned to it by a mighty and invisible Power; we can, therefore, form but a faint idea of the impression which it produced upon the spirit of a people whose intellect was still in its infancy, and who believed, with child-like simplicity, that every power of nature was a divinity, which, according as its character was baleful or benefi-cent, worked for the destruction or benefit of the human race.

Helios, who was the son of the Titans Hyperion and Theia, is described as rising every morning in the east, preceded by his sister Eos (the Dawn), who, with her rosy fingers, paints the tips of the mountains, and draws aside that misty veil through which her brother is about to appear. When he has burst forth in all the glorious light of day, Eos disap-pears, and Helios now drives his flame-darting chariot along the accustomed track. This chariot, which is of burnished gold, is drawn by four fire-breathing steeds, behind which the young god stands erect with flashing eyes, his head surrounded with rays, holding in one hand the reins of those fiery coursers which in all hands save his are unmanageable. When towards evening he descends the curve[26] in order to cool his burning forehead in the waters of the deep sea, he is followed closely by his sister Selene (the Moon), who is now prepared to take charge of the world, and illumine with her silver crescent the dusky night. Helios meanwhile rests from his labours, and, reclining softly on the cool fragrant couch prepared for him by the sea-nymphs, recruits himself for another life-giving, joy-inspiring, and beauteous day.

It may appear strange that, although the Greeks considered the earth to be a flat circle, no explanation is given of the fact that Helios sinks down in the far west regularly every evening, and yet reappears as regularly every morning in the east. Whether he was supposed to pass through Tartarus, and thus regain the opposite extremity through the bowels of the earth, or whether they thought he possessed any other means of making this transit, there is not a line in either Homer or Hesiod to prove. In later times, however, the poets invented the graceful fiction, that when Helios had finished his course, and reached the western side of the curve, a winged-boat, or cup, which had been made for him by Hephæstus, awaited him there, and conveyed him rapidly, with his glorious equipage, to the east, where he recommenced his bright and glowing career.

This divinity was invoked as a witness when a solemn oath was taken, as it was believed that nothing escaped his all-seeing eye, and it was this fact which enabled him to inform Demeter of the fate of her daughter, as already related. He was supposed to possess flocks and herds in various localities, which may possibly be intended to represent the days and nights of the year, or the stars of heaven.

Helios is said to have loved Clytie, a daughter of Oceanus, who ardently returned his affection; but in the course of time the fickle sun-god transferred his devotion to Leucothea, the daughter of Orchamus, king of the eastern countries, which so angered the forsaken Clytie that she informed Orchamus of his daughter's attachment, and he punished her by inhumanly burying her alive. Helios, overcome with grief, endeavoured, by every means in his power, to recall her to life. At last, finding all his efforts unavailing, he sprinkled her grave with heavenly nectar, and immediately there sprang forth from the spot a shoot of frankincense, which spread around its aromatic perfume.

The jealous Clytie gained nothing by her cruel conduct, for the sun-god came to her no more. Inconsolable at his loss, she threw herself upon the ground, and refused all sustenance. For nine long days she turned her face towards the glorious god of day, as he moved along the heavens, till at length her limbs became rooted in the ground, and she was transformed into a flower, which ever turns towards the sun.

Helios married Perse, daughter of Oceanus, and their children were, Aëtes, king of Colchis (celebrated in the legend of the Argonauts as the possessor of the Golden Fleece), and Circe, the renowned sorceress.

Helios had another son named Phaethon, whose mother was Clymene, one of the Oceanides. The youth was very beautiful, and a great favourite with Aphrodite, who intrusted him with the care of one of her temples, which flattering proof of her regard caused him to become vain and presumptuous. His friend Epaphus, son of Zeus and Io, endeavoured to check his youthful vanity by pretending to disbelieve his assertion that the sun-god was his father. Phaethon, full of resentment, and eager to be able to refute the calumny, hastened to his mother Clymene, and besought her to tell him whether Helios was really his father. Moved by his entreaties, and at the same time angry at the reproach of Epaphus, Clymene pointed to the glorious sun, then shining down upon them, and assured her son that in that bright orb he beheld the author of his being, adding that if he had still any doubt, he might visit the radiant dwelling of the great god of light and inquire for himself. Overjoyed at his mother's reassuring words, and following the directions she gave him, Phaethon quickly wended his way to his father's palace.

As he entered the palace of the sun-god the dazzling rays almost blinded him, and prevented him from approaching the throne on which his father was seated, surrounded by the Hours, Days, Months, Years, and Seasons. Helios, who with his all-seeing eye had watched him from afar, removed his crown of glittering rays, and bade him not to be afraid, but to draw near to his father. Encouraged by this kind reception, Phaethon entreated him to bestow upon him such a proof of his love, that all the world might be convinced that he was indeed his son; whereupon Helios desired him to ask any favour he pleased, and swore by the Styx that it should be granted. The impetuous youth immediately requested permission to drive the chariot of the sun for one whole day. His father listened horror-struck to this presumptuous demand, and by representing the many dangers which would beset his path, endeavoured to dissuade him from so perilous an undertaking; but his son, deaf to all advice, pressed his point with such pertinacity, that Helios was reluctantly compelled to lead him to the chariot. Phaethon paused for a moment to admire the beauty of the glittering equipage, the gift of the god of fire, who had formed it of gold, and ornamented it with precious stones, which reflected the rays of the sun. And now Helios, seeing his sister, the Dawn, opening her doors in the rosy east, ordered the Hours to yoke the horses. The goddesses speedily obeyed the command, and the father then anointed the face of his son with a sacred balm, to enable him to endure the burning flames which issued from the nostrils of the steeds, and sorrowfully placing his crown of rays upon his head, desired him to ascend the chariot.

The eager youth joyfully took his place and grasped the coveted reins, but no sooner did the fiery coursers of the sun feel the inexperienced hand which attempted to guide them, than they became restive and unmanageable. Wildly they rushed out of their accustomed track, now soaring so high as to threaten the heavens with destruction, now descending so low as nearly to set the earth on fire. At last the unfortunate charioteer, blinded with the glare, and terrified at the awful devastation he had caused, dropped the reins from his trembling hands. Mountains and forests were in flames, rivers and streams were dried up, and a general conflagration was imminent. The scorched earth now called on Zeus for help, who hurled his thunderbolt at Phaethon, and with a flash of lightning brought the fiery steeds to a standstill. The lifeless body of the youth fell headlong into the river Eridanus,[27] where it was received and buried by the nymphs of the stream. His sisters mourned so long for him that they were transformed by Zeus into poplars, and the tears they shed, falling into the waters, became drops of clear, transparent amber. Cycnus, the faithful friend of the unhappy Phaethon, felt such overwhelming grief at his terrible fate, that he pined and wasted away. The gods, moved with compassion, transformed him into a swan, which for ever brooded over the fatal spot where the waters had closed over the head of his unfortunate friend.

The chief seat of the worship of Helios was the island of Rhodes, which according to the following myth was his especial territory. At the time of the Titanomachia, when the gods were dividing the world by lot, Helios happened to be absent, and consequently received no share. He, therefore, complained to Zeus, who proposed to have a new allotment, but this Helios would not allow, saying, that as he pursued his daily journey, his penetrating eye had beheld a lovely, fertile island lying beneath the waves of the ocean, and that if the immortals would swear to give him the undisturbed possession of this spot, he would be content to accept it as his share of the universe. The gods took the oath, whereupon the island of Rhodes immediately raised itself above the surface of the waters.

The famous Colossus of Rhodes, which was one of the seven wonders of the world, was erected in honour of Helios. This wonderful statue was 105 feet high, and was formed entirely of brass; it formed the entrance to the harbour at Rhodes, and the largest vessel could easily sail between the legs, which stood on moles, each side of the harbour. Though so gigantic, it was perfectly proportioned in every part. Some idea of its size may be gained from the fact that very few people were able to span the thumb of this statue with their arms. In the interior of the Colossus was a winding staircase leading to the top, from the summit of which, by means of a telescope, the coast of Syria, and also the shores of Egypt, are said to have been visible.[28]

EOS (Aurora).

Eos, the Dawn, like her brother Helios, whose advent she always announced, was also deified by the early Greeks. She too had her own chariot, which she drove across the vast horizon both morning and night, before and after the sun-god. Hence she is not merely the personification of the rosy morn, but also of twilight, for which reason her palace is placed in the west, on the island Æææ. The abode of Eos is a magnificent structure, surrounded by flowery meads and velvety lawns, where nymphs and other immortal beings, wind in and out in the mazy figures of the dance, whilst the music of a sweetly-tuned melody accompanies their graceful, gliding movements.

Eos is described by the poets as a beautiful maiden with rosy arms and fingers, and large wings, whose plumage is of an ever-changing hue; she bears a star on her forehead, and a torch in her hand. Wrapping round her the rich folds of her violet-tinged mantle, she leaves her couch before the break of day, and herself yokes her two horses, Lampetus and Phaethon, to her glorious chariot. She then hastens with active cheerfulness to open the gates of heaven, in order to herald the approach of her brother, the god of day, whilst the tender plants and flowers, revived by the morning dew, lift their heads to welcome her as she passes.

Eos first married the Titan Astræus,[29] and their children were Heosphorus (Hesperus), the evening star, and the winds. She afterwards became united to Tithonus, son of Laomedon, king of Troy, who had won her affection by his unrivalled beauty; and Eos, unhappy at the thought of their being ever separated by death, obtained for him from Zeus the gift of immortality, forgetting, however, to add to it that of eternal youth. The consequence was that when, in the course of time, Tithonus grew old and decrepid, and lost all the beauty which had won her admiration, Eos became disgusted with his infirmities, and at last shut him up in a chamber, where soon little else was left of him but his voice, which had now sunk into a weak, feeble quaver. According to some of the later poets, he became so weary of his cheerless and miserable existence, that he entreated to be allowed to die. This was, however, impossible; but Eos, pitying his unhappy condition, exerted her divine power, and changed him into a grasshopper, which is, as it were, all voice, and whose monotonous, ceaseless chirpings may not inaptly be compared to the meaningless babble of extreme old age.

PHŒBUS-APOLLO.

Phœbus-Apollo, the god of Light, Prophecy, Music, Poetry, and the Arts and Sciences, is by far the noblest conception within the whole range of Greek mythology, and his worship, which not only extended to all the states of Greece, but also to Asia Minor and to every Greek colony throughout the world, stands out among the most ancient and strongly-marked features of Grecian history, and exerted a more decided influence over the Greek nation, than that of any other deity, not excepting Zeus himself.

Apollo was the son of Zeus and Leto, and was born beneath the shade of a palm tree which grew at the foot of Mount Cynthus, on the barren and rocky island of Delos. The poets tell us that the earth smiled when the young god first beheld the light of day, and that Delos became so proud and exultant at the honour thus conferred upon her, that she covered herself with golden flowers; swans surrounded the island, and the Delian nymphs celebrated his birth with songs of joy.

The unhappy Leto, driven to Delos by the relentless persecutions of Hera, was not long permitted to enjoy her haven of refuge. Being still tormented by her enemy, the young mother was once more obliged to fly; she therefore resigned the charge of her new-born babe to the goddess Themis, who carefully wrapped the helpless infant in swaddling-clothes, and fed him with nectar and ambrosia; but he had no sooner partaken of the heavenly food than, to the amazement of the goddess, he burst asunder the bands which confined his infant limbs, and springing to his feet, appeared before her as a full-grown youth of divine strength and beauty. He now demanded a lyre and a bow, declaring that henceforth he would announce to mankind the will of his father Zeus. "The golden lyre," said he, "shall be my friend, the bent bow my delight, and in oracles will I foretell the dark future." With these words he ascended to Olympus, where he was received with joyful acclamations into the assembly of the celestial gods, who acknowledged him as the most beautiful and glorious of all the sons of Zeus.

Phœbus-Apollo was the god of light in a twofold signification: first, as representing the great orb of day which illumines the world; and secondly, as the heavenly light which animates the soul of man. He inherited his function as sun-god from Helios, with whom, in later times, he was so completely identified, that the personality of the one became gradually merged in that of the other. We, accordingly, find Helios frequently confounded with Apollo, myths belonging to the former attributed to the latter; and with some tribes—the Ionic, for instance—so complete is this identification, that Apollo is called by them Helios-Apollo.

As the divinity whose power is developed in the broad light of day, he brings joy and delight to nature, and health and prosperity to man. By the influence of his warm and gentle rays he disperses the noxious vapours of the night, assists the grain to ripen and the flowers to bloom.

But although, as god of the sun, he is a life-giving and life-preserving power, who, by his genial influence, dispels the cold of winter, he is, at the same time, the god who, by means of his fiercely darting rays, could spread disease and send sudden death to men and animals; and it is to this phase of his character that we must look for the explanation of his being considered, in conjunction with his twin-sister, Artemis (as moon-goddess), a divinity of death. The brother and sister share this function between them, he taking man and she woman as her aim, and those especially who died in the bloom of youth, or at an advanced age, were believed to have been killed by their gentle arrows. But Apollo did not always send an easy death. We see in the *Iliad* how, when angry with the Greeks, the "god of the silver bow" strode down from Olympus, with his quiver full of death-bringing darts, and sent a raging pestilence into their camp. For nine days he let fly his fatal arrows, first on animals and then on men, till the air became darkened with the smoke from the funeral pyres.

In his character as god of light, Phœbus-Apollo is the protecting deity of shepherds, because it is he who warms the fields and meadows, and gives rich pastures to the flocks, thereby gladdening the heart of the herdsman.

As the temperate heat of the sun exercises so invigorating an effect on man and animals, and promotes the growth of those medicinal herbs and vegetable productions necessary for the cure of diseases, Phœbus-Apollo was supposed to possess the power of restoring life and health; hence he was regarded as the god of healing; but this feature in his character we shall find more particularly developed in his son Asclepius (Æsculapius), the veritable god of the healing art.

Pursuing our analysis of the various phases in the character of Phœbus-Apollo, we find that with the first beams of his genial light, all nature awakens to renewed life, and the woods re-echo with the jubilant sound of the untaught lays, warbled by thousands of feathered choristers. Hence, by a natural inference, he is the god of music, and as, according to the belief of the ancients, the inspirations of genius were inseparably connected with the glorious light of heaven, he is also the god of poetry, and acts as the special patron of the arts and sciences. Apollo is himself the heavenly musician among the Olympic gods, whose banquets are gladdened by the wondrous strains which he produces from his favourite instrument, the seven-stringed lyre. In the cultus of Apollo, music formed a distinguishing feature. All sacred dances, and even the sacrifices in his honour, were performed to the sound of musical instruments; and it is, in a great measure, owing to the influence which the music in his worship exercised on the Greek nation, that Apollo came to be regarded as the leader of the nine Muses, the legitimate divinities of poetry and song. In this character he is called Musagetes, and is always represented robed in a long flowing garment; his lyre, to the tones of which he appears to be singing, is suspended by a band across the chest; his head is encircled by a wreath of laurel, and his long hair, streaming down over his shoulders, gives him a somewhat effeminate appearance.

And now we must view the glorious god of light under another, and (as far as regards his influence over the Greek nation) a much more important aspect; for, in historical times, all the other functions and attributes of Apollo sink into comparative insignificance before the great power which he exercised as god of prophecy. It is true that all Greek gods were endowed, to a certain extent, with the faculty of fore-telling future events; but Apollo, as sun-god, was the concentration of all prophetic power, as it was supposed that nothing escaped his all-seeing eye, which penetrated the most hidden recesses, and laid bare the secrets which lay concealed behind the dark veil of the future.

We have seen that when Apollo assumed his god-like form, he took his place among the immortals; but he had not long enjoyed the rapturous delights of Olympus, before he felt within him an ardent desire to fulfil his great mission of interpreting to mankind the will of his mighty father. He accordingly descended to earth, and travelled through many countries, seeking a fitting site upon which to establish an oracle. At length he reached the southern side of the rocky heights of Parnassus, beneath which lay the harbour of Crissa.

Here, under the overhanging cliff, he found a secluded spot, where, from the most ancient times, there had existed an oracle, in which Gæa herself had revealed the future to man, and which, in Deucalion's time, she had resigned to Themis. It was guarded by the huge serpent Python, the scourge of the surrounding neighbourhood, and the terror alike of men and cattle. The young god, full of confidence in his unerring aim, attacked and slew the monster with his arrows, thus freeing land and people from their mighty enemy.

The grateful inhabitants, anxious to do honour to their deliverer, flocked round Apollo, who proceeded to mark out a plan for a temple, and, with the assistance of numbers of eager volunteers, a suitable edifice was soon erected. It now became necessary to choose ministers, who would offer up sacrifices, interpret his prophecies to the people, and take charge of the temple. Looking round, he saw in the far distance a vessel bound from Crete to the Peloponnesus, and determined to avail himself of her crew for his service. Assuming the shape of an enormous dolphin, he agitated the waters to such a degree, that the ship was tossed violently to and fro, to the great alarm of the mariners; at the same time he raised a mighty wind, which drove the ship into the harbour of Crissa, where she ran aground. The terrified sailors dared not set foot on shore; but Apollo, under the form of a vigorous youth, stepped down to the vessel, revealed himself in his true character, and informed them that it was he who had driven them to Crissa, in order that they might become his priests, and serve him in his temple. Arrived at the sacred fane, he instructed them how to perform the services in his honour, and desired them to worship him under the name of Apollo-Delphinios, because he had first appeared to them under the form of a dolphin. Thus was established the far-famed oracle of Delphi, the only institution of the kind which was not exclusively national, for it was consulted by Lydians, Phrygians, Etruscans, Romans, &c., and, in fact, was held in the highest repute all over the world. In obedience to its decrees, the laws of Lycurgus were introduced, and the earliest Greek colonies founded. No cities were built without first consulting the Delphic oracle, for it was believed that Apollo took special delight in the founding of cities, the first stone of which he laid in person; nor was any enterprise ever undertaken, without inquiring at this sacred fane as to its probable success.

But that which brought Apollo more closely home to the hearts of the people, and raised the whole moral tone of the Greek nation, was the belief, gradually developed with the intelligence of the people, that he was the god who accepted repentance as an atonement for sin, who pardoned the contrite sinner, and who acted as the special protector of those, who, like Orestes, had committed a crime, which required long years of expiation.

Apollo is represented by the poets as being eternally young; his countenance, glowing with joyous life, is the embodiment of immortal beauty; his eyes are of a deep blue; his forehead low, but broad and intellectual; his hair, which falls over his shoulders in long waving locks, is of a golden, or warm chestnut hue. He is crowned with laurel, and wears a purple robe; in his hand he bears his silver bow, which is unbent when he smiles, but ready for use when he menaces evil-doers.

But Apollo, the eternally beautiful youth, the perfection of all that is graceful and refined, rarely seems to have been happy in his love; either his advances met with a repulse, or his union with the object of his affection was attended with fatal consequences.

His first love was Daphne (daughter of Peneus, the river-god), who was so averse to marriage that she entreated her father to allow her to lead a life of celibacy, and devote herself to the chase, which she loved to the exclusion of all other pursuits. But one day, soon after his victory over the Python, Apollo happened to see Eros bending his bow, and proud of his own superior strength and skill, he laughed at the efforts of the little archer, saying that such a weapon was more suited to the one who had just killed the terrible serpent. Eros angrily replied that his arrow should pierce the heart of the mocker himself, and flying off to the summit of Mount Parnassus, he drew from his quiver two darts of different workmanship—one of gold, which had the effect of inspiring love; the other of lead, which created aversion. Taking aim at Apollo, he pierced his breast with the golden shaft, whilst the leaden one he discharged into the bosom of the beautiful Daphne. The son of Leto instantly felt the most ardent affection for the nymph, who, on her part, evinced the greatest dislike towards her divine lover, and, at his approach, fled from him like a hunted deer. He called upon her in the most endearing accents to stay, but she still sped on, until at length, becoming faint with fatigue, and fearing that she was about to succumb, she called upon the gods to come to her aid. Hardly had she uttered her prayer before a heavy torpor seized her limbs, and just as Apollo threw out his arms to embrace her, she became transformed into a laurel-bush. He sorrowfully crowned his head with its leaves, and declared, that in memory of his love, it should henceforth remain evergreen, and be held sacred to him.

He next sought the love of Marpessa, the daughter of Evenus; but though her father approved his suit, the maiden preferred a youth named Idas, who contrived to carry her off in a winged chariot which he had procured from Poseidon. Apollo pursued the fugitives, whom he quickly overtook, and forcibly seizing the bride, refused to resign her. Zeus then interfered, and declared that Marpessa herself must decide which of her lovers should claim her as his wife. After due reflection she accepted Idas as her husband, judiciously concluding that although the attractions of the divine Apollo were superior to those of her lover, it would be wiser to unite herself to a mortal, who, growing old with herself, would be less likely to forsake her, when advancing years should rob her of her charms.

Cassandra, daughter of Priam, king of Troy, was another object of the love of Apollo. She feigned to return his affection, and promised to marry him, provided he would confer upon her the gift of prophecy; but having received the boon she desired, the treacherous maiden refused to comply with the conditions upon which it had been granted. Incensed at her breach of faith, Apollo, unable to recall the gift he had bestowed, rendered it useless by causing her predictions to fail in obtaining credence. Cassandra became famous in history for her prophetic powers, but her prophecies were never believed. For instance, she warned her brother Paris that if he brought back a wife from Greece he would cause the destruction of his father's house and kingdom; she also warned the Trojans not to admit the wooden horse within the walls of the city, and foretold to Agamemnon all the disasters which afterwards befell him.

Apollo afterwards married Coronis, a nymph of Larissa, and thought himself happy in the possession of her faithful love; but once more he was doomed to disappointment, for one day his favourite bird, the crow, flew to him with the intelligence that his wife had transferred her affections to a youth of Haemonia. Apollo, burning with rage, instantly destroyed her with one of his death-bringing darts. Too late he repented of his rashness, for she had been tenderly beloved by him, and he would fain have recalled her to life; but, although he exerted all his healing powers, his efforts were in vain. He punished the crow for its garrulity by changing the colour of its plumage from pure white to intense black, and forbade it to fly any longer among the other birds.

Coronis left an infant son named Asclepius, who afterwards became god of medicine. His powers were so extraordinary that he could not only cure the sick, but could even restore the dead to life. At last Aïdes complained to Zeus that the number of shades conducted to his dominions was daily decreasing, and the great ruler of Olympus, fearing that mankind, thus protected against sickness and death, would be able to defy the gods themselves, killed Asclepius with one of his thunderbolts. The loss of his highly gifted son so exasperated Apollo that, being unable to vent his anger on Zeus, he destroyed the Cyclops, who had forged the fatal thunderbolts. For this offence, Apollo would have been banished by Zeus to Tartarus, but at the earnest intercession of Leto he partially relented, and contented himself with depriving him of all power and dignity, and imposing on him a temporary servitude in the house of Admetus, king of Thessaly. Apollo faithfully served his royal master for nine years in the humble capacity of a shepherd, and was treated by him with every kindness and consideration. During the period of his service the king sought the hand of Alcestis, the beautiful daughter of Pelias, son of Poseidon; but her father declared that he would only resign her to the suitor who should succeed in yoking a lion and a wild boar to his chariot. By the aid of his divine herdsman, Admetus accomplished this difficult task, and gained his bride. Nor was this the only favour which the king received from the exiled god, for Apollo obtained from the Fates the gift of immortality for his benefactor, on condition that when his last hour approached, some member of his own family should be willing to die in his stead. When the fatal hour arrived, and Admetus felt that he was at the point of death, he implored his aged parents to yield to him their few remaining days. But "life is sweet" even to old age, and they both refused to make the sacrifice demanded of them. Alcestis, however, who had secretly devoted herself to death for her husband, was seized with a mortal sickness, which kept pace with his rapid recovery. The devoted wife breathed her last in the arms of Admetus, and he had just consigned her to the tomb, when Heracles chanced to come to the palace. Admetus held the rites of hospitality so sacred, that he at first kept silence with regard to his great bereavement; but as soon as his friend heard what had occurred, he bravely descended into the tomb, and when death came to claim his prey, he exerted his marvellous strength, and held him in his arms, until he promised to restore the beautiful and heroic queen to the bosom of her family.

Whilst pursuing the peaceful life of a shepherd, Apollo formed a strong friendship with two youths named Hyacinthus and Cyparissus, but the great favour shown to them by the god did not suffice to shield them from misfortune. The former was one day throwing the discus with Apollo, when, running too eagerly to take up the one thrown by the god, he was struck on the head with it and killed on the spot. Apollo was overcome with grief at the sad end of his young favourite, but being unable to restore him to life, he changed him into the flower called after him the Hyacinth. Cyparissus had the misfortune to kill by accident one of Apollo's favourite stags, which so preyed on his mind that he gradually pined away, and died of a broken heart. He was transformed by the god into a cypress-tree, which owes its name to this story.

After these sad occurrences Apollo quitted Thessaly and repaired to Phrygia, in Asia Minor, where he met Poseidon, who, like himself, was in exile, and condemned to a temporary servitude on earth. The two gods now entered the service of Laomedon, king of Troy, Apollo undertaking to tend his flocks, and Poseidon to build the walls of the city. But Apollo also contributed his assistance in the erection of those wonderful walls, and, by the aid of his marvellous musical powers, the labours of his fellow-worker, Poseidon, were rendered so light and easy that his otherwise arduous task advanced with astonishing celerity; for, as the master-hand of the god of music grasped the chords of his lyre,[30] the huge blocks of stone moved of their own accord, adjusting themselves with the utmost nicety into the places designed for them.

But though Apollo was so renowned in the art of music, there were two individuals who had the effrontery to consider themselves equal to him in this respect, and, accordingly, each challenged him to compete with them in a musical contest.

These were Marsyas and Pan. Marsyas was a satyr, who, having picked up the flute which Athene had thrown away in disgust, discovered, to his great delight and astonishment, that, in consequence of its having touched the lips of a goddess, it played of itself in the most charming manner. Marsyas, who was a great lover of music, and much beloved on this account by all the elf-like denizens of the woods and glens, was so intoxicated with joy at this discovery, that he foolishly challenged Apollo to compete with him in a musical contest. The challenge being accepted, the Muses were chosen umpires, and it was decided that the unsuccessful candidate should suffer the punishment of being flayed alive. For a long time the merits of both claimants remained so equally balanced, that it was impossible to award the palm of victory to either, seeing which, Apollo, resolved to conquer, added the sweet tones of his melodious voice to the strains of his lyre, and this at once turned the scale in his favour. The unhappy Marsyas being defeated, had to undergo the terrible penalty, and his untimely fate was universally lamented; indeed the Satyrs and Dryads, his companions, wept so incessantly at his fate, that their tears, uniting together, formed a river in Phrygia which is still known by the name of Marsyas.

The result of the contest with Pan was by no means of so serious a character. The god of shepherds having affirmed that he could play more skilfully on his flute of seven reeds (the syrinx or Pan's pipe), than Apollo on his world-renowned lyre, a contest ensued, in which Apollo was pronounced the victor by all the judges appointed to decide between the rival candidates. Midas, king of Phrygia, alone demurred at this decision, having the bad taste to prefer the uncouth tones of the Pan's pipe to the refined melodies of Apollo's lyre. Incensed at the obstinacy and stupidity of the Phrygian king, Apollo punished him by giving him the ears of an ass. Midas, horrified at being thus disfigured, determined to hide his disgrace from his subjects by means of a cap; his barber, however, could not be kept in ignorance of the fact, and was therefore bribed with rich gifts never to reveal it. Finding, however, that he could not keep the secret any longer, he dug a hole in the ground into which he whispered it; then closing up the aperture he returned home, feeling greatly relieved at having thus eased his mind of its burden. But after all, this very humiliating secret was revealed to the world, for some reeds which sprung up from the spot murmured incessantly, as they waved to and fro in the wind: "King Midas has the ears of an ass."

In the sad and beautiful story of Niobe, daughter of Tantalus, and wife of Amphion, king of Thebes, we have another instance of the severe punishments meted out by Apollo to those who in any way incurred his displeasure. Niobe was the proud mother of seven sons and seven daughters, and exulting in the number of her children, she, upon one occasion, ridiculed the worship of Leto, because she had but one son and daughter, and desired the Thebans, for the future, to give to her the honours and sacrifices which they had hitherto offered to the mother of Apollo and Artemis. The sacrilegious words had scarcely passed her lips before Apollo called upon his sister Artemis to assist him in avenging the insult offered to their mother, and soon their invisible arrows sped through the air. Apollo slew all the sons, and Artemis had already slain all the daughters save one, the youngest and best beloved, whom Niobe clasped in her arms, when the agonized mother implored the enraged deities to leave her, at least, one out of all her beautiful children; but, even as she prayed, the deadly arrow reached the heart of this child also. Meanwhile the unhappy father, unable to bear the loss of his children, had destroyed himself, and his dead body lay beside the lifeless corpse of his favourite son. Widowed and childless, the heart-broken mother sat among her dead, and the gods, in pity for her unutterable woe, turned her into a stone, which they transferred to Siphylus, her native Phrygian mountain, where it still continues to shed tears.

The punishment of Niobe forms the subject of a

magnificent marble group, which was found at Rome in the year 1553, and is now in the gallery of Uffizi, at Florence.

The renowned singer Orpheus was the son of Apollo and Calliope, the muse of epic poetry, and, as might be expected with parents so highly gifted, was endowed with most distinguished intellectual qualifications. He was a poet, a teacher of the religious doctrines known as the Orphic mysteries, and a great musician, having inherited from his father an extraordinary genius for music. When he sang to the sweet tones of his lyre, he charmed all nature, and summoned round him the wild beasts of the forests, who, under the influence of his music, became tame and gentle as lambs. The madly rushing torrents stopped their rapid course, and the very mountains and trees moved from their places at the sound of his entrancing melodies.

Orpheus became united to a lovely nymph named Eurydice, the daughter of the sea-god Nereus, whom he fondly loved. She was no less attached to him, and their married life was full of joy and happiness. But it was only short-lived; for Aristæus,[31] the half-brother of Orpheus, having fallen in love with the beautiful Eurydice, forcibly endeavoured to take her from her husband, and as she fled across some fields to elude his pursuit, she was bitten in the foot by a venomous snake, which lay concealed in the long grass. Eurydice died of the wound, and her sorrowing husband filled the groves and valleys with his piteous and unceasing lamentations.

His longing to behold her once more became at last so unconquerable, that he determined to brave the horrors of the lower world, in order to entreat Aïdes to restore to him his beloved wife. Armed only with his golden lyre, the gift of Apollo, he descended into the gloomy depths of Hades, where his heavenly music arrested for a while the torments of the unhappy sufferers. The stone of Sisyphus remained motionless; Tantalus forgot his perpetual thirst; the wheel of Ixion ceased to revolve; and even the Furies shed tears, and withheld for a time their persecutions. Undismayed at the scenes of horror and suffering which met his view on every side, he pursued his way until he arrived at the palace of Aïdes. Presenting himself before the throne on which sat the stony-hearted king and his consort Persephone, Orpheus recounted his woes to the sound of his lyre. Moved to pity by his sweet strains, they listened to his melancholy story, and consented to release Eurydice on condition that he should not look upon her until they reached the upper world. Orpheus gladly promised to comply with this injunction, and, followed by Eurydice, ascended the steep and gloomy path which led to the realms of life and light. All went well until he was just about to pass the extreme limits of Hades, when, forgetting for the moment the hard condition, he turned to convince himself that his beloved wife was really behind him. The glance was fatal, and destroyed all his hopes of happiness; for, as he yearningly stretched out his arms to embrace her, she was caught back, and vanished from his sight for ever. The grief of Orpheus at this second loss was even more intense than before, and he now avoided all human society. In vain did the nymphs, his once chosen companions, endeavour to win him back to his accustomed haunts; their power to charm was gone, and music was now his sole consolation. He wandered forth alone, choosing the wildest and most secluded paths, and the hills and vales resounded with his pathetic melodies. At last he happened to cross the path of some Thracian women, who were performing the wild rites of Dionysus (Bacchus), and in their mad fury at his refusing to join them, they furiously attacked him, and tore him in pieces. In pity for his unhappy fate, the Muses collected his remains, which they buried at the foot of Mount Olympus, and the nightingale warbled a funeral dirge over his grave. His head was thrown into the river Hebrus, and as it floated down the stream, the lips still continued to murmur the beloved name of Eurydice.

The chief seat of the worship of Apollo was at Delphi,

and here was the most magnificent of all his temples, the foundation of which reaches far beyond all historical knowledge, and which contained immense riches, the offerings of kings and private persons, who had received favourable replies from the oracle. The Greeks believed Delphi to be the central point of the earth, because two eagles sent forth by Zeus, one from the east, the other from the west, were said to have arrived there at the same moment.

The Pythian games, celebrated in honour of the victory of Apollo over the Python, took place at Delphi every four years. At the first celebration of these games, gods, goddesses, and heroes contended for the prizes, which were at first of gold or silver, but consisted, in later times, of simple laurel wreaths.

On account of its being the place of his birth, the whole island of Delos was consecrated to Apollo, where he was worshipped with great solemnity; the greatest care was taken to preserve the sanctity of the spot, for which reason no one was suffered to be buried there. At the foot of Mount Cynthus was a splendid temple of Apollo which possessed an oracle, and was enriched with magnificent offerings from all parts of Greece. Even foreign nations held this island sacred, for when the Persians passed it on their way to attack Greece, they not only sailed by, leaving it uninjured, but sent rich presents to the temple. Games, called Delia, instituted by Theseus, were celebrated at Delos every four years.

A festival termed the Gymnopedæa was held at Sparta in honour of Apollo, in which boys sang the praises of the gods, and of the three hundred Lacedæmonians who fell at the battle of Thermopylæ.

Wolves and hawks were sacrificed to Apollo, and the birds sacred to him were the hawk, raven, and swan.

ROMAN APOLLO.

The worship of Apollo never occupied the all-important position in Rome which it held in Greece, nor was it introduced till a comparatively late period. There was no sanctuary erected to this divinity until B.C. 430, when the Romans, in order to avert a plague, built a temple in his honour; but we do not find the worship of Apollo becoming in any way prominent until the time of Augustus, who, having called upon this god for aid before the famous battle of Actium, ascribed the victory which he gained, to his influence, and accordingly erected a temple there, which he enriched with a portion of the spoil.

Augustus afterwards built another temple in honour of Apollo, on the Palatine Hill, in which at the foot of his statue, were deposited two gilt chests, containing the Sibylline oracles. These oracles were collected to replace the Sibylline books originally preserved in the temple of Jupiter, which were destroyed when that edifice was burned.

The Sibyls were maidens who had received the gift of prophecy, and the privilege of living to an incredible age. One of these Sibyls (known as the Cumæan) appeared to Tarquinius Superbus, the last king of Rome, offering for sale nine books, which she informed him had been written by herself. Not knowing who she was, Tarquin refused to buy them, upon which she burned three, and returned with six, demanding the same price as before. Being again driven away as an impostor, she again retired and burned three more, returning with the remaining three, for which she still asked the same price as at first. Tarquin, amazed at her inconsistency, now consulted the Augurs, who blamed him for not having bought the nine books when they were first offered to him, and desired him to secure the remaining three, at whatever price they were to be had. He, accordingly, purchased the volumes, which were found to contain predictions of great importance to the Romans. After the disposal of the books, the Sibyl vanished, and was seen no more.

The most beautiful and renowned of all the statues of Apollo now in existence, is that known as the Apollo Belvedere, which was found in 1503 among the ruins of ancient Antium. It was purchased by Pope Julius II., who removed it to the Belvedere of the Vatican, from whence it takes its name, and where it has been, for more than three hundred years, the admiration of the world. When Rome was taken, and plundered by the French, this celebrated statue was transported to Paris, and placed in the museum there, but in 1815 it was restored to its former place in the Vatican. The attitude of the figure, which is more than seven feet high, is inimitable in its freedom, grace, and majesty. The forehead is noble and intellectual, and the whole countenance so exquisite in its beauty, that one pauses spell-bound to gaze on so perfect a conception. The god has a very youthful appearance, as is usual in all his representations, and with the exception of a short mantle which falls from his shoulders, is unclothed. He stands against the trunk of a tree, up which a serpent is creeping, and his left arm is outstretched, as though about to punish.

HECATE.

Hecate would appear to have been originally a moon-goddess worshipped by the Thracians. She became confounded, and eventually identified with Selene and Persephone, and is one of those divinities of whom the ancients had various conflicting accounts.

Hecate was the daughter of Perses and "gold-wreathed" Astræa (the starry night[32]), and her sway extended over earth, heaven, and hell, for which reason she is represented in works of art as a triple divinity, having three female bodies, all young and beautiful, and united together.

In later times, when this divinity becomes identified with Persephone, she is supposed to inhabit the lower world as a malignant deity, and henceforward it is the gloomy, awe-inspiring side of her character which alone develops itself. She now presides over all practices connected with witchcraft and enchantments, haunts sepulchres, and the point where two roads cross, and lonely spots where murders have been committed. She was supposed to be connected with the appearance of ghosts and spectres, to possess unlimited influence over the powers of the lower world, and to be able to lay to rest unearthly apparitions by her magic spells and incantations.

Hecate appears as a gigantic woman, bearing a torch and a sword. Her feet and hair are formed of snakes, and her passage is accompanied by voices of thunder, weird shrieks and yells, and the deep baying and howling of dogs.

Her favour was propitiated by offerings and sacrifices, principally consisting of black lambs. Her festivals were celebrated at night, by torchlight, when these animals were offered to her, accompanied by many peculiar ceremonies. These ceremonies were carried out with the minutest attention to details, as it was believed that the omission of the slightest particular would afford to her ministers, the evil spirits of the lower world, who hovered round the worshippers, an opportunity for entering among them, and exerting their baneful influence. At the end of every month food was placed wherever two roads met, in readiness for her and other malignant divinities.

In studying the peculiar characteristics which Hecate assumes when she usurps the place of Persephone, the rightful mistress of the lower world, we are reminded of the various superstitions with regard to spectres, witchcraft, &c., which have, even down to our own times, exerted so powerful an influence over the minds of the ignorant, and which would appear to owe their origin to a remote pagan source.

SELENE (LUNA).

Just as Helios personified the sun, so his sister Selene represented the moon, and was supposed to drive her chariot across the sky whilst her brother was reposing after the toils of the day.

When the shades of evening began to enfold the earth, the two milk-white steeds of Selene rose out of the mysterious depths of Oceanus. Seated in a silvery chariot, and accompanied by her daughter Herse, the goddess of the dew, appeared the mild and gentle queen of the night, with a crescent on her fair brow, a gauzy veil flowing behind, and a lighted torch in her hand.

Selene greatly admired a beautiful young shepherd named Endymion, to whom Zeus had accorded the privilege of eternal youth, combined with the faculty of sleeping whenever he desired, and as long as he wished. Seeing this lovely youth fast asleep on Mount Latmus, Selene was so struck with his beauty, that she came down every night from heaven to watch over and protect him.

ARTEMIS (DIANA).

Artemis was worshipped by the Greeks under various appellations, to each of which belonged special characteristics. Thus she is known as the Arcadian, Ephesian and Brauronian Artemis, and also as Selene-Artemis, and in order fully to comprehend the worship of this divinity, we must consider her under each aspect.

ARCADIAN ARTEMIS.

The Arcadian Artemis (the real Artemis of the Greeks) was the daughter of Zeus and Leto, and twin-sister of Apollo. She was the goddess of Hunting and Chastity, and having obtained from her father permission to lead a life of celibacy, she ever remained a maiden-divinity. Artemis is the feminine counterpart of her brother, the glorious god of Light, and, like him, though she deals out destruction and sudden death to men and animals, she is also able to alleviate suffering and cure diseases. Like Apollo also, she is skilled in the use of the bow, but in a far more eminent degree, for in the character of

Artemis, who devoted herself to the chase with passionate ardour, this becomes an all-distinguishing feature. Armed with her bow and quiver, and attended by her train of huntresses, who were nymphs of the woods and springs, she roamed over the mountains in pursuit of her favourite exercise, destroying in her course the wild animals of the forest. When the chase was ended, Artemis and her maidens loved to assemble in a shady grove, or on the banks of a favourite stream, where they joined in the merry song, or graceful dance, and made the hills resound with their joyous shouts.

As the type of purity and chastity, Artemis was especially venerated by young maidens, who, before marrying, sacrificed their hair to her. She was also the patroness of those vowed to celibacy, and punished severely any infringement of their obligation.

The huntress-goddess is represented as being a head taller than her attendant nymphs, and always appears as a youthful and slender maiden. Her features are beautiful, but wanting in gentleness of expression; her hair is gathered negligently into a knot at the back of her well-shaped head; and her figure, though somewhat masculine, is most graceful in its attitude and proportions. The short robe she wears, leaves her limbs free for the exercise of the chase, her devotion to which is indicated by the quiver which is slung over her shoulder, and the bow which she bears in her hand.

There are many famous statues of this divinity; but the most celebrated is that known as the Diana of Versailles, now in the Louvre, which forms a not unworthy companion to the Apollo-Belvedere of the Vatican. In this statue, the goddess appears in the act of rescuing a hunted deer from its pursuers, on whom she is turning with angry mien. One hand is laid protectingly on the head of the stag, whilst with the other she draws an arrow from the quiver which hangs over her shoulder.

Her attributes are the bow, quiver, and spear. The animals sacred to her are the hind, dog, bear, and wild boar.

Artemis promptly resented any disregard or neglect of her worship; a remarkable instance of this is shown in the story of the Calydonian boar-hunt, which is as follows:—

Oeneus, king of Calydon in Ætolia, had incurred the displeasure of Artemis by neglecting to include her in a general sacrifice to the gods which he had offered up, out of gratitude for a bountiful harvest. The goddess, enraged at this neglect, sent a wild boar of extraordinary size and prodigious strength, which destroyed the sprouting grain, laid waste the fields, and threatened the inhabitants with famine and death. At this juncture, Meleager, the brave son of Oeneus, returned from the Argonautic expedition, and finding his country ravaged by this dreadful scourge, entreated the assistance of all the celebrated heroes of the age to join him in hunting the ferocious monster. Among the most famous of those who responded to his call were Jason, Castor and Pollux, Idas and Lynceus, Peleus, Telamon, Admetus, Perithous, and Theseus. The brothers of Althea, wife of Oeneus, joined the hunters, and Meleager also enlisted into his service the fleet-footed huntress Atalanta.

The father of this maiden was Schoeneus, an Arcadian, who, disappointed at the birth of a daughter when he had particularly desired a son, had exposed her on the Parthenian Hill, where he left her to perish. Here she was nursed by a she-bear, and at last found by some hunters, who reared her, and gave her the name of Atalanta. As the maiden grew up, she became an ardent lover of the chase, and was alike distinguished for her beauty and courage. Though often wooed, she led a life of strict celibacy, an oracle having predicted that inevitable misfortune awaited her, should she give herself in marriage to any of her numerous suitors.

Many of the heroes objected to hunt in company with a maiden; but Meleager, who loved Atalanta, overcame their opposition, and the valiant band set out on their expedition. Atalanta was the first to wound the boar with her spear, but not before two of the heroes had met their death from his fierce tusks. After a long and desperate encounter, Meleager succeeded in killing the monster, and presented the head and hide to Atalanta, as trophies of the victory. The uncles of Meleager, however, forcibly took the hide from the maiden, claiming their right to the spoil as next of kin, if Meleager resigned it. Artemis, whose anger was still unappeased, caused a violent quarrel to arise between uncles and nephew, and, in the struggle which ensued, Meleager killed his mother's brothers, and then restored the hide to Atalanta. When Althea beheld the dead bodies of the slain heroes, her grief and anger knew no bounds. She swore to revenge the death of her brothers on her own son, and unfortunately for him, the instrument of vengeance lay ready to her hand.

At the birth of Meleager, the Moirae, or Fates, entered the house of Oeneus, and pointing to a piece of wood then burning on the hearth, declared that as soon as it was consumed the babe would surely die. On hearing this, Althea seized the brand, laid it up carefully in a chest, and henceforth preserved it as her most precious possession. But now, love for her son giving place to the resentment she felt against the murderer of her brothers, she threw the fatal brand into the devouring flames. As it consumed, the vigour of Meleager wasted away, and when it was reduced to ashes, he expired. Repenting too late the terrible effects of her rash deed, Althea, in remorse and despair, took away her own life.

The news of the courage and intrepidity displayed by Atalanta in the famous boar-hunt, being carried to the ears of her father, caused him to acknowledge his long-lost child. Urged by him to choose one of her numerous suitors, she consented to do so, but made it a condition that he alone, who could outstrip her in the race, should become her husband, whilst those she defeated should be put to death by her, with the lance which she bore in her hand. Thus many suitors had perished, for the maiden was unequalled for swiftness of foot, but at last a beautiful youth, named Hippomenes, who had vainly endeavoured to win her love by his assiduous attentions in the chase, ventured to enter the fatal lists. Knowing that only by stratagem could he hope to be successful, he obtained, by the help of Aphrodite, three golden apples from the garden of the Hesperides, which he threw down at intervals during his course. Atalanta, secure of victory, stooped to pick up the tempting fruit, and, in the meantime, Hippomenes arrived at the goal. He became the husband of the lovely Atalanta, but forgot, in his newly found happiness, the gratitude which he owed to Aphrodite, and the goddess withdrew her favour from the pair. Not long after, the prediction which foretold misfortune to Atalanta, in the event of her marriage, was verified, for she and her husband, having strayed unsanctioned into a sacred grove of Zeus, were both transformed into lions.

The trophies of the ever-memorable boar-hunt had been carried by Atalanta into Arcadia, and, for many centuries, the identical hide and enormous tusks of the Calydonian boar hung in the temple of Athene at Tegea. The tusks were afterwards conveyed to Rome, and shown there among other curiosities.

A forcible instance of the manner in which Artemis resented any intrusion on her retirement, is seen in the fate which befell the famous hunter Actaeon, who happening one day to see Artemis and her attendants bathing, imprudently ventured to approach the spot. The goddess, incensed at his audacity, sprinkled him with water, and transformed him into a stag, whereupon he was torn in pieces and devoured by his own dogs.

EPHESIAN ARTEMIS.

The Ephesian Artemis, known to us as "Diana of the Ephesians," was a very ancient Asiatic divinity of Persian origin called Metra,[33] whose worship the Greek colonists found already established, when they first settled in Asia Minor, and whom they identified with their own Greek Artemis, though she really possessed but one single attribute in common with their home deity.

Metra was a twofold divinity, and represented, in one phase of her character, all-pervading love; in the other she was the light of heaven; and as Artemis, in her character as Selene, was the only Greek female divinity who represented celestial light, the Greek settlers, according to their custom of fusing foreign deities into their own, seized at once upon this point of resemblance, and decided that Metra should henceforth be regarded as identical with Artemis.

In her character as the love which pervades all nature, and penetrates everywhere, they believed her also to be present in the mysterious Realm of Shades, where she exercised her benign sway, replacing to a certain extent that ancient divinity Hecate, and partly usurping also the place of Persephone, as mistress of the lower world. Thus they believed that it was she who permitted the spirits of the departed to revisit the earth, in order to communicate with those they loved, and to give them timely warning of coming evil. In fact, this great, mighty, and omnipresent power of love, as embodied in the Ephesian Artemis, was believed by the great thinkers of old, to be the ruling spirit of the universe, and it was to her influence, that all the mysterious and beneficent workings of nature were ascribed.

There was a magnificent temple erected to this divinity at Ephesus (a city of Asia Minor), which was ranked among the seven wonders of the world, and was unequalled in beauty and grandeur. The interior of this edifice was adorned with statues and paintings, and contained one hundred and twenty-seven columns, sixty feet in height, each column having been placed there by a different king. The wealth deposited in this temple was enormous, and the goddess was here worshipped with particular awe and solemnity. In the interior of the edifice stood a statue of her, formed of ebony, with lions on her arms and turrets on her head, whilst a number of breasts indicated the fruitfulness of the earth and of nature. Ctesiphon was the principal architect of this world-renowned structure, which, however, was not entirely completed till two hundred and twenty years after the foundation-stone was laid. But the labour of centuries was destroyed in a single night; for a man called Herostratus, seized with the insane desire of making his name famous to all succeeding generations, set fire to it and completely destroyed it.[34] So great was the indignation and sorrow of the Ephesians at this calamity, that they enacted a law, forbidding the incendiary's name to be mentioned, thereby however, defeating their own object, for thus the name of Herostratus has been handed down to posterity, and will live as long as the memory of the famous temple of Ephesus.

BRAURONIAN ARTEMIS.

In ancient times, the country which we now call the Crimea, was known by the name of the Taurica Chersonnesus. It was colonized by Greek settlers, who, finding that the Scythian inhabitants had a native divinity somewhat resembling their own Artemis, identified her with the huntress-goddess of the mother-country. The worship of this Taurian Artemis was attended with the most barbarous practices, for, in accordance with a law which she had enacted, all strangers, whether male or female, landing, or shipwrecked on her shores, were sacrificed upon her altars. It is supposed that this decree was issued by the Taurian goddess of Chastity, to protect the purity of her followers, by keeping them apart from foreign influences.

The interesting story of Iphigenia, a priestess in the temple of Artemis at Tauris, forms the subject of one of Schiller's most beautiful plays. The circumstances occurred at the commencement of the Trojan war, and are as follows:—
The fleet, collected by the Greeks for the siege of Troy, had

assembled at Aulis, in Bœotia, and was about to set sail, when Agamemnon, the commander-in-chief, had the misfortune to kill accidentally a stag which was grazing in a grove, sacred to Artemis. The offended goddess sent continuous calms that delayed the departure of the fleet, and Calchas, the soothsayer, who had accompanied the expedition, declared that nothing less than the sacrifice of Agamemnon's favorite daughter, Iphigenia, would appease the wrath of the goddess. At these words, the heroic heart of the brave leader sank within him, and he declared that rather than consent to so fearful an alternative, he would give up his share in the expedition and return to Argos. In this dilemma Odysseus and other great generals called a council to discuss the matter, and, after much deliberation, it was decided that private feeling must yield to the welfare of the state. For a long time the unhappy Agamemnon turned a deaf ear to their arguments, but at last they succeeded in persuading him that it was his duty to make the sacrifice. He, accordingly, despatched a messenger to his wife, Clytemnæstra, begging her to send Iphigenia to him, alleging as a pretext that the great hero Achilles desired to make her his wife. Rejoicing at the brilliant destiny which awaited her beautiful daughter, the fond mother at once obeyed the command, and sent her to Aulis. When the maiden arrived at her destination, and discovered, to her horror, the dreadful fate which awaited her, she threw herself in an agony of grief at her father's feet, and with sobs and tears entreated him to have mercy on her, and to spare her young life. But alas! her doom was sealed, and her now repentant and heart-broken father was powerless to avert it. The unfortunate victim was bound to the altar, and already the fatal knife was raised to deal the death-blow, when suddenly Iphigenia disappeared from view, and in her place on the altar, lay a beautiful deer ready to be sacrificed. It was Artemis herself, who, pitying the youth and beauty of her victim, caused her to be conveyed in a cloud to Taurica, where she became one of her priestesses, and intrusted with the charge of her temple; a dignity, however, which necessitated the offering of those human sacrifices presented to Artemis.

Many years passed away, during which time the long and wearisome siege of Troy had come to an end, and the brave Agamemnon had returned home to meet death at the hands of his wife and Aegisthus. But his daughter, Iphigenia, was still an exile from her native country, and continued to perform the terrible duties which her office involved. She had long given up all hopes of ever being restored to her friends, when one day two Greek strangers landed on Taurica's inhospitable shores. These were Orestes and Pylades, whose romantic attachment to each other has made their names synonymous for devoted self-sacrificing friendship. Orestes was Iphigenia's brother, and Pylades her cousin, and their object in undertaking an expedition fraught with so much peril, was to obtain the statue of the Taurian Artemis. Orestes, having incurred the anger of the Furies for avenging the murder of his father Agamemnon, was pursued by them wherever he went, until at last he was informed by the oracle of Delphi that, in order to pacify them, he must convey the image of the Taurian Artemis from Tauris to Attica. This he at once resolved to do, and accompanied by his faithful friend Pylades, who insisted on sharing the dangers of the undertaking, he set out for Taurica. But the unfortunate youths had hardly stepped on shore before they were seized by the natives, who, as usual, conveyed them for sacrifice to the temple of Artemis. Iphigenia, discovering that they were Greeks, though unaware of their near relationship to herself, thought the opportunity a favourable one for sending tidings of her existence to her native country, and, accordingly, requested one of the strangers to be the bearer of a letter from her to her family. A magnanimous dispute now arose between the friends, and each besought the other to accept the precious privilege of life and freedom. Pylades, at length overcome by the urgent entreaties of Orestes, agreed to be the bearer of the missive, but on looking more closely at the superscription, he observed, to his intense surprise, that it was addressed to Orestes. Hereupon an explanation followed; the brother and sister recognized each other, amid joyful tears and loving embraces, and assisted by her friends and kinsmen, Iphigenia escaped with them from a country where she had spent so many unhappy days, and witnessed so many scenes of horror and anguish.

The fugitives, having contrived to obtain the image of the Taurian Artemis, carried it with them to Brauron in Attica. This divinity was henceforth known as the Brauronian Artemis, and the rites which had rendered her worship so infamous in Taurica were now introduced into Greece, and human victims bled freely under the sacrificial knife, both in Athens and Sparta. The revolting practice of offering human sacrifices to her, was continued until the time of Lycurgus, the great Spartan lawgiver, who put an end to it by substituting in its place one, which was hardly less barbarous, namely, the scourging of youths, who were whipped on the altars of the Brauronian Artemis in the most cruel manner; sometimes indeed they expired under the lash, in which case their mothers, far from lamenting their fate, are said to have rejoiced, considering this an honourable death for their sons.

SELENE-ARTEMIS.

Hitherto we have seen Artemis only in the various phases of her terrestrial character; but just as her brother Apollo drew into himself by degrees the attributes of that more ancient divinity Helios, the sun-god, so, in like manner, she came to be identified in later times with Selene, the moon-goddess, in which character she is always represented as wearing on her forehead a glittering crescent, whilst a flowing veil, bespangled with stars, reaches to her feet, and a long robe completely envelops her.

DIANA.

The Diana of the Romans was identified with the Greek Artemis, with whom she shares that peculiar tripartite character, which so strongly marks the individuality of the Greek goddess. In heaven she was Luna (the moon), on earth Diana (the huntress-goddess), and in the lower world Proserpine; but, unlike the Ephesian Artemis, Diana, in her character as Proserpine, carries with her into the lower world no element of love or sympathy; she is, on the contrary, characterized by practices altogether hostile to man, such as the exercise of witchcraft, evil charms, and other antagonistic influences, and is, in fact, the Greek Hecate, in her later development.

The statues of Diana were generally erected at a point where three roads met, for which reason she is called Trivia (from *tri*, three, and *via*, way).

A temple was dedicated to her on the Aventine hill by Servius Tullius, who is said to have first introduced the worship of this divinity into Rome.

The Nemoralia, or Grove Festivals, were celebrated in her honour on the 13th of August, on the Lacus Nemorensis, or forest-buried lake, near Aricia. The priest who officiated in her temple on this spot, was always a fugitive slave, who had gained his office by murdering his predecessor, and hence was constantly armed, in order that he might thus be prepared to encounter a new aspirant.

HEPHÆSTUS (VULCAN).

Hephæstus, the son of Zeus and Hera, was the god of fire in its beneficial aspect, and the presiding deity over all workmanship accomplished by means of this useful element. He was universally honoured, not only as the god of all mechanical arts, but also as a house and hearth divinity, who exercised a beneficial influence on civilized society in general. Unlike the other Greek divinities, he was ugly and deformed, being awkward in his movements, and limping in his gait. This latter defect originated, as we have already seen, in the wrath of his father Zeus, who hurled him down from heaven[35] in consequence of his taking the part of Hera, in one of the domestic disagreements, which so frequently arose between this royal pair. Hephæstus was a whole day falling from Olympus to the earth, where he at length alighted on the island of Lemnos. The inhabitants of the country, seeing him descending through the air, received him in their arms; but in spite of their care, his leg was broken by the fall, and he remained ever afterwards lame in one foot. Grateful for the kindness of the Lemnians, he henceforth took up his abode in their island, and there built for himself a superb palace, and forges for the pursuit of his avocation. He instructed the people how to work in metals, and also taught them other valuable and useful arts.

It is said that the first work of Hephæstus was a most ingenious throne of gold, with secret springs, which he presented to Hera. It was arranged in such a manner that, once seated, she found herself unable to move, and though all the gods endeavoured to extricate her, their efforts were unavailing. Hephæstus thus revenged himself on his mother for the cruelty she had always displayed towards him, on account of his want of comeliness and grace. Dionysus, the wine god, contrived, however, to intoxicate Hephæstus, and then induced him to return to Olympus, where, after having released the queen of heaven from her very undignified position, he became reconciled to his parents.

He now built for himself a glorious palace on Olympus, of shining gold, and made for the other deities those magnificent edifices which they inhabited. He was assisted in his various and exquisitely skilful works of art, by two female statues of pure gold, formed by his own hand, which possessed the power of motion, and always accompanied him wherever he went. With the assistance of the Cyclops, he forged for Zeus his wonderful thunderbolts, thus investing his mighty father with a new power of terrible import. Zeus testified his appreciation of this precious gift, by bestowing upon Hephæstus the beautiful Aphrodite in marriage,[36] but this was a questionable boon; for the lovely Aphrodite, who was the personification of all grace and beauty, felt no affection for her ungainly and unattractive spouse, and amused herself by ridiculing his awkward movements and unsightly person. On one occasion especially, when Hephæstus good-naturedly took upon himself the office of cup-bearer to the gods, his hobbling gait and extreme awkwardness created the greatest mirth amongst the celestials, in which his disloyal partner was the first to join, with unconcealed merriment.

Aphrodite greatly preferred Ares to her husband, and this preference naturally gave rise to much jealousy on the part of Hephæstus, and caused them great unhappiness.

Hephæstus appears to have been an indispensable member of the Olympic Assembly, where he plays the part of smith, armourer, chariot-builder, &c. As already mentioned, he constructed the palaces where the gods resided, fashioned the golden shoes with which they trod the air or water, built for them their wonderful chariots, and shod with brass the horses of celestial breed, which conveyed these glittering equipages over land and sea. He also made the tripods which moved of themselves in and out of the celestial halls, formed for Zeus the far-famed ægis, and erected the magnificent palace of the sun. He also created the brazen-footed bulls of Aetes, which breathed flames from their nostrils, sent forth clouds of smoke, and filled the air with their roaring.

Among his most renowned works of art for the use of mortals were: the armour of Achilles and Æneas, the beautiful necklace of Harmonia, and the crown of Ariadne; but his masterpiece was Pandora, of whom a detailed account has already been given.

There was a temple on Mount Etna erected in his honour, which none but the pure and virtuous were permitted to enter. The entrance to this temple was guarded by dogs, which possessed the extraordinary faculty of being able to discriminate between the righteous and the unrighteous, fawning upon and caressing the good, whilst they rushed upon all evil-doers and drove them away.

Hephæstus is usually represented as a powerful, brawny, and very muscular man of middle height and mature age; his strong uplifted arm is raised in the act of striking the anvil with a hammer, which he holds in one hand, whilst with the other he is turning a thunderbolt, which an eagle beside him is waiting to carry to Zeus. The principal seat of his worship was the island of Lemnos, where he was regarded with peculiar veneration.

VULCAN.

The Roman Vulcan was merely an importation from Greece, which never at any time took firm root in Rome, nor entered largely into the actual life and sympathies of the nation, his worship being unattended by the devotional feeling and enthusiasm which characterized the religious rites of the other deities. He still, however, retained in Rome his Greek attributes as god of fire, and unrivalled master of the art of working in metals, and was ranked among the twelve great gods of Olympus, whose gilded statues were arranged consecutively along the Forum. His Roman name, Vulcan, would seem to indicate a connection with the first great metal-working artificer of Biblical history, Tubal-Cain.

POSEIDON (Neptune).

Poseidon was the son of Kronos and Rhea, and the brother of Zeus. He was god of the sea, more particularly of the Mediterranean, and, like the element over which he presided, was of a variable disposition, now violently agitated, and now calm and placid, for which reason he is sometimes represented by the poets as quiet and composed, and at others as disturbed and angry.

In the earliest ages of Greek mythology, he merely symbolized the watery element; but in later times, as navigation and intercourse with other nations engendered greater traffic by sea, Poseidon gained in importance, and came to be regarded as a distinct divinity, holding indisputable dominion over the sea, and over all sea-divinities, who acknowledged him as their sovereign ruler. He possessed the power of causing at will, mighty and destructive tempests, in which the billows rise mountains high, the wind becomes a hurricane, land and sea being enveloped in thick mists, whilst destruction assails the unfortunate mariners exposed to their fury. On the other hand, his alone was the power of stilling the angry waves, of soothing the troubled waters, and granting safe voyages to mariners. For this reason, Poseidon was always invoked and propitiated by a libation before a voyage was undertaken, and sacrifices and thanksgivings were gratefully offered to him after a safe and prosperous journey by sea.

The symbol of his power was the fisherman's fork or trident,[37] by means of which he produced earthquakes, raised up islands from the bottom of the sea, and caused wells to spring forth out of the earth.

Poseidon was essentially the presiding deity over fishermen, and was on that account, more particularly worshipped and revered in countries bordering on the sea-coast, where fish naturally formed a staple commodity of trade. He was supposed to vent his displeasure by sending disastrous inundations, which completely destroyed whole countries, and were usually accompanied by terrible marine monsters, who swallowed up and devoured those whom the floods had spared. It is probable that these sea-monsters are the poetical figures which represent the demons of hunger and famine, necessarily accompanying a general inundation.

Poseidon is generally represented as resembling his

brother Zeus in features, height, and general aspect; but we miss in the countenance of the sea-god the kindness and benignity which so pleasingly distinguish his mighty brother. The eyes are bright and piercing, and the contour of the face somewhat sharper in its outline than that of Zeus, thus corresponding, as it were, with his more angry and violent nature. His hair waves in dark, disorderly masses over his shoulders; his chest is broad, and his frame powerful and stalwart; he wears a short, curling beard, and a band round his head. He usually appears standing erect in a graceful shell-chariot, drawn by hippocamps, or sea-horses, with golden manes and brazen hoofs, who bound over the dancing waves with such wonderful swiftness, that the chariot scarcely touches the water. The monsters of the deep, acknowledging their mighty lord, gambol playfully around him, whilst the sea joyfully smooths a path for the passage of its all-powerful ruler.

He inhabited a beautiful palace at the bottom of the sea at Ægea in Eubœa, and also possessed a royal residence on Mount Olympus, which, however, he only visited when his presence was required at the council of the gods.

His wonderful palace beneath the waters was of vast extent; in its lofty and capacious halls thousands of his followers could assemble. The exterior of the building was of bright gold, which the continual wash of the waters preserved untarnished; in the interior, lofty and graceful columns supported the gleaming dome. Everywhere fountains of glistening, silvery water played; everywhere groves and arbours of feathery-leaved sea-plants appeared, whilst rocks of pure crystal glistened with all the varied colours of the rainbow. Some of the paths were strewn with white sparkling sand, interspersed with jewels, pearls, and amber. This delightful abode was surrounded on all sides by wide fields, where there were whole groves of dark purple coralline, and tufts of beautiful scarlet-leaved plants, and sea-anemones of every tint. Here grew bright, pinky sea-weeds, mosses of all hues and shades, and tall grasses, which, growing upwards, formed emerald caves and grottoes such as the Nereides love, whilst fish of various kinds playfully darted in and out, in the full enjoyment of their native element. Nor was illumination wanting in this fairy-like region, which at night was lit up by the glow-worms of the deep.

But although Poseidon ruled with absolute power over the ocean and its inhabitants, he nevertheless bowed submissively to the will of the great ruler of Olympus, and appeared at all times desirous of conciliating him. We find him coming to his aid when emergency demanded, and frequently rendering him valuable assistance against his opponents. At the time when Zeus was harassed by the attacks of the Giants, he proved himself a most powerful ally, engaging in single combat with a hideous giant named Polybotes, whom he followed over the sea, and at last succeeded in destroying, by hurling upon him the island of Cos.

These amicable relations between the brothers were, however, sometimes interrupted. Thus, for instance, upon one occasion Poseidon joined Hera and Athene in a secret conspiracy to seize upon the ruler of heaven, place him in fetters, and deprive him of the sovereign power. The conspiracy being discovered, Hera, as the chief instigator of this sacrilegious attempt on the divine person of Zeus, was severely chastised, and even beaten, by her enraged spouse, as a punishment for her rebellion and treachery, whilst Poseidon was condemned, for the space of a whole year, to forego his dominion over the sea, and it was at this time that, in conjunction with Apollo, he built for Laomedon the walls of Troy.

Poseidon married a sea-nymph named Amphitrite, whom he wooed under the form of a dolphin. She afterwards became jealous of a beautiful maiden called Scylla, who was beloved by Poseidon, and in order to revenge herself she threw some herbs into a well where Scylla was bathing, which had the effect of metamorphosing her into a monster of terrible aspect, having twelve feet, six heads with six long necks, and a voice which resembled the bark of a dog. This awful monster is said to have inhabited a cave at a very great height in the famous rock which still bears her name,[38] and was supposed to swoop down from her rocky eminence upon every ship that passed, and with each of her six heads to secure a victim.

Amphitrite is often represented assisting Poseidon in attaching the sea-horses to his chariot.

The Cyclops, who have been already alluded to in the history of Cronus, were the sons of Poseidon and Amphitrite. They were a wild race of gigantic growth, similar in their nature to the earth-born Giants, and had only one eye each in the middle of their foreheads. They led a lawless life, possessing neither social manners nor fear of the gods, and were the workmen of Hephæstus, whose workshop was supposed to be in the heart of the volcanic mountain Ætna.

Here we have another striking instance of the manner in which the Greeks personified the powers of nature, which they saw in active operation around them. They beheld with awe, mingled with astonishment, the fire, stones, and ashes which poured forth from the summit of this and other volcanic mountains, and, with their vivacity of imagination, found a solution of the mystery in the supposition, that the god of Fire must be busy at work with his men in the depths of the earth, and that the mighty flames which they beheld, issued in this manner from his subterranean forge.

The chief representative of the Cyclops was the man-eating monster Polyphemus, described by Homer as having been blinded and outwitted at last by Odysseus. This monster fell in love with a beautiful nymph called Galatea; but, as may be supposed, his addresses were not acceptable to the fair maiden, who rejected them in favour of a youth named Acis, upon which Polyphemus, with his usual barbarity, destroyed the life of his rival by throwing upon him a gigantic rock. The blood of the murdered Acis, gushing out of the rock, formed a stream which still bears his name.

Triton, Rhoda,[39] and Benthesicyme were also children of Poseidon and Amphitrite.

The sea-god was the father of two giant sons called Otus and Ephialtes.[40] When only nine years old they were said to be twenty-seven cubits[41] in height and nine in breadth. These youthful giants were as rebellious as they were powerful, even presuming to threaten the gods themselves with hostilities. During the war of the Gigantomachia, they endeavoured to scale heaven by piling mighty mountains one upon another. Already had they succeeded in placing Mount Ossa on Olympus and Pelion on Ossa, when this impious project was frustrated by Apollo, who destroyed them with his arrows. It was supposed that had not their lives been thus cut off before reaching maturity, their sacrilegious designs would have been carried into effect.

Pelias and Neleus were also sons of Poseidon. Their mother Tyro was attached to the river-god Enipeus, whose form Poseidon assumed, and thus won her love. Pelias became afterwards famous in the story of the Argonauts, and Neleus was the father of Nestor, who was distinguished in the Trojan War.

The Greeks believed that it was to Poseidon they were indebted for the existence of the horse, which he is said to have produced in the following manner: Athene and Poseidon both claiming the right to name Cecropia (the ancient name of Athens), a violent dispute arose, which was finally settled by an assembly of the Olympian gods, who decided that whichever of the contending parties presented mankind with the most useful gift, should obtain the privilege of naming the city. Upon this Poseidon struck the ground with his trident, and the horse sprang forth in all his untamed strength and graceful beauty. From the spot which Athene touched with her wand, issued the olive-tree, whereupon the gods unanimously awarded to her the victory, declaring her gift to be the emblem of peace and plenty, whilst that of Poseidon was thought to be the symbol of war and bloodshed. Athene accordingly called the city Athens, after herself, and it has ever since retained this name.

Poseidon tamed the horse for the use of mankind, and was believed to have taught men the art of managing horses by the bridle. The Isthmian games (so named because they were held on the Isthmus of Corinth), in which horse and chariot races were a distinguishing feature, were instituted in honour of Poseidon.

He was more especially worshipped in the Peloponnesus, though universally revered throughout Greece and in the south of Italy. His sacrifices were generally black and white bulls, also wild boars and rams. His usual attributes are the trident, horse, and dolphin.

In some parts of Greece this divinity was identified with the sea-god Nereus, for which reason the Nereides, or daughters of Nereus, are represented as accompanying him.

NEPTUNE.

The Romans worshipped Poseidon under the name of Neptune, and invested him with all the attributes which belong to the Greek divinity.

The Roman commanders never undertook any naval expedition without propitiating Neptune by a sacrifice.

His temple at Rome was in the Campus Martius, and the festivals commemorated in his honour were called Neptunalia.

SEA DIVINITIES—

OCEANUS.

Oceanus was the son of Uranus and Gæa. He was the personification of the ever-flowing stream, which, according to the
primitive notions of the early Greeks, encircled the world,
and from which sprang all the rivers and streams that watered
the earth. He was married to Tethys, one of the Titans, and
was the father of a numerous progeny called the Oceanides,
who are said to have been three thousand in number. He
alone, of all the Titans, refrained from taking part against
Zeus in the Titanomachia, and was, on that account, the only
one of the primeval divinities permitted to retain his dominion
under the new dynasty.

NEREUS.

Nereus appears to have been the personification of the sea in
its calm and placid moods, and was, after Poseidon, the most
important of the sea-deities. He is represented as a kind and
benevolent old man, possessing the gift of prophecy, and
presiding more particularly over the Ægean Sea, of which he
was considered to be the protecting spirit. There he dwelt

with his wife Doris and their fifty blooming daughters, the Nereides, beneath the waves in a beautiful grotto-palace, and was ever ready to assist distressed mariners in the hour of danger.

PROTEUS.

Proteus, more familiarly known as "The Old Man of the Sea," was a son of Poseidon, and gifted with prophetic power. But he had an invincible objection to being consulted in his capacity as seer, and those who wished him to foretell events, watched for the hour of noon, when he was in the habit of coming up to the island of Pharos,[42] with Poseidon's flock of seals, which he tended at the bottom of the sea. Surrounded by these creatures of the deep, he used to slumber beneath the grateful shade of the rocks. This was the favourable moment to seize the prophet, who, in order to avoid importunities, would change himself into an infinite variety of forms. But patience gained the day; for if he were only held long enough, he became wearied at last, and, resuming his true form, gave the information desired, after which he dived down again to the bottom of the sea, accompanied by the animals he tended.

TRITON and the TRITONS.

Triton was the only son of Poseidon and Amphitrite, but he possessed little influence, being altogether a minor divinity. He is usually represented as preceding his father and acting as his trumpeter, using a conch-shell for this purpose. He lived with his parents in their beautiful golden palace beneath the sea at Ægea, and his favourite pastime was to ride over the billows on horses or sea-monsters. Triton is always represented as half man, half fish, the body below the waist terminating in the tail of a dolphin. We frequently find mention of Tritons who are either the offspring or kindred of Triton.

GLAUCUS.

Glaucus is said to have become a sea-divinity in the following manner. While angling one day, he observed that the fish he caught and threw on the bank, at once nibbled at the grass and then leaped back into the water. His curiosity was naturally excited, and he proceeded to gratify it by taking up a few blades and tasting them. No sooner was this done than, obeying an irresistible impulse, he precipitated himself into the deep, and became a sea-god.

Like most sea-divinities he was gifted with prophetic power, and each year visited all the islands and coasts with a train of marine monsters, foretelling all kinds of evil. Hence fishermen dreaded his approach, and endeavoured, by prayer and fasting, to avert the misfortunes which he prophesied. He is often represented floating on the billows, his body covered with mussels, sea-weed, and shells, wearing a full beard and long flowing hair, and bitterly bewailing his immortality.

THETIS.

The silver-footed, fair-haired Thetis, who plays an important part in the mythology of Greece, was the daughter of Nereus, or, as some assert, of Poseidon. Her grace and beauty were so remarkable that Zeus and Poseidon both sought an alliance with her; but, as it had been foretold that a son of hers would gain supremacy over his father, they relinquished their intentions, and she became the wife of Peleus, son of Æacus. Like Proteus, Thetis possessed the power of transforming herself into a variety of different shapes, and when wooed by Peleus she exerted this power in order to elude him. But, knowing that persistence would eventually succeed, he held her fast until she assumed her true form. Their nuptials were celebrated with the utmost pomp and magnificence, and were honoured by the presence of all the gods and goddesses, with the exception of Eris. How the goddess of discord resented her exclusion from the marriage festivities has already been shown.

Thetis ever retained great influence over the mighty lord of heaven, which, as we shall see hereafter, she used in favour of her renowned son, Achilles, in the Trojan War.

When Halcyone plunged into the sea in despair after the shipwreck and death of her husband King Ceyx, Thetis transformed both husband and wife into the birds called kingfishers (halcyones), which, with the tender affection which characterized the unfortunate couple, always fly in pairs. The idea of the ancients was that these birds brought forth their young in nests, which float on the surface of the sea in calm weather, before and after the shortest day, when Thetis was said to keep the waters smooth and tranquil for their especial benefit; hence the term "halcyon-days," which signifies a period of rest and untroubled felicity.

THAUMAS, PHORCYS, and CETO.

The early Greeks, with their extraordinary power of personifying all and every attribute of Nature, gave a distinct personality to those mighty wonders of the deep, which, in all ages, have afforded matter of speculation to educated and uneducated alike. Among these personifications we find Thaumas, Phorcys, and their sister Ceto, who were the offspring of Pontus.

Thaumas (whose name signifies Wonder) typifies that peculiar, translucent condition of the surface of the sea when it reflects, mirror-like, various images, and appears to hold in its transparent embrace the flaming stars and illuminated cities, which are so frequently reflected on its glassy bosom.

Thaumas married the lovely Electra (whose name signifies the sparkling light produced by electricity), daughter of Oceanus. Her amber-coloured hair was of such rare beauty that none of her fair-haired sisters could compare with her, and when she wept, her tears, being too precious to be lost, formed drops of shining amber.

Phorcys and Ceto personified more especially the hidden perils and terrors of the ocean. They were the parents of the Gorgons, the Græa, and the Dragon which guarded the golden apples of the Hesperides.

LEUCOTHEA.

Leucothea was originally a mortal named Ino, daughter of Cadmus, king of Thebes. She married Athamas, king of Orchomenus, who, incensed at her unnatural conduct to her step-children,[43] pursued her and her son to the sea-shore, when, seeing no hope of escape, she flung herself with her child into the deep. They were kindly received by the Nereides, and became sea-divinities under the name of Leucothea and Palæmon.

THE SIRENS.

The Sirens would appear to have been personifications of those numerous rocks and unseen dangers, which abound on the S.W. coast of Italy. They were sea-nymphs, with the upper part of the body that of a maiden and the lower that of a sea-bird, having wings attached to their shoulders, and were endowed with such wonderful voices, that their sweet songs are said to have lured mariners to destruction.

ARES (MARS).

Ares, the son of Zeus and Hera, was the god of war, who gloried in strife for its own sake; he loved the tumult and havoc of the battlefield, and delighted in slaughter and extermination; in fact he presents no benevolent aspect which could possibly react favourably upon human life.

Epic poets, in particular, represent the god of battles as a wild ungovernable warrior, who passes through the armies like a whirlwind, hurling to the ground the brave and cowardly alike; destroying chariots and helmets, and triumphing over the terrible desolation which he produces.

In all the myths concerning Ares, his sister Athene ever appears in opposition to him, endeavouring by every means in her power to defeat his bloodthirsty designs. Thus she assists the divine hero Diomedes at the siege of Troy, to overcome Ares in battle, and so well does he profit by her timely aid, that he succeeds in wounding the sanguinary war-god, who makes his exit from the field, roaring like ten thousand bulls.

Ares appears to have been an object of aversion to all the gods of Olympus, Aphrodite alone excepted. As the son of Hera, he had inherited from his mother the strongest feelings of independence and contradiction, and as he took delight in upsetting that peaceful course of state-life which it was pre-eminently the care of Zeus to establish, he was naturally disliked and even hated by him.

When wounded by Diomedes, as above related, he complains to his father, but receives no sympathy from the otherwise kindly and beneficent ruler of Olympus, who thus angrily addresses him: "Do not trouble me with thy complaints, thou who art of all the gods of Olympus most hateful to me, for thou delightest in nought save war and strife. The very spirit of thy mother lives in thee, and wert thou not my son, long ago wouldst thou have lain deeper down in the bowels of the earth than the son of Uranus."

Ares, upon one occasion, incurred the anger of Poseidon by slaying his son Halirrhothios, who had insulted Alcippe, the daughter of the war-god. For this deed, Poseidon summoned Ares to appear before the tribunal of the Olympic gods, which was held upon a hill in Athens. Ares was acquitted, and this event is supposed to have given rise to the name Areopagus (or Hill of Ares), which afterwards became so famous as a court of justice. In the Gigantomachia, Ares was defeated by the Aloidæ, the two giant-sons of Poseidon, who put him in chains, and kept him in prison for thirteen months.

Ares is represented as a man of youthful appearance; his tall muscular form combines great strength with wonderful agility. In his right hand he bears a sword or a mighty lance, while on the left arm he carries his round shield. His demoniacal surroundings are Terror and Fear;[44] Enyo, the goddess of the war-cry; Keidomos, the demon of the noise of battles; and Eris (Contention), his twin-sister and companion, who always precedes his chariot when he rushes to the fight, the latter being evidently a simile of the poets to express the fact that war follows contention.

Eris is represented as a woman of florid complexion, with dishevelled hair, and her whole appearance angry and menacing. In one hand she brandishes a poniard and a hissing adder, whilst in the other she carries a burning torch. Her dress is torn and disorderly, and her hair intertwined with venomous snakes. This divinity was never invoked by mortals, except when they desired her assistance for the accomplishment of evil purposes.

MARS.

The Roman divinity most closely resembling the Greek Ares, and identified with him, was called Mars, Mamers, and Marspiter or Father Mars.

The earliest Italian tribes, who were mostly engaged in the pursuit of husbandry, regarded this deity more especially as the god of spring, who vanquished the powers of winter, and encouraged the peaceful arts of agriculture. But with the Romans, who were an essentially warlike nation, Mars gradually loses his peaceful character, and, as god of war, attains, after Jupiter, the highest position among the Olympic gods. The Romans looked upon him as their special protector, and declared him to have been the father of Romulus and Remus, the founders of their city. But although he was especially worshipped in Rome as god of war, he still continued to preside over agriculture, and was also the protecting deity who watched over the welfare of the state.

As the god who strode with warlike step to the battlefield, he was called Gradivus (from *gradus*, a step), it being popularly believed by the Romans that he himself marched before them to battle, and acted as their invisible protector. As the presiding deity over agriculture, he was styled Sylvanus, whilst in his character as guardian of the state, he bore the name of Quirinus.[45]

The priests of Mars were twelve in number, and were called Salii, or the dancers, from the fact that sacred dances, in full armour, formed an important item in their peculiar ceremonial. This religious order, the members of which were always chosen from the noblest families in Rome, was first instituted by Numa Pompilius, who intrusted to their special charge the Anciliæ, or sacred shields. It is said that one morning, when Numa was imploring the protection of Jupiter for the newly-founded city of Rome, the god of heaven, as though in answer to his prayer, sent down an oblong brazen shield, and, as it fell at the feet of the king, a voice was heard announcing that on its preservation depended the future safety and prosperity of Rome. In order, therefore, to lessen the chances of this sacred treasure being abstracted, Numa caused eleven more to be made exactly like it, which were then given into the care of the Salii.

The assistance and protection of the god of war was always solemnly invoked before the departure of a Roman army for the field of battle, and any reverses of fortune were invariably ascribed to his anger, which was accordingly propitiated by means of extraordinary sin-offerings and prayers.

In Rome a field, called the Campus Martius, was dedicated to Mars. It was a large, open space, in which armies were collected and reviewed, general assemblies of the people held, and the young nobility trained to martial exercises.

The most celebrated and magnificent of the numerous temples built by the Romans in honour of this deity was the one erected by Augustus in the Forum, to commemorate the overthrow of the murderers of Cæsar.

Of all existing statues of Mars the most renowned is that in the Villa Ludovisi at Rome, in which he is represented as a powerful, muscular man in the full vigour of youth. The attitude is that of thoughtful repose, but the short, curly hair, dilated nostrils, and strongly marked features leave no doubt as to the force and turbulence of his character. At his feet, the sculptor has placed the little god of love, who looks up all undaunted at the mighty war-god, as though mischievously conscious that this unusually quiet mood is attributable to his influence.

Religious festivals in honour of Mars were generally held in the month of March; but he had also a festival on the Ides of October, when chariot-races took place, after which, the right-hand horse of the team which had drawn the victorious chariot, was sacrificed to him. In ancient times, human sacrifices, more especially prisoners of war, were offered to him; but, at a later period, this cruel practice was discontinued.

The attributes of this divinity are the helmet, shield, and spear. The animals consecrated to him were the wolf, horse, vulture, and woodpecker.

Intimately associated with Mars in his character as god of war, was a goddess called **BELLONA**, who was evidently the female divinity of battle with one or other of the primitive nations of Italy (most probably the Sabines), and is usually seen accompanying Mars, whose war-chariot she guides. Bellona appears on the battle-field, inspired with mad rage, cruelty, and the love of extermination. She is in full armour, her hair is dishevelled, and she bears a scourge in one hand, and a lance in the other.

A temple was erected to her on the Campus Martius. Before the entrance to this edifice stood a pillar, over which a spear was thrown when war was publicly declared.

NIKE (VICTORIA).

Nike, the goddess of victory, was the daughter of the Titan Pallas, and of Styx, the presiding nymph of the river of that name in the lower world.

In her statues, Nike somewhat resembles Athene, but may easily be recognized by her large, graceful wings and flowing drapery, which is negligently fastened on the right shoulder, and only partially conceals her lovely form. In her left hand, she holds aloft a crown of laurel, and in the right, a palm-branch. In ancient sculpture, Nike is usually represented in connection with colossal statues of Zeus or Pallas-Athene, in which case she is life-sized, and stands on a ball, held in the open palm of the deity she accompanies. Sometimes she is represented engaged in inscribing the victory of a conqueror on his shield, her right foot being slightly raised and placed on a ball.

A celebrated temple was erected to this divinity on the Acropolis at Athens, which is still to be seen, and is in excellent preservation.

VICTORIA.

Under the name of Victoria, Nike was highly honoured by the Romans, with whom love of conquest was an all-absorbing characteristic. There were several sanctuaries in Rome dedicated to her, the principal of which was on the Capitol, where it was the custom of generals, after success had attended their arms, to erect statues of the goddess in commemoration of their victories. The most magnificent of these statues, was that raised by Augustus after the battle of Actium. A festival was celebrated in honour of Nike on the 12th of April.

HERMES (Mercury).

Hermes was the swift-footed messenger, and trusted ambassador of all the gods, and conductor of shades to Hades. He presided over the rearing and education of the young, and encouraged gymnastic exercises and athletic pursuits, for which reason, all gymnasiums and wrestling schools throughout Greece were adorned with his statues. He is said to have invented the alphabet, and to have taught the art of interpreting foreign languages, and his versatility, sagacity, and cunning were so extraordinary, that Zeus invariably chose him as his attendant, when, disguised as a mortal, he journeyed on earth.

Hermes was worshipped as god of eloquence, most probably from the fact that, in his office as ambassador, this faculty was indispensable to the successful issue of the negotiations with which he was intrusted. He was regarded as the god who granted increase and prosperity to flocks and herds, and, on this account, was worshipped with special veneration by herdsmen.

In ancient times, trade was conducted chiefly by means of the exchange of cattle. Hermes, therefore, as god of herdsmen, came to be regarded as the protector of merchants, and, as ready wit and adroitness are valuable qualities both in buying and selling, he was also looked upon as the patron of artifice and cunning. Indeed, so deeply was this notion rooted in the minds of the Greek people, that he was popularly believed to be also god of thieves, and of all persons who live by their wits.

As the patron of commerce, Hermes was naturally supposed to be the promoter of intercourse among nations; hence, he is essentially the god of travellers, over whose safety he presided, and he severely punished those who refused assistance to the lost or weary wayfarer. He was also guardian of streets and roads, and his statues, called Hermæ (which were pillars of stone surmounted by a head of Hermes), were placed at cross-roads, and frequently in streets and public squares.

Being the god of all undertakings in which gain was a feature, he was worshipped as the giver of wealth and good luck, and any unexpected stroke of fortune was attributed to his influence. He also presided over the game of dice, in which he is said to have been instructed by Apollo.

Hermes was the son of Zeus and Maia, the eldest and most beautiful of the seven Pleiades (daughters of Atlas), and was born in a cave of Mount Cyllene in Arcadia. As a mere babe, he exhibited an extraordinary faculty for cunning and dissimulation; in fact, he was a thief from his cradle, for, not many hours after his birth, we find him creeping stealthily out of the cave in which he was born, in order to steal some oxen belonging to his brother Apollo, who was at this time feeding the flocks of Admetus. But he had not proceeded very far on his expedition before he found a tortoise, which he killed, and, stretching seven strings across the empty shell, invented a lyre, upon which he at once began to play with exquisite skill. When he had sufficiently amused himself with the instrument, he placed it in his cradle, and then resumed his journey to Pieria, where the cattle of Admetus were grazing. Arriving at sunset at his destination, he succeeded in separating fifty oxen from his brother's herd, which he now drove before him, taking the precaution to cover his feet with sandals made of twigs of myrtle, in order to escape detection. But the little rogue was not unobserved, for the theft had been witnessed by an old shepherd named Battus, who was tending the flocks of Neleus, king of Pylos (father of Nestor). Hermes, frightened at being discovered, bribed him with the finest cow in the herd not to betray him, and Battus promised to keep the secret. But Hermes, astute as he was dishonest, determined to test the shepherd's integrity. Feigning to go away, he assumed the form of Admetus, and then returning to the spot offered the old man two of his best oxen if he would disclose the author of the theft. The ruse succeeded, for the avaricious shepherd, unable to resist the tempting bait, gave the desired information, upon which Hermes, exerting his divine power, changed him into a lump of touchstone, as a punishment for his treachery and avarice. Hermes now killed two of the oxen, which he sacrificed to himself and the other gods, concealing the remainder in the cave. He then carefully extinguished the fire, and, after throwing his twig shoes into the river Alpheus, returned to Cyllene.

Apollo, by means of his all-seeing power, soon discovered who it was that had robbed him, and hastening to Cyllene, demanded restitution of his property. On his complaining to Maia of her son's conduct, she pointed to the innocent babe then lying, apparently fast asleep, in his cradle, whereupon, Apollo angrily aroused the pretended sleeper, and charged him with the theft; but the child stoutly denied all knowledge of it, and so cleverly did he play his part, that he even inquired in the most naive manner what sort of animals cows were. Apollo threatened to throw him into Tartarus if he would not confess the truth, but all to no purpose. At last, he seized the babe in his arms, and brought him into the presence of his august father, who was seated in the council chamber of the gods. Zeus listened to the charge made by Apollo, and then sternly desired Hermes to say where he had hidden the cattle. The child, who was still in swaddling-clothes, looked up bravely into his father's face and said, "Now, do I look capable of driving away a herd of cattle; I, who was only born yesterday, and whose feet are much too soft and tender to tread in rough places? Until this moment, I lay in sweet sleep on my mother's bosom, and have never even crossed the threshold of our dwelling. You know well that I am not guilty; but, if you wish, I will affirm it by the most solemn oaths." As the child stood before him, looking the picture of innocence, Zeus could not refrain from smiling at his cleverness and cunning, but, being perfectly aware of his guilt, he commanded him to conduct Apollo to the cave where he had concealed the herd, and Hermes, seeing that further subterfuge was useless, unhesitatingly obeyed. But when the divine shepherd was about to drive his cattle back into Pieria, Hermes, as though by chance, touched the chords of his lyre. Hitherto Apollo had heard nothing but the music of his own three-stringed lyre and the syrinx, or Pan's pipe, and, as he listened entranced to the delightful strains of this new instrument, his longing to possess it became so great, that he gladly offered the oxen in exchange, promising at the same time, to give Hermes full dominion over flocks and herds, as well as over horses, and all the wild animals of the woods and forests. The offer was accepted, and, a reconciliation being thus effected between the brothers, Hermes became henceforth god of herdsmen, whilst Apollo devoted himself enthusiastically to the art of music.

They now proceeded together to Olympus, where Apollo introduced Hermes as his chosen friend and companion, and, having made him swear by the Styx, that he would never steal his lyre or bow, nor invade his sanctuary at Delphi, he presented him with the Caduceus, or golden wand. This wand was surmounted by wings, and on presenting it to Hermes, Apollo informed him that it possessed the faculty of uniting in love, all beings divided by hate. Wishing to prove the truth of this assertion, Hermes threw it down between two snakes which were fighting, whereupon the angry combatants clasped each other in a loving embrace, and curling round the staff, remained ever after permanently attached to it. The wand itself typified power; the serpents, wisdom; and the wings, despatch—all qualities characteristic of a trustworthy ambassador.

The young god was now presented by his father with a winged silver cap (Petasus), and also with silver wings for his feet (Talaria), and was forthwith appointed herald of the gods, and conductor of shades to Hades, which office had hitherto been filled by Aïdes.

As messenger of the gods, we find him employed on all occasions requiring special skill, tact, or despatch. Thus he conducts Hera, Athene, and Aphrodite to Paris, leads Priam to

Achilles to demand the body of Hector, binds Prometheus to Mount Caucasus, secures Ixion to the eternally revolving wheel, destroys Argus, the hundred-eyed guardian of Io, &c. &c.

As conductor of shades, Hermes was always invoked by the dying to grant them a safe and speedy passage across the Styx. He also possessed the power of bringing back departed spirits to the upper world, and was, therefore, the mediator between the living and the dead.

The poets relate many amusing stories of the youthful tricks played by this mischief-loving god upon the other immortals. For instance, he had the audacity to extract the Medusa's head from the shield of Athene, which he playfully attached to the back of Hephæstus; he also stole the girdle of Aphrodite; deprived Artemis of her arrows, and Ares of his spear, but these acts were always performed with such graceful dexterity, combined with such perfect good humour, that even the gods and goddesses he thus provoked, were fain to pardon him, and he became a universal favourite with them all.

It is said that Hermes was one day flying over Athens, when, looking down into the city, he beheld a number of maidens returning in solemn procession from the temple of Pallas-Athene. Foremost among them was Herse, the beautiful daughter of king Cecrops, and Hermes was so struck with her exceeding loveliness that he determined to seek an interview with her. He accordingly presented himself at the royal palace, and begged her sister Agraulos to favour his suit; but, being of an avaricious turn of mind, she refused to do so without the payment of an enormous sum of money. It did not take the messenger of the gods long to obtain the means of fulfilling this condition, and he soon returned with a well-filled purse. But meanwhile Athene, to punish the cupidity of Agraulos, had caused the demon of envy to take possession of her, and the consequence was, that, being unable to contemplate the happiness of her sister, she sat down before the door, and resolutely refused to allow Hermes to enter. He tried every persuasion and blandishment in his power, but she still remained obstinate. At last, his patience being exhausted, he changed her into a mass of black stone, and, the obstacle to his wishes being removed, he succeeded in persuading Herse to become his wife.

In his statues, Hermes is represented as a beardless youth, with broad chest and graceful but muscular limbs; the face is handsome and intelligent, and a genial smile of kindly benevolence plays round the delicately chiselled lips.

As messenger of the gods he wears the Petasus and Talaria, and bears in his hand the Caduceus or herald's staff.

As god of eloquence, he is often represented with chains of gold hanging from his lips, whilst, as the patron of merchants, he bears a purse in his hand.

The wonderful excavations in Olympia, to which allusion has already been made, have brought to light an exquisite marble group of Hermes and the infant Bacchus, by Praxiteles. In this great work of art, Hermes is represented as a young and handsome man, who is looking down kindly and affectionately at the child resting on his arm, but unfortunately nothing remains of the infant save the right hand, which is laid lovingly on the shoulder of his protector.

The sacrifices to Hermes consisted of incense, honey, cakes, pigs, and especially lambs and young goats. As god of eloquence, the tongues of animals were sacrificed to him.

MERCURY.

Mercury was the Roman god of commerce and gain. We find mention of a temple having been erected to him near the Circus Maximus as early as B.C. 495; and he had also a temple and a sacred fount near the Porta Capena. Magic powers were ascribed to the latter, and on the festival of Mercury, which took place on the 25th of May, it was the custom for merchants to sprinkle themselves and their merchandise with this holy water, in order to insure large profits from their wares.

The Fetiales (Roman priests whose duty it was to act as

guardians of the public faith) refused to recognize the identity of Mercury with Hermes, and ordered him to be represented with a sacred branch as the emblem of peace, instead of the Caduceus. In later times, however, he was completely identified with the Greek Hermes.

DIONYSUS (BACCHUS).

Dionysus, also called Bacchus (from *bacca*, berry), was the god of wine, and the personification of the blessings of Nature in general.

The worship of this divinity, which is supposed to have been introduced into Greece from Asia (in all probability from India), first took root in Thrace, whence it gradually spread into other parts of Greece.

Dionysus was the son of Zeus and Semele, and was snatched by Zeus from the devouring flames in which his mother perished, when he appeared to her in all the splendour of his divine glory. The motherless child was intrusted to the charge of Hermes, who conveyed him to Semele's sister, Ino. But Hera, still implacable in her vengeance, visited Athamas, the husband of Ino, with madness, and the child's life being no longer safe, he was transferred to the fostering care of the nymphs of Mount Nysa. An aged satyr named Silenus, the son of Pan, took upon himself the office of guardian and preceptor to the young god, who, in his turn, became much attached to his kind tutor; hence we see Silenus always figuring as one of the chief personages in the various expeditions of the wine-god.

Dionysus passed an innocent and uneventful childhood, roaming through the woods and forests, surrounded by nymphs, satyrs, and shepherds. During one of these rambles, he found a fruit growing wild, of a most refreshing and cooling nature. This was the vine, from which he subsequently learnt to extract a juice which formed a most exhilarating beverage. After his companions had partaken freely of it, they felt their whole being pervaded by an unwonted sense of pleasurable excitement, and gave full vent to their overflowing exuberance, by shouting, singing, and dancing. Their numbers were soon swelled by a crowd, eager to taste a beverage productive of such extraordinary results, and anxious to join in the worship of a divinity to whom they were indebted for this new enjoyment. Dionysus, on his part, seeing how agreeably his discovery had affected his immediate followers, resolved to extend the boon to mankind in general. He saw that wine, used in moderation, would enable man to enjoy a happier, and more sociable existence, and that, under its invigorating influence, the sorrowful might, for a while, forget their grief and the sick their pain. He accordingly gathered round him his zealous followers, and they set forth on their travels, planting the vine and teaching its cultivation wherever they went.

We now behold Dionysus at the head of a large army composed of men, women, fauns, and satyrs, all bearing in their hands the Thyrsus (a staff entwined with vine-branches surmounted by a fir-cone), and clashing together cymbals and other musical instruments. Seated in a chariot drawn by panthers, and accompanied by thousands of enthusiastic followers, Dionysus made a triumphal progress through Syria, Egypt, Arabia, India, &c., conquering all before him, founding cities, and establishing on every side a more civilized and sociable mode of life among the inhabitants of the various countries through which he passed.

When Dionysus returned to Greece from his Eastern expedition, he encountered great opposition from Lycurgus, king of Thrace, and Pentheus, king of Thebes. The former, highly disapproving of the wild revels which attended the worship of the wine-god, drove away his attendants, the nymphs of Nysa, from that sacred mountain, and so effectually intimidated Dionysus, that he precipitated himself into the sea, where he was received into the arms of the ocean-nymph, Thetis. But the impious king bitterly expiated his sacrilegious conduct. He was punished with the loss of his reason, and, during one of his mad paroxysms, killed his own son Dryas, whom he mistook for a vine.

Pentheus, king of Thebes, seeing his subjects so completely infatuated by the riotous worship of this new divinity, and fearing the demoralizing effects of the unseemly nocturnal orgies held in honour of the wine-god, strictly prohibited his people from taking any part in the wild Bacchanalian revels. Anxious to save him from the consequences of his impiety, Dionysus appeared to him under the form of a youth in the king's train, and earnestly warned him to desist from his denunciations. But the well-meant admonition failed in its purpose, for Pentheus only became more incensed at this interference, and, commanding Dionysus to be cast into prison, caused the most cruel preparations to be made for his immediate execution. But the god soon freed himself from his ignoble confinement, for scarcely had his jailers departed, ere the prison-doors opened of themselves, and, bursting asunder his iron chains, he escaped to rejoin his devoted followers.

Meanwhile, the mother of the king and her sisters, inspired with Bacchanalian fury, had repaired to Mount Cithæron, in order to join the worshippers of the wine-god in those dreadful orgies which were solemnized exclusively by women, and at which no man was allowed to be present. Enraged at finding his commands thus openly disregarded by the members of his own family, Pentheus resolved to witness for himself the excesses of which he had heard such terrible reports, and for this purpose, concealed himself behind a tree on Mount Cithæron; but his hiding-place being discovered, he was dragged out by the half-maddened crew of Bacchantes and, horrible to relate, he was torn in pieces by his own mother Agave and her two sisters.

An incident which occurred to Dionysus on one of his travels has been a favourite subject with the classic poets. One day, as some Tyrrhenian pirates approached the shores of

Greece, they beheld Dionysus, in the form of a beautiful youth, attired in radiant garments. Thinking to secure a rich prize, they seized him, bound him, and conveyed him on board their vessel, resolved to carry him with them to Asia and there sell him as a slave. But the fetters dropped from his limbs, and the pilot, who was the first to perceive the miracle, called upon his companions to restore the youth carefully to the spot whence they had taken him, assuring them that he was a god, and that adverse winds and storms would, in all probability, result from their impious conduct. But, refusing to part with their prisoner, they set sail for the open sea. Suddenly, to the alarm of all on board, the ship stood still, masts and sails were covered with clustering vines and wreaths of ivy-leaves, streams of fragrant wine inundated the vessel, and heavenly strains of music were heard around. The terrified crew, too late repentant, crowded round the pilot for protection, and entreated him to steer for the shore. But the hour of retribution had arrived. Dionysus assumed the form of a lion, whilst beside him appeared a bear, which, with a terrific roar, rushed upon the captain and tore him in pieces; the sailors, in an agony of terror, leaped over-board, and were changed into dolphins. The discreet and pious steersman was alone permitted to escape the fate of his companions, and to him Dionysus, who had resumed his true form, addressed words of kind and affectionate encouragement, and announced his name and dignity. They now set sail, and Dionysus desired the pilot to land him at the island of Naxos, where he found the lovely Ariadne, daughter of Minos, king of Crete. She had been abandoned by Theseus on this lonely spot, and, when Dionysus now beheld her, was lying fast asleep on a rock, worn out with sorrow and weeping. Wrapt in admiration, the god stood gazing at the beautiful vision before him, and when she at length unclosed her eyes, he revealed himself to her, and, in gentle tones, sought to banish her grief. Grateful for his kind sympathy, coming as it did at a moment when she had deemed herself forsaken and friendless, she gradually regained her former serenity, and, yielding to his entreaties, consented to become his wife.

Dionysus, having established his worship in various parts of the world, descended to the realm of shades in search of his ill-fated mother, whom he conducted to Olympus, where, under the name of Thyone, she was admitted into the assembly of the immortal gods.

Among the most noted worshippers of Dionysus was Midas,[46] the wealthy king of Phrygia, the same who, as already related, gave judgment against Apollo. Upon one occasion Silenus, the preceptor and friend of Dionysus, being in an intoxicated condition, strayed into the rose-gardens of this monarch, where he was found by some of the king's attendants, who bound him with roses and conducted him to the presence of their royal master. Midas treated the aged satyr with the greatest consideration, and, after entertaining him hospitably for ten days, led him back to Dionysus, who was so grateful for the kind attention shown to his old friend, that he offered to grant Midas any favour he chose to demand; whereupon the avaricious monarch, not content with his boundless wealth, and still thirsting for more, desired that everything he touched might turn to gold. The request was complied with in so literal a sense, that the now wretched Midas bitterly repented his folly and cupidity, for, when the pangs of hunger assailed him, and he essayed to appease his cravings, the food became gold ere he could swallow it; as he raised the cup of wine to his parched lips, the sparkling draught was changed into the metal he had so coveted, and when at length, wearied and faint, he stretched his aching frame on his hitherto luxurious couch, this also was transformed into the substance which had now become the curse of his existence. The despairing king at last implored the god to take back the fatal gift, and Dionysus, pitying his unhappy plight, desired him to bathe in the river Pactolus, a small stream in Lydia, in order to lose the power which had become the bane of his life. Midas joyfully obeying the injunction, was at once freed from the consequences of his avaricious demand, and from this time forth the sands of the river Pactolus have ever contained grains of gold.

Representations of Dionysus are of two kinds. According to the earliest conceptions, he appears as a grave and dignified man in the prime of life; his countenance is earnest, thoughtful, and benevolent; he wears a full beard, and is draped from head to foot in the garb of an Eastern monarch. But the sculptors of a later period represent him as a youth of singular beauty, though of somewhat effeminate appearance; the expression of the countenance is gentle and winning; the limbs are supple and gracefully moulded; and the hair, which is adorned by a wreath of vine or ivy leaves, falls over the shoulders in long curls. In one hand he bears the Thyrsus, and in the other a drinking-cup with two handles, these being his distinguishing attributes. He is often represented riding on a panther, or seated in a chariot drawn by lions, tigers, panthers, or lynxes.

Being the god of wine, which is calculated to promote sociability, he rarely appears alone, but is usually accompanied by Bacchantes, satyrs, and mountain-nymphs.

The finest modern representation of Ariadne is that by Danneker, at Frankfort-on-the-Maine. In this statue she appears riding on a panther; the beautiful upturned face inclines slightly over the left shoulder; the features are regular and finely cut, and a wreath of ivy-leaves encircles the well-shaped head. With her right hand she gracefully clasps the folds of drapery which fall away negligently from her rounded form, whilst the other rests lightly and caressingly on the head of the animal.

Dionysus was regarded as the patron of the drama, and at the state festival of the Dionysia, which was celebrated with great pomp in the city of Athens, dramatic entertainments took place in his honour, for which all the renowned Greek dramatists of antiquity composed their immortal tragedies and comedies.

He was also a prophetic divinity, and possessed oracles, the principal of which was that on Mount Rhodope in Thrace.

The tiger, lynx, panther, dolphin, serpent, and ass were sacred to this god. His favourite plants were the vine, ivy, laurel, and asphodel. His sacrifices consisted of goats, probably on account of their being destructive to vineyards.

BACCHUS OR LIBER.

The Romans had a divinity called Liber who presided over vegetation, and was, on this account, identified with the Greek Dionysus, and worshipped under the name of Bacchus.

The festival of Liber, called the Liberalia, was celebrated on the 17th of March.

AÏDES (PLUTO).

Aïdes, Aïdoneus, or Hades, was the son of Cronus and Rhea, and the youngest brother of Zeus and Poseidon. He was the ruler of that subterranean region called Erebus, which was inhabited by the shades or spirits of the dead, and also by those dethroned and exiled deities who had been vanquished by Zeus and his allies. Aïdes, the grim and gloomy monarch of this lower world, was the successor of Erebus, that ancient primeval divinity after whom these realms were called.

The early Greeks regarded Aïdes in the light of their greatest foe, and Homer tells us that he was "of all the gods the most detested," being in their eyes the grim robber who stole from them their nearest and dearest, and eventually deprived each of them of their share in terrestrial existence. His name was so feared that it was never mentioned by mortals, who, when they invoked him, struck the earth with their hands, and in sacrificing to him turned away their faces.

The belief of the people with regard to a future state was, in the Homeric age, a sad and cheerless one. It was supposed that when a mortal ceased to exist, his spirit tenanted the shadowy outline of the human form it had quitted. These shadows, or shades as they were called, were driven by Aïdes into his dominions, where they passed their time, some in brooding over the vicissitudes of fortune which they had experienced on earth, others in regretting the lost pleasures they had enjoyed in life, but all in a condition of semi-consciousness, from which the intellect could only be roused to full activity by drinking of the blood of the sacrifices offered to their shades by living friends, which, for a time, endowed them with their former mental vigour. The only beings supposed to enjoy any happiness in a future state were the heroes, whose acts of daring and deeds of prowess had, during their life, reflected honour on the land of their birth; and even these, according to Homer, pined after their career of earthly activity. He tells us that when Odysseus visited the lower world at the command of Circe, and held communion with the shades of the heroes of the Trojan war, Achilles assured him that he would rather be the poorest day-labourer on earth than reign supreme over the realm of shades.

The early Greek poets offer but scanty allusions to Erebus. Homer appears purposely to envelop these realms in vagueness and mystery, in order, probably, to heighten the sensation of awe inseparably connected with the lower world. In the Odyssey he describes the entrance to Erebus as being beyond the furthermost edge of Oceanus, in the far west, where dwelt the Cimmerians, enveloped in eternal mists and darkness.

In later times, however, in consequence of extended intercourse with foreign nations, new ideas became gradually introduced, and we find Egyptian theories with regard to a future state taking root in Greece, which become eventually the religious belief of the whole nation. It is now that the poets and philosophers, and more especially the teachers of the Eleusinian Mysteries, begin to inculcate the doctrine of the future reward and punishment of good and bad deeds. Aïdes, who had hitherto been regarded as the dread enemy of mankind, who delights in his grim office, and keeps the shades imprisoned in his dominions after withdrawing them from the joys of existence, now receives them with hospitality and friendship, and Hermes replaces him as conductor of shades to Hades. Under this new aspect Aïdes usurps the functions of a totally different divinity called Plutus (the god of riches), and is henceforth regarded as the giver of wealth to mankind, in the shape of those precious metals which lie concealed in the bowels of the earth.

The later poets mention various entrances to Erebus, which were for the most part caves and fissures. There was one in the mountain of Taenarum, another in Thesprotia, and a third, the most celebrated of all, in Italy, near the pestiferous Lake Avernus, over which it is said no bird could fly, so noxious were its exhalations.

In the dominions of Aïdes there were four great rivers, three of which had to be crossed by all the shades. These three were Acheron (sorrow), Cocytus (lamentation), and Styx (intense darkness), the sacred stream which flowed nine times round these realms.

The shades were ferried over the Styx by the grim, unshaven old boatman Charon, who, however, only took those whose bodies had received funereal rites on earth, and who had brought with them his indispensable toll, which was a small coin or obolus, usually placed under the tongue of a dead person for this purpose. If these conditions had not been fulfilled, the unhappy shades were left behind to wander up and down the banks for a hundred years as restless spirits.

On the opposite bank of the Styx was the tribunal of Minos, the supreme judge, before whom all shades had to appear, and who, after hearing full confession of their actions whilst on earth, pronounced the sentence of happiness or misery to which their deeds had entitled them. This tribunal was guarded by the terrible triple-headed dog Cerberus, who, with his three necks bristling with snakes, lay at full length on the ground;—a formidable sentinel, who permitted all shades to enter, but none to return.

The happy spirits, destined to enjoy the delights of Elysium, passed out on the right, and proceeded to the golden palace where Aïdes and Persephone held their royal court, from whom they received a kindly greeting, ere they set out for the Elysian Fields which lay beyond.[47] This blissful region was replete with all that could charm the senses or please the imagination; the air was balmy and fragrant, rippling brooks flowed peacefully through the smiling meadows, which glowed with the varied hues of a thousand flowers, whilst the groves resounded with the joyous songs of birds. The occupations and amusements of the happy shades were of the same nature as those which they had delighted in whilst on earth. Here the warrior found his horses, chariots, and arms, the musician his lyre, and the hunter his quiver and bow.

In a secluded vale of Elysium there flowed a gentle, silent stream, called Lethe (oblivion), whose waters had the effect of dispelling care, and producing utter forgetfulness of former events. According to the Pythagorean doctrine of the transmigration of souls, it was supposed that after the shades had inhabited Elysium for a thousand years they were destined to animate other bodies on earth, and before leaving Elysium they drank of the river Lethe, in order that they might enter upon their new career without any remembrance of the past.

The guilty souls, after leaving the presence of Minos, were conducted to the great judgment-hall of Hades, whose massive walls of solid adamant were surrounded by the river Phlegethon, the waves of which rolled flames of fire, and lit up, with their lurid glare, these awful realms. In the interior sat the dread judge Rhadamanthus, who declared to each comer the precise torments which awaited him in Tartarus. The wretched sinners were then seized by the Furies, who scourged them with their whips, and dragged them along to the great gate, which closed the opening to Tartarus, into whose awful depths they were hurled, to suffer endless torture.

Tartarus was a vast and gloomy expanse, as far below Hades as the earth is distant from the skies. There the Titans, fallen from their high estate, dragged out a dreary and monotonous existence; there also were Otus and Ephialtes, those giant sons of Poseidon, who, with impious hands, had attempted to scale Olympus and dethrone its mighty ruler. Principal among the sufferers in this abode of gloom were Tityus, Tantalus, Sisyphus, Ixion, and the Danaïdes.

TITYUS, one of the earth-born giants, had insulted Hera on her way to Peitho, for which offence Zeus flung him into Tartarus, where he suffered dreadful torture, inflicted by two vultures, which perpetually gnawed his liver.

TANTALUS was a wise and wealthy king of Lydia, with whom the gods themselves condescended to associate; he was even permitted to sit at table with Zeus, who delighted in his conversation, and listened with interest to the wisdom of his observations. Tantalus, however, elated at these distinguished marks of divine favour, presumed upon his position, and used unbecoming language to Zeus himself; he also stole nectar and ambrosia from the table of the gods, with which he regaled his friends; but his greatest crime consisted in killing his own son, Pelops, and serving him up at one of the banquets to the gods, in order to test their omniscience. For these heinous offences he was condemned by Zeus to eternal punishment in Tartarus, where, tortured with an ever-burning thirst, he was plunged up to the chin in water, which, as he stooped to drink, always receded from his parched lips. Tall trees, with spreading branches laden with delicious fruits, hung temptingly over his head; but no sooner did he raise himself to grasp them, than a wind arose, and carried them beyond his reach.

SISYPHUS was a great tyrant who, according to some accounts, barbarously murdered all travellers who came into his dominions, by hurling upon them enormous pieces of rock.

In punishment for his crimes he was condemned to roll incessantly a huge block of stone up a steep hill, which, as soon as it reached the summit, always rolled back again to the plain below.

IXION was a king of Thessaly to whom Zeus accorded the privilege of joining the festive banquets of the gods; but, taking advantage of his exalted position, he presumed to aspire to the favour of Hera, which so greatly incensed Zeus, that he struck him with his thunderbolts, and commanded Hermes to throw him into Tartarus, and bind him to an ever-revolving wheel.

The **DANAÏDES** were the fifty daughters of Danaus, king of Argos, who had married their fifty cousins, the sons of Ægyptus. By the command of their father, who had been warned by an oracle that his son-in-law would cause his death, they all killed their husbands in one night, Hypermnestra alone excepted. Their punishment in the lower world was to fill with water a vessel full of holes,—a never-ending and useless task.

Aïdes is usually represented as a man of mature years and stern majestic mien, bearing a striking resemblance to his brother Zeus; but the gloomy and inexorable expression of the face contrasts forcibly with that peculiar benignity which so characterizes the countenance of the mighty ruler of heaven. He is seated on a throne of ebony, with his queen, the grave and sad Persephone, beside him, and wears a full beard, and long flowing black hair, which hangs straight down over his forehead; in his hand he either bears a two-pronged fork or the keys of the lower world, and at his feet sits Cerberus. He is sometimes seen in a chariot of gold, drawn by four black horses, and wearing on his head a helmet made for him by the Cyclops, which rendered the wearer invisible. This helmet he frequently lent to mortals and immortals.

Aïdes, who was universally worshipped throughout Greece, had temples erected to his honour in Elis, Olympia, and also at Athens.

His sacrifices, which took place at night, consisted of black sheep, and the blood, instead of being sprinkled on the altars or received in vessels, as at other sacrifices, was permitted to run down into a trench, dug for this purpose. The officiating priests wore black robes, and were crowned with cypress.

The narcissus, maiden-hair, and cypress were sacred to this divinity.

PLUTO.

Before the introduction into Rome of the religion and literature of Greece, the Romans had no belief in a realm of future happiness or misery, corresponding to the Greek Hades; hence they had no god of the lower world identical with Aïdes. They supposed that there was, in the centre of the earth, a vast, gloomy, and impenetrably dark cavity called Orcus, which formed a place of eternal rest for the dead. But with the introduction of Greek mythology, the Roman Orcus became the Greek Hades, and all the Greek notions with regard to a future state now obtained with the Romans, who worshipped Aïdes under the name of Pluto, his other appellations being Dis (from *dives*, rich) and Orcus from the dominions over which he ruled. In Rome there were no temples erected to this divinity.

PLUTUS.

Plutus, the son of Demeter and a mortal called Iasion, was the god of wealth, and is represented as being lame when he makes his appearance, and winged when he takes his departure. He was supposed to be both blind and foolish, because he bestows his gifts without discrimination, and frequently upon the most unworthy objects.

Plutus was believed to have his abode in the bowels of the earth, which was probably the reason why, in later times, Aïdes became confounded with this divinity.

MINOR DIVINITIES—

THE HARPIES.

The Harpies, who, like the Furies, were employed by the gods as instruments for the punishment of the guilty, were three female divinities, daughters of Thaumas and Electra, called Aello, Ocypete, and Celæno.

They were represented with the head of a fair-haired maiden and the body of a vulture, and were perpetually devoured by the pangs of insatiable hunger, which caused them to torment their victims by robbing them of their food; this they either devoured with great gluttony, or defiled in such a manner as to render it unfit to be eaten.

Their wonderfully rapid flight far surpassed that of birds, or even of the winds themselves. If any mortal suddenly and unaccountably disappeared, the Harpies were believed to have carried him off. Thus they were supposed to have borne away the daughters of King Pandareos to act as servants to the Erinyes.

The Harpies would appear to be personifications of sudden tempests, which, with ruthless violence, sweep over whole districts, carrying off or injuring all before them.

ERINYES, EUMENIDES (Furiæ, Diræ).

The Erinyes or Furies were female divinities who personified the torturing pangs of an evil conscience, and the remorse which inevitably follows wrong-doing.

Their names were Alecto, Megæra, and Tisiphone, and their origin was variously accounted for. According to Hesiod, they sprang from the blood of Uranus, when wounded by Cronus, and were hence supposed to be the embodiment of all the terrible imprecations, which the defeated deity called down upon the head of his rebellious son. According to other accounts they were the daughters of Night.

Their place of abode was the lower world, where they were employed by Aïdes and Persephone to chastise and torment those shades who, during their earthly career, had committed crimes, and had not been reconciled to the gods before descending to Hades.

But their sphere of action was not confined to the realm of shades, for they appeared upon earth as the avenging deities who relentlessly pursued and punished murderers, perjurers, those who had failed in duty to their parents, in hospitality to strangers, or in the respect due to old age. Nothing escaped the piercing glance of these terrible divinities, from whom flight was unavailing, for no corner of the earth was so remote as to be beyond their reach, nor did any mortal dare to offer to their victims an asylum from their persecutions.

The Furies are frequently represented with wings; their bodies are black, blood drips from their eyes, and snakes twine in their hair. In their hands they bear either a dagger, scourge, torch, or serpent.

When they pursued Orestes they constantly held up a mirror to his horrified gaze, in which he beheld the face of his murdered mother.

These divinities were also called Eumenides, which signifies the "well-meaning" or "soothed goddesses;" This appellation was given to them because they were so feared and dreaded that people dared not call them by their proper title, and hoped by this means to propitiate their wrath.

In later times the Furies came to be regarded as salutary agencies, who, by severely punishing sin, upheld the cause of morality and social order, and thus contributed to the welfare of mankind. They now lose their awe-inspiring aspect, and are represented, more especially in Athens, as earnest maidens, dressed, like Artemis, in short tunics suitable for the chase, but still retaining, in their hands, the wand of office in the form of a snake.

Their sacrifices consisted of black sheep and a libation composed of a mixture of honey and water, called Nephalia. A celebrated temple was erected to the Eumenides at Athens, near the Areopagus.

MOIRÆ or FATES (PARCÆ).

The ancients believed that the duration of human existence and the destinies of mortals were regulated by three sister-goddesses, called Clotho, Lachesis, and Atropos, who were the daughters of Zeus and Themis.

The power which they wielded over the fate of man was significantly indicated under the figure of a thread, which they spun out for the life of each human being from his birth to the grave. This occupation they divided between them. Clotho wound the flax round the distaff, ready for her sister Lachesis, who span out the thread of life, which Atropos, with her scissors, relentlessly snapt asunder, when the career of an individual was about to terminate.

Homer speaks of one Moira only, the daughter of Night, who represents the moral force by which the universe is governed, and to whom both mortals and immortals were forced to submit, Zeus himself being powerless to avert her decrees; but in later times this conception of one inexorable, all-conquering fate became amplified by the poets into that above described, and the Moiræ are henceforth the special presiding deities over the life and death of mortals.

The Moiræ are represented by the poets as stern, inexorable female divinities, aged, hideous, and also lame, which is evidently meant to indicate the slow and halting march of destiny, which they controlled. Painters and sculptors, on the other hand, depicted them as beautiful maidens of a grave but kindly aspect.

There is a charming representation of Lachesis, which depicts her in all the grace of youth and beauty. She is sitting spinning, and at her feet lie two masks, one comic, the other tragic, as though to convey the idea, that, to a divinity of fate, the brightest and saddest scenes of earthly existence are alike indifferent, and that she quietly and steadily pursues her occupation, regardless of human weal or woe.

When represented at the feet of Aïdes in the lower world they are clad in dark robes; but when they appear in Olympus they wear bright garments, bespangled with stars, and are seated on radiant thrones, with crowns on their heads.

It was considered the function of the Moiræ to indicate to the Furies the precise torture which the wicked should undergo for their crimes.

They were regarded as prophetic divinities, and had sanctuaries in many parts of Greece.

The Moiræ are mentioned as assisting the Charites to conduct Persephone to the upper world at her periodical reunion with her mother Demeter. They also appear in company with Eileithyia, goddess of birth.

NEMESIS.

Nemesis, the daughter of Nyx, represents that power which adjusts the balance of human affairs, by awarding to each individual the fate which his actions deserve. She rewards, humble, unacknowledged merit, punishes crime, deprives the worthless of undeserved good fortune, humiliates the proud and overbearing, and visits all evil on the wrong-doer; thus maintaining that proper balance of things, which the Greeks recognized as a necessary condition of all civilized life. But though Nemesis, in her original character, was the distributor of rewards as well as punishments, the world was so full of sin, that she found but little occupation in her first capacity, and hence became finally regarded as the avenging goddess only.

We have seen a striking instance of the manner in which this divinity punishes the proud and arrogant in the history of Niobe. Apollo and Artemis were merely the instruments for avenging the insult offered to their mother; but it was Nemesis who prompted the deed, and presided over its execution.

Homer makes no mention of Nemesis; it is therefore evident that she was a conception of later times, when higher views of morality had obtained among the Greek nation.

Nemesis is represented as a beautiful woman of thoughtful and benign aspect and regal bearing; a diadem crowns her majestic brow, and she bears in her hand a rudder, balance, and cubit;—fitting emblems of the manner in which she guides, weighs, and measures all human events. She is also sometimes seen with a wheel, to symbolize the rapidity with which she executes justice. As the avenger of evil she appears winged, bearing in her hand either a scourge or a sword, and seated in a chariot drawn by griffins.

Nemesis is frequently called Adrastia, and also Rhamnusia, from Rhamnus in Attica, the chief seat of her worship, which contained a celebrated statue of the goddess.

Nemesis was worshipped by the Romans, (who invoked her on the Capitol), as a divinity who possessed the power of averting the pernicious consequences of envy.

NIGHT AND HER CHILDREN (DEATH, SLEEP, AND DREAMS).

Nyx (NOX).

Nyx, the daughter of Chaos, being the personification of Night, was, according to the poetic ideas of the Greeks, considered to be the mother of everything mysterious and inexplicable, such as death, sleep, dreams, &c. She became united to Erebus, and their children were Aether and Hemera (Air and Daylight), evidently a simile of the poets, to indicate that darkness always precedes light.

Nyx inhabited a palace in the dark regions of the lower world, and is represented as a beautiful woman, seated in a chariot, drawn by two black horses. She is clothed in dark robes, wears a long veil, and is accompanied by the stars, which follow in her train.

Thanatos (MORS) and Hypnus (SOMNUS).

Thanatos (Death) and his twin-brother Hypnus (Sleep) were the children of Nyx.

Their dwelling was in the realm of shades, and when they appear among mortals, Thanatos is feared and hated as the enemy of mankind, whose hard heart knows no pity, whilst his brother Hypnus is universally loved and welcomed as their kindest and most beneficent friend.

But though the ancients regarded Thanatos as a gloomy and mournful divinity, they did not represent him with any exterior repulsiveness. On the contrary, he appears as a beautiful youth, who holds in his hand an inverted torch, emblematical of the light of life being extinguished, whilst his disengaged arm is thrown lovingly round the shoulder of his brother Hypnus.

Hypnus is sometimes depicted standing erect with closed eyes; at others he is in a recumbent position beside his brother Thanatos, and usually bears a poppy-stalk in his hand.

A most interesting description of the abode of Hypnus is given by Ovid in his Metamorphoses. He tells us how the god of Sleep dwelt in a mountain-cave near the realm of the Cimmerians, which the sun never pierced with his rays. No sound disturbed the stillness, no song of birds, not a branch moved, and no human voice broke the profound silence which reigned everywhere. From the lowermost rocks of the cave issued the river Lethe, and one might almost have supposed that its course was arrested, were it not for the low, monotonous hum of the water, which invited slumber. The entrance was partially hidden by numberless white and red poppies, which Mother Night had gathered and planted there, and from the juice of which she extracts drowsiness, which she scatters in liquid drops all over the earth, as soon as the sun-god has sunk to rest. In the centre of the cave stands a couch of blackest ebony, with a bed of down, over which is laid a coverlet of sable hue. Here the god himself reposes, surrounded by innumerable forms. These are idle dreams, more numerous than the sands of the sea. Chief among them is Morpheus, that changeful god, who may assume any shape or form he pleases. Nor can the god of Sleep resist his own power; for though he may rouse himself for a while, he soon succumbs to the drowsy influences which surround him.

Morpheus.

Morpheus, the son of Hypnus, was the god of Dreams.

He is always represented winged, and appears sometimes as a youth, sometimes as an old man. In his hand he bears a cluster of poppies, and as he steps with noiseless footsteps over the earth, he gently scatters the seeds of this sleep-producing plant over the eyes of weary mortals.

Homer describes the House of Dreams as having two gates: one, whence issue all deceptive and flattering visions, being formed of ivory; the other, through which proceed those dreams which are fulfilled, of horn.

THE GORGONS.

The Gorgons, Stheno, Euryale, and Medusa, were the three daughters of Phorcys and Ceto, and were the personification of those benumbing, and, as it were, petrifying sensations, which result from sudden and extreme fear.

They were frightful winged monsters, whose bodies were covered with scales; hissing, wriggling snakes clustered round their heads instead of hair; their hands were of brass; their teeth resembled the tusks of a wild boar; and their whole aspect was so appalling, that they are said to have turned into stone all who beheld them.

These terrible sisters were supposed to dwell in that remote and mysterious region in the far West, beyond the sacred stream of Oceanus.

The Gorgons were the servants of Aïdes, who made use of them to terrify and overawe those shades, doomed to be kept in a constant state of unrest as a punishment for their misdeeds, whilst the Furies, on their part, scourged them with their whips and tortured them incessantly.

The most celebrated of the three sisters was Medusa, who alone was mortal. She was originally a golden-haired and very beautiful maiden, who, as a priestess of Athene, was devoted to a life of celibacy; but, being wooed by Poseidon, whom she loved in return, she forgot her vows, and became united to him in marriage. For this offence she was punished by the goddess in a most terrible manner. Each wavy lock of the beautiful hair which had so charmed her husband, was changed into a venomous snake; her once gentle, love-in-spiring eyes now became blood-shot, furious orbs, which excited fear and disgust in the mind of the beholder; whilst her former roseate hue and milk-white skin assumed a loathsome greenish tinge. Seeing herself thus transformed into so repulsive an object, Medusa fled from her home, never to return. Wandering about, abhorred, dreaded, and shunned by all the world, she now developed into a character, worthy of her outward appearance. In her despair she fled to Africa, where, as she passed restlessly from place to place, infant snakes dropped from her hair, and thus, according to the belief of the ancients, that country became the hotbed of these venomous reptiles. With the curse of Athene upon her, she turned into stone whomsoever she gazed upon, till at last, after a life of nameless misery, deliverance came to her in the shape of death, at the hands of Perseus.

It is well to observe that when the Gorgons are spoken of in the singular, it is Medusa who is alluded to.

Medusa was the mother of Pegasus and Chrysaor, father of the three-headed, winged giant Geryones, who was slain by Heracles.

GRÆÆ.

The Grææ, who acted as servants to their sisters the Gorgons, were also three in number; their names were Pephredo, Enyo, and Dino.

In their original conception they were merely personifications of kindly and venerable old age, possessing all its benevolent attributes without its natural infirmities. They were old and gray from their birth, and so they ever remained. In later times, however, they came to be regarded as misshapen females, decrepid, and hideously ugly, having only one eye, one tooth, and one gray wig between them, which they lent to each other, when one of them wished to appear before the world.

When Perseus entered upon his expedition to slay the Medusa, he repaired to the abode of the Grææ, in the far west, to inquire the way to the Gorgons, and on their refusing to give any information, he deprived them of their one eye, tooth, and wig, and did not restore them until he received the necessary directions.

SPHINX.

The Sphinx was an ancient Egyptian divinity, who personified wisdom, and the fertility of nature. She is represented as a lion-couchant, with the head and bust of a woman, and wears a peculiar sort of hood, which completely envelops her head, and falls down on either side of the face.

Transplanted into Greece, this sublime and mysterious Egyptian deity degenerates into an insignificant, and yet malignant power, and though she also deals in mysteries, they are, as we shall see, of a totally different character, and altogether inimical to human life.

The Sphinx is represented, according to Greek genealogy, as the offspring of Typhon and Echidna.[48] Hera, being upon one occasion displeased with the Thebans, sent them this awful monster, as a punishment for their offences. Taking her seat on a rocky eminence near the city of Thebes, commanding a pass which the Thebans were compelled to traverse in their usual way of business, she propounded to all comers a riddle, and if they failed to solve it, she tore them in pieces.

During the reign of King Creon, so many people had fallen a sacrifice to this monster, that he determined to use every effort to rid the country of so terrible a scourge. On consulting the oracle of Delphi, he was informed that the only way to destroy the Sphinx was to solve one of her riddles, when she would immediately precipitate herself from the rock on which she was seated.

Creon, accordingly, made a public declaration to the effect, that whoever could give the true interpretation of a riddle propounded by the monster, should obtain the crown, and the hand of his sister Jocaste. Œdipus offered himself as a candidate, and proceeding to the spot where she kept guard, received from her the following riddle for solution: "What creature goes in the morning on four legs, at noon on two, and in the evening on three?" Œdipus replied, that it must be man, who during his infancy creeps on all fours, in his prime walks erect on two legs, and when old age has enfeebled his powers, calls a staff to his assistance, and thus has, as it were, three legs.

The Sphinx no sooner heard this reply, which was the correct solution of her riddle, than she flung herself over the precipice, and perished in the abyss below.

The Greek Sphinx may be recognized by having wings and by being of smaller dimensions than the Egyptian Sphinx.

TYCHE (Fortuna) AND ANANKE (Necessitas).

Tyche (Fortuna).

Tyche personified that peculiar combination of circumstances which we call luck or fortune, and was considered to be the source of all unexpected events in human life, whether good or evil. If a person succeeded in all he undertook without possessing any special merit of his own, Tyche was supposed to have smiled on his birth. If, on the other hand, undeserved ill-luck followed him through life, and all his efforts resulted in failure, it was ascribed to her adverse influence.

This goddess of Fortune is variously represented. Sometimes she is depicted bearing in her hand two rudders, with one of which she steers the bark of the fortunate, and with the other that of the unfortunate among mortals. In later times she appears blindfolded, and stands on a ball or wheel, indicative of the fickleness and ever-revolving changes of fortune. She frequently bears the sceptre and cornucopia[49] or horn of plenty, and is usually winged. In her temple at Thebes, she is represented holding the infant Plutus in her arms, to symbolize her power over riches and prosperity.

Tyche was worshipped in various parts of Greece, but

more particularly by the Athenians, who believed in her special predilection for their city.

FORTUNA.

Tyche was worshipped in Rome under the name of Fortuna, and held a position of much greater importance among the Romans than the Greeks.

In later times Fortuna is never represented either winged or standing on a ball; she merely bears the cornucopia. It is evident, therefore, that she had come to be regarded as the goddess of good luck only, who brings blessings to man, and not, as with the Greeks, as the personification of the fluctuations of fortune.

In addition to Fortuna, the Romans worshipped Felicitas as the giver of positive good fortune.

Ananke (NECESSITAS).

As Ananke, Tyche assumes quite another character, and becomes the embodiment of those immutable laws of nature, by which certain causes produce certain inevitable results.

In a statue of this divinity at Athens she was represented with hands of bronze, and surrounded with nails and hammers. The hands of bronze probably indicated the irresistible power of the inevitable, and the hammer and chains the fetters which she forged for man.

Ananke was worshipped in Rome under the name of Necessitas.

KER.

In addition to the Moiræ, who presided over the life of mortals, there was another divinity, called Ker, appointed for each human being at the moment of his birth. The Ker belonging to an individual was believed to develop with his growth, either for good or evil; and when the ultimate fate of a mortal was about to be decided, his Ker was weighed in the balance, and, according to the preponderance of its worth or worthlessness, life or death was awarded to the human being in question. It becomes evident, therefore, that according to the belief of the early Greeks, each individual had it in his power, to a certain extent, to shorten or prolong his own existence.

The Keres, who are frequently mentioned by Homer, were the goddesses who delighted in the slaughter of the battle-field.

ATE.

Ate, the daughter of Zeus and Eris, was a divinity who delighted in evil.

Having instigated Hera to deprive Heracles of his birthright, her father seized her by the hair of her head, and hurled her from Olympus, forbidding her, under the most solemn imprecations, ever to return. Henceforth she wandered among mankind, sowing dissension, working mischief, and luring men to all actions inimical to their welfare and happiness. Hence, when a reconciliation took place between friends who had quarrelled, Ate was blamed as the original cause of disagreement.

MOMUS.

Momus, the son of Nyx, was the god of raillery and ridicule, who delighted to criticise, with bitter sarcasm, the actions of gods and men, and contrived to discover in all things some defect or blemish. Thus when Prometheus created the first man, Momus considered his work incomplete because there was no aperture in the breast through which his inmost thoughts might be read. He also found fault with a house built by Athene because, being unprovided with the means of locomotion, it could never be removed from an unhealthy locality. Aphrodite alone defied his criticism, for, to his great chagrin, he could find no fault with her perfect form.[50]

In what manner the ancients represented this god is unknown. In modern art he is depicted like a king's jester, with a fool's cap and bells.

EROS (CUPID, AMOR) AND PSYCHE.

According to Hesiod's Theogony, Eros, the divine spirit of Love, sprang forth from Chaos, while all was still in confusion, and by his beneficent power reduced to order and harmony the shapeless, conflicting elements, which, under his influence, began to assume distinct forms. This ancient Eros is represented as a full-grown and very beautiful youth, crowned with flowers, and leaning on a shepherd's crook.

In the course of time, this beautiful conception gradually faded away, and though occasional mention still continues to be made of the Eros of Chaos, he is replaced by the son of Aphrodite, the popular, mischief-loving little god of Love, so familiar to us all.

In one of the myths concerning Eros, Aphrodite is described as complaining to Themis, that her son, though so beautiful, did not appear to increase in stature; whereupon Themis suggested that his small proportions were probably attributable to the fact of his being always alone, and advised his mother to let him have a companion. Aphrodite accordingly gave him, as a playfellow, his younger brother Anteros (requited love), and soon had the gratification of seeing the little Eros begin to grow and thrive; but, curious to relate, this desirable result only continued as long as the brothers remained together, for the moment they were separated, Eros shrank once more to his original size.

By degrees the conception of Eros became multiplied and we hear of little love-gods (Amors), who appear under the most charming and diversified forms. These love-gods, who afforded to artists inexhaustible subjects for the exercise of their imagination, are represented as being engaged in various occupations, such as hunting, fishing, rowing, driving chariots, and even busying themselves in mechanical labour.

Perhaps no myth is more charming and interesting than that of Eros and Psyche, which is as follows:—Psyche, the youngest of three princesses, was so transcendently beautiful that Aphrodite herself became jealous of her, and no mortal dared to aspire to the honour of her hand. As her sisters, who were by no means equal to her in attractions, were married, and Psyche still remained unwedded, her father consulted the oracle of Delphi, and, in obedience to the divine response, caused her to be dressed as though for the grave, and conducted to the edge of a yawning precipice. No sooner was she alone than she felt herself lifted up, and wafted away by the gentle west wind Zephyrus, who transported her to a verdant meadow, in the midst of which stood a stately palace, surrounded by groves and fountains.

Here dwelt Eros, the god of Love, in whose arms Zephyrus deposited his lovely burden. Eros, himself unseen, wooed her in the softest accents of affection; but warned her, as she valued his love, not to endeavour to behold his form. For some time Psyche was obedient to the injunction of her immortal spouse, and made no effort to gratify her natural curiosity; but, unfortunately, in the midst of her happiness she was seized with an unconquerable longing for the society of her sisters, and, in accordance with her desire, they were conducted by Zephyrus to her fairy-like abode. Filled with envy at the sight of her felicity, they poisoned her mind against her husband, and telling her that her unseen lover was a frightful monster, they gave her a sharp dagger, which they persuaded her to use for the purpose of delivering herself from his power.

After the departure of her sisters, Psyche resolved to take the first opportunity of following their malicious counsel. She accordingly rose in the dead of night, and taking a lamp in one hand and a dagger in the other, stealthily approached the couch where Eros was reposing, when, instead of the frightful monster she had expected to see, the beauteous form of the god of Love greeted her view. Overcome with surprise and admiration, Psyche stooped down to gaze more closely on his lovely features, when, from the lamp which she held in her trembling hand, there fell a drop of burning oil upon the shoulder of the sleeping god, who instantly awoke, and seeing Psyche standing over him with the instrument of death in her hand, sorrowfully reproached her for her treacherous designs, and, spreading out his wings, flew away.

In despair at having lost her lover, the unhappy Psyche endeavoured to put an end to her existence by throwing herself into the nearest river; but instead of closing over her, the waters bore her gently to the opposite bank, where Pan (the god of shepherds) received her, and consoled her with the hope of becoming eventually reconciled to her husband.

Meanwhile her wicked sisters, in expectation of meeting with the same good fortune which had befallen Psyche, placed themselves on the edge of the rock, but were both precipitated into the chasm below.

Psyche herself, filled with a restless yearning for her lost love, wandered all over the world in search of him. At length she appealed to Aphrodite to take compassion on her; but the goddess of Beauty, still jealous of her charms, imposed upon her the hardest tasks, the accomplishment of which often appeared impossible. In these she was always assisted by invisible, beneficent beings, sent to her by Eros, who still loved her, and continued to watch over her welfare.

Psyche had to undergo a long and severe penance before she became worthy to regain the happiness, which she had so foolishly trifled away. At last Aphrodite commanded her to descend into the under world, and obtain from Persephone a box containing all the charms of beauty. Psyche's courage now failed her, for she concluded that death must of necessity precede her entrance into the realm of shades. About to abandon herself to despair, she heard a voice which warned her of every danger to be avoided on her perilous journey, and instructed her with regard to certain precautions to be observed. These were as follows:—not to omit to provide herself with the ferryman's toll for Charon, and the cake to pacify Cerberus, also to refrain from taking any part in the banquets of Aïdes and Persephone, and, above all things, to bring the box of beauty charms unopened to Aphrodite. In conclusion, the voice assured her, that compliance with the above conditions would insure for her a safe return to the realms of light. But, alas, Psyche, who had implicitly followed all injunctions, could not withstand the temptation of the last condition; and, hardly had she quitted the lower world, when, unable to resist the curiosity which devoured her, she raised the lid of the box with eager expectation. But, instead of the wondrous charms of beauty which she expected to behold, there issued from the casket a dense black vapour, which had the effect of throwing her into a death-like sleep, out of which Eros, who had long hovered round her unseen, at length awoke her with the point of one of his golden arrows. He gently reproached her with this second proof of her curiosity and folly, and then, having persuaded Aphrodite to be reconciled to his beloved, he induced Zeus to admit her among the immortal gods.

Their reunion was celebrated amidst the rejoicings of all the Olympian deities. The Graces shed perfume on their path, the Hours sprinkled roses over the sky, Apollo added the music of his lyre, and the Muses united their voices in a glad chorus of delight.

This myth would appear to be an allegory, which signifies that the soul, before it can be reunited to its original divine essence, must be purified by the chastening sorrows and sufferings of its earthly career.[51]

Eros is represented as a lovely boy, with rounded limbs, and a merry, roguish expression. He has golden wings, and a quiver slung over his shoulder, which contained his magical and unerring arrows; in one hand he bears his golden bow, and in the other a torch.

He is also frequently depicted riding on a lion, dolphin, or eagle, or seated in a chariot drawn by stags or wild boars, undoubtedly emblematical of the power of love as the subduer of all nature, even of the wild animals.

In Rome, Eros was worshipped under the name of Amor or Cupid.

HYMEN.

Hymen or Hymenæus, the son of Apollo and the muse Urania, was the god who presided over marriage and nuptial solemnities, and was hence invoked at all marriage festivities.

There is a myth concerning this divinity, which tells us that Hymen was a beautiful youth of very poor parents, who fell in love with a wealthy maiden, so far above him in rank, that he dared not cherish the hope of ever becoming united to her. Still he missed no opportunity of seeing her, and, upon one occasion, disguised himself as a girl, and joined a troop of maidens, who, in company with his beloved, were proceeding from Athens to Eleusis, in order to attend a festival of Demeter. On their way thither they were surprised by pirates, who carried them off to a desert island, where the ruffians, after drinking deeply, fell into a heavy sleep. Hymen, seizing the opportunity, slew them all, and then set sail for Athens, where he found the parents of the maidens in the greatest distress at their unaccountable disappearance. He comforted them with the assurance that their children should be restored to them, provided they would promise to give him in marriage the maiden he loved. The condition being gladly complied with, he at once returned to the island, and brought back the maidens in safety to Athens, whereupon he became united to the object of his love; and their union proved so remarkably happy, that henceforth the name of Hymen became synonymous with conjugal felicity.

IRIS (THE RAINBOW).

Iris, the daughter of Thaumas and Electra, personified the rainbow, and was the special attendant and messenger of the queen of heaven, whose commands she executed with singular tact, intelligence, and swiftness.

Most primitive nations have regarded the rainbow as a bridge of communication between heaven and earth, and this is doubtless the reason why Iris, who represented that beautiful phenomenon of nature, should have been invested by the Greeks with the office of communicating between gods and men.

Iris is usually represented seated behind the chariot of Hera, ready to do the bidding of her royal mistress. She appears under the form of a slender maiden of great beauty, robed in an airy fabric of variegated hues, resembling mother-of-pearl; her sandals are bright as burnished silver, she has golden wings, and wherever she appears, a radiance of light, and a sweet odour, as of delicate spring flowers, pervades the air.

HEBE (JUVENTAS).

Hebe was the personification of eternal youth under its most attractive and joyous aspect.

She was the daughter of Zeus and Hera, and though of such distinguished rank, is nevertheless represented as cup-bearer to the gods; a forcible exemplification of the old patriarchal custom, in accordance with which the daughters of the house, even when of the highest lineage, personally assisted in serving the guests.

Hebe is represented as a comely, modest maiden, small, of a beautifully rounded contour, with nut-brown tresses and sparkling eyes. She is often depicted pouring out nectar from an upraised vessel, or bearing in her hand a shallow dish, supposed to contain ambrosia, the ever youth-renewing food of the immortals.

In consequence of an act of awkwardness, which caused her to slip while serving the gods, Hebe was deprived of her office, which was henceforth delegated to Ganymedes, son of Tros.

Hebe afterwards became the bride of Heracles, when, after his apotheosis, he was received among the immortals.

JUVENTAS.

Juventas was the Roman divinity identified with Hebe, whose attributes, however, were regarded by the Romans as applying more particularly to the imperishable vigour and immortal glory of the state.

In Rome, several temples were erected in honour of this goddess.

GANYMEDES.

Ganymedes, the youngest son of Tros, king of Troy, was one day drawing water from a well on Mount Ida, when he was observed by Zeus, who, struck with his wonderful beauty, sent his eagle to transport him to Olympus, where he was endowed with immortality, and appointed cup-bearer to the gods.

Ganymedes is represented as a youth of exquisite beauty, with short golden locks, delicately chiselled features, beaming blue eyes, and pouting lips.

THE MUSES.

Of all the Olympic deities, none occupy a more distinguished position than the Muses, the nine beautiful daughters of Zeus and Mnemosyne.

In their original signification, they presided merely over music, song, and dance; but with the progress of civilization the arts and sciences claimed their special presiding divinities, and we see these graceful creations, in later times, sharing among them various functions, such as poetry, astronomy, &c.

The Muses were honoured alike by mortals and immortals. In Olympus, where Apollo acted as their leader, no banquet or festivity was considered complete without their joy-inspiring presence, and on earth no social gathering was celebrated without libations being poured out to them; nor was any task involving intellectual effort ever undertaken, without earnestly supplicating their assistance. They endowed their chosen favourites with knowledge, wisdom, and understanding; they bestowed upon the orator the gift of eloquence, inspired the poet with his noblest thoughts, and the musician with his sweetest harmonies.

Like so many of the Greek divinities, however, the refined conception of the Muses is somewhat marred by the acerbity with which they punished any effort on the part of mortals to rival them in their divine powers. An instance of this is seen in the case of Thamyris, a Thracian bard, who presumed to invite them to a trial of skill in music. Having vanquished him, they not only afflicted him with blindness, but deprived him also of the power of song.

Another example of the manner in which the gods punished presumption and vanity is seen in the story of the daughters of King Pierus. Proud of the perfection to which they had brought their skill in music, they presumed to challenge the Muses themselves in the art over which they specially presided. The contest took place on Mount Helicon, and it is said that when the mortal maidens commenced their song, the sky became dark and misty, whereas when the Muses raised their heavenly voices, all nature seemed to rejoice, and Mount Helicon itself moved with exultation. The Pierides were signally defeated, and were transformed by the Muses into singing birds, as a punishment for having dared to challenge comparison with the immortals.

Undeterred by the above example, the Sirens also entered into a similar contest. The songs of the Muses were loyal and true, whilst those of the Sirens were the false and deceptive strains with which so many unfortunate mariners had been lured to their death. The Sirens were defeated by the Muses, and as a mark of humiliation, were deprived of the feathers with which their bodies were adorned.

The oldest seat of the worship of the Muses was Pieria in Thrace, where they were supposed to have first seen the light of day. Pieria is a district on one of the sloping declivities of Mount Olympus, whence a number of rivulets, as they flow towards the plains beneath, produce those sweet, soothing sounds, which may possibly have suggested this spot as a fitting home for the presiding divinities of song.

They dwelt on the summits of Mounts Helicon, Parnassus, and Pindus, and loved to haunt the springs and fountains which gushed forth amidst these rocky heights, all of which were sacred to them and to poetic inspiration. Aganippe and Hippocrene on Mount Helicon, and the Castalian spring on Mount Parnassus, were sacred to the Muses. The latter flowed between two lofty rocks above the city of Delphi, and in ancient times its waters were introduced into a square stone basin, where they were retained for the use of the Pythia and the priests of Apollo.

The libations to these divinities consisted of water, milk, and honey, but never of wine.

Their names and functions are as follows:—

CALLIOPE, the most honoured of the Muses, presided over heroic song and epic poetry, and is represented with a pencil in her hand, and a slate upon her knee.

CLIO, the muse of History, holds in her hand a roll of parchment, and wears a wreath of laurel.

MELPOMENE, the muse of Tragedy, bears a tragic mask.

THALIA, the muse of Comedy, carries in her right hand a shepherd's crook, and has a comic mask beside her.

POLYHYMNIA, the muse of Sacred Hymns, is crowned with a wreath of laurel. She is always represented in a thoughtful attitude, and entirely enveloped in rich folds of drapery.

TERPSICHORE, the muse of Dance and Roundelay, is represented in the act of playing on a seven-stringed lyre.

URANIA, the muse of Astronomy, stands erect, and bears in her left hand a celestial globe.

EUTERPE, the muse of Harmony, is represented bearing a musical instrument, usually a flute.

ERATO, the muse of Love and hymeneal songs, wears a wreath of laurel, and is striking the chords of a lyre.

With regard to the origin of the Muses, it is said that they were created by Zeus in answer to a request on the part of the victorious deities, after the war with the Titans, that some special divinities should be called into existence, in order to commemorate in song the glorious deeds of the Olympian gods.

PEGASUS.

Pegasus was a beautiful winged horse who sprang from the body of Medusa when she was slain by the hero Perseus, the son of Zeus and Danaë. Spreading out his wings he immediately flew to the top of Mount Olympus, where he was received with delight and admiration by all the immortals. A place in his palace was assigned to him by Zeus, who employed him to carry his thunder and lightning. Pegasus permitted none but the gods to mount him, except in the case of Bellerophon, whom, at the command of Athene, he carried aloft, in order that he might slay the Chimæra with his arrows.

The later poets represent Pegasus as being at the service

of the Muses, and for this reason he is more celebrated in modern times than in antiquity. He would appear to represent that poetical inspiration, which tends to develop man's higher nature, and causes the mind to soar heavenwards. The only mention by the ancients of Pegasus in connection with the Muses, is the story of his having produced with his hoofs, the famous fountain Hippocrene.

It is said that during their contest with the Pierides, the Muses played and sang on the summit of Mount Helicon with such extraordinary power and sweetness, that heaven and earth stood still to listen, whilst the mountain raised itself in joyous ecstasy towards the abode of the celestial gods. Poseidon, seeing his special function thus interfered with, sent Pegasus to check the boldness of the mountain, in daring to move without his permission. When Pegasus reached the summit, he stamped the ground with his hoofs, and out gushed the waters of Hippocrene, afterwards so renowned as the sacred fount, whence the Muses quaffed their richest draughts of inspiration.

THE HESPERIDES.

The Hesperides, the daughters of Atlas, dwelt in an island in the far west, whence they derived their name.

They were appointed by Hera to act as guardians to a tree bearing golden apples, which had been presented to her by Gæa on the occasion of her marriage with Zeus.

It is said that the Hesperides, being unable to withstand the temptation of tasting the golden fruit confided to their care, were deprived of their office, which was henceforth delegated to the terrible dragon Ladon, who now became the ever-watchful sentinel of these precious treasures.

The names of the Hesperides were Aegle, Arethusa, and Hesperia.

CHARITES (Gratiæ) OR GRACES.

All those gentler attributes which beautify and refine human existence were personified by the Greeks under the form of three lovely sisters, Euphrosyne, Aglaia, and Thalia, the daughters of Zeus and Eurynome (or, according to later writers, of Dionysus and Aphrodite).

They are represented as beautiful, slender maidens in the full bloom of youth, with hands and arms lovingly intertwined, and are either undraped, or wear a fleecy, transparent garment of an ethereal fabric.

They portray every gentle emotion of the heart, which vents itself in friendship and benevolence, and were believed to preside over those qualities which constitute grace, modesty, unconscious beauty, gentleness, kindliness, innocent joy, purity of mind and body, and eternal youth.

They not only possessed the most perfect beauty themselves, but also conferred this gift upon others. All the enjoyments of life were enhanced by their presence, and were deemed incomplete without them; and wherever joy or pleasure, grace and gaiety reigned, there they were supposed to be present.

Temples and altars were everywhere erected in their honour, and people of all ages and of every rank in life entreated their favour. Incense was burnt daily upon their altars, and at every banquet they were invoked, and a libation poured out to them, as they not only heightened all enjoyment, but also by their refining influence moderated the exciting effects of wine.

Music, eloquence, poetry, and art, though the direct work of the Muses, received at the hands of the Graces an additional touch of refinement and beauty; for which reason they are always regarded as the friends of the Muses, with whom they lived on Mount Olympus.

Their special function was to act, in conjunction with the Seasons, as attendants upon Aphrodite, whom they adorned with wreaths of flowers, and she emerges from their hands like the Queen of Spring, perfumed with the odour of roses and violets, and all sweet-scented blossoms.

The Graces are frequently seen in attendance on other divinities; thus they carry music for Apollo, myrtles for Aphrodite, &c., and frequently accompany the Muses, Eros, or Dionysus.

HORÆ (SEASONS).

Closely allied to the Graces were the Horæ, or Seasons, who were also represented as three beautiful maidens, daughters of Zeus and Themis. Their names were Eunomia, Dice, and Irene.

It may appear strange that these divinities, presiding over the seasons, should be but three in number, but this is quite in accordance with the notions of the ancient Greeks, who only recognized spring, summer, and autumn as seasons; nature being supposed to be wrapt in death or slumber, during that cheerless and unproductive portion of the year which we call winter. In some parts of Greece there were but two Horæ, Thallo, goddess of the bloom, and Carpo, of the corn and fruit-bearing season.

The Horæ are always regarded as friendly towards mankind, and totally devoid of guile or subtlety; they are represented as joyous, but gentle maidens, crowned with flowers, and holding each other by the hand in a round dance. When they are depicted separately as personifications of the different seasons, the Hora representing spring appears laden with flowers, that of summer bears a sheaf of corn, whilst the personification of autumn has her hands filled with clusters of grapes and other fruits. They also appear in company with the Graces in the train of Aphrodite, and are seen with Apollo and the Muses.

They are inseparably connected with all that is good and beautiful in nature, and as the regular alternation of the seasons, like all her other operations, demands the most perfect order and regularity, the Horæ, being the daughters of Themis, came to be regarded as the representatives of order, and the just administration of human affairs in civilized communities. Each of these graceful maidens took upon herself a separate function: Eunomia presided more especially over state life, Dice guarded the interests of individuals, whilst Irene, the gayest and brightest of the three sisters, was the light-hearted companion of Dionysus.

The Horæ were also the deities of the fast-fleeting hours, and thus presided over the smaller, as well as the larger divisions of time. In this capacity they assist every morning in yoking the celestial horses to the glorious chariot of the sun, which they again help to unyoke when he sinks to rest.

In their original conception they were personifications of the clouds, and are described as opening and closing the gates of heaven, and causing fruits and flowers to spring forth, when they pour down upon them their refreshing and life-giving streams.

THE NYMPHS.

The graceful beings called the Nymphs were the presiding deities of the woods, grottoes, streams, meadows, &c.

These divinities were supposed to be beautiful maidens of fairy-like form, and robed in more or less shadowy garments. They were held in the greatest veneration, though, being minor divinities, they had no temples dedicated to them, but were worshipped in caves or grottoes, with libations of milk, honey, oil, &c.

They may be divided into three distinct classes, viz., water, mountain, and tree or wood nymphs.

Water Nymphs (Oceanides, Nereides, and Naiades).

The worship of water-deities is common to most primitive nations. The streams, springs, and fountains of a country bear the same relation to it which the blood, coursing through the numberless arteries of a human being, bears to the body; both represent the living, moving, life-awakening element, without which existence would be impossible. Hence we find among most nations a deep feeling of attachment to the streams and waters of their native land, the remembrance of which, when absent in foreign climes, is always treasured with peculiar fondness. Thus among the early Greeks, each tribe came to regard the rivers and springs of its individual state as beneficent powers, which brought blessing and prosperity to the country. It is probable also that the charm which ever accompanies the sound of running water exercised its power over their imagination. They heard with delight the gentle whisper of the fountain, lulling the senses with its low, rippling tones; the soft purling of the brook as it rushes over the pebbles, or the mighty voice of the waterfall as it dashes on in its headlong course; and the beings which they pictured to themselves as presiding over all these charming sights and sounds of nature, corresponded, in their graceful appearance, with the scenes with which they were associated.

OCEANIDES.

The OCEANIDES, or Ocean Nymphs, were the daughters of Oceanus and Tethys, and, like most sea divinities, were endowed with the gift of prophecy.

They are personifications of those delicate vapour-like exhalations, which, in warm climates, are emitted from the surface of the sea, more especially at sunset, and are impelled forwards by the evening breeze. They are accordingly represented as misty, shadowy beings, with graceful swaying forms, and robed in pale blue, gauze-like fabrics.

THE NEREIDES.

The NEREIDES were the daughters of Nereus and Doris, and were nymphs of the Mediterranean Sea.

They are similar in appearance to the Oceanides, but their beauty is of a less shadowy order, and is more like that of mortals. They wear a flowing, pale green robe; their liquid eyes resemble, in their clear depths, the lucid waters of the sea they inhabit; their hair floats carelessly over their shoulders, and assumes the greenish tint of the water itself, which, far from deteriorating from their beauty, greatly adds to its effect. The Nereides either accompany the chariot of the mighty ruler of the sea, or follow in his train.

We are told by the poets that the lonely mariner watches the Nereides with silent awe and wondering delight, as they rise from their grotto-palaces in the deep, and dance, in joyful groups, over the sleeping waves. Some, with arms entwined, follow with their movements the melodies which seem to hover over the sea, whilst others scatter liquid gems around, these being emblematical of the phosphorescent light, so frequently observed at night by the traveller in southern waters.

The best known of the Nereides were Thetis, the wife of Peleus, Amphitrite, the spouse of Poseidon, and Galatea, the beloved of Acis.

THE NAIADES.

The NAIADES were the nymphs of fresh-water springs, lakes, brooks, rivers, &c.

As the trees, plants, and flowers owed their nourishment to their genial, fostering care, these divinities were regarded by the Greeks as special benefactors to mankind. Like all the nymphs, they possessed the gift of prophecy, for which reason many of the springs and fountains over which they presided were believed to inspire mortals who drank of their waters with the power of foretelling future events. The Naiades are intimately connected in idea with those flowers which are called after them Nymphæ, or water-lilies, whose broad, green leaves and yellow cups float upon the surface of the water, as though proudly conscious of their own grace and beauty.

We often hear of the Naiades forming alliances with

mortals, and also of their being wooed by the sylvan deities of the woods and dales.

Dryades, or Tree Nymphs.

The tree nymphs partook of the distinguishing characteristics of the particular tree to whose life they were wedded, and were known collectively by the name of the Dryades.

The HAMADRYADES, or oak nymphs, represent in their peculiar individuality the quiet, self-reliant power which appears to belong essentially to the grand and lordly king of the forest.

The BIRCH NYMPH is a melancholy maiden with floating hair, resembling the branches of the pale and fragile-looking tree which she inhabits.

The BEECH NYMPH is strong and sturdy, full of life and joyousness, and appears to give promise of faithful love and undisturbed repose, whilst her rosy cheeks, deep brown eyes, and graceful form bespeak health, vigour, and vitality.

The nymph of the LINDEN TREE is represented as a little coy maiden, whose short silver-gray dress reaches a little below the knee, and displays to advantage her delicately formed limbs. The sweet face, which is partly averted, reveals a pair of large blue eyes, which appear to look at you with wondering surprise and shy mistrust; her pale, golden hair is bound by the faintest streak of rose-coloured ribbon.

The tree nymph, being wedded to the life of the tree she inhabited, ceased to exist when it was either felled, or so injured as to wither away and die.

Nymphs of the Valleys and Mountains (Napææ and Oreades).

The NAPÆÆ were the kind and gentle nymphs of the valleys and glens who appear in the train of Artemis. They are represented as lovely maidens with short tunics, which, reaching only to the knee, do not impede their swift and graceful movements in the exercise of the chase. Their pale brown tresses are fastened in a knot at the back of the head, whence a few stray curls escape over their shoulders. The Napææ are shy as the fawns, and quite as frolicsome.

The OREADES, or mountain nymphs, who are the principal and constant companions of Artemis, are tall, graceful maidens, attired as huntresses. They are ardent followers of the chase, and spare neither the gentle deer nor the timid hare, nor indeed any animal they meet with in their rapid course. Wherever their wild hunt goes the shy Napææ are represented as hiding behind the leaves, whilst their favourites, the fawns, kneel tremblingly beside them, looking up beseechingly for protection from the wild huntresses; and even the bold Satyrs dart away at their approach, and seek safety in flight.

There is a myth connected with one of these mountain nymphs, the unfortunate Echo. She became enamoured of a beautiful youth named Narcissus, son of the river-god Cephissus, who, however, failed to return her love, which so grieved her that she gradually pined away, becoming a mere shadow of her former self, till, at length, nothing remained of her except her voice, which henceforth gave back, with unerring fidelity, every sound that was uttered in the hills and dales. Narcissus himself also met with an unhappy fate, for Aphrodite punished him by causing him to fall in love with his own image, which he beheld in a neighbouring fountain, whereupon, consumed with unrequited love, he wasted away, and was changed into the flower which bears his name.

The LIMONIADES, or meadow nymphs, resemble the Naiades, and are usually represented dancing hand in hand in a circle.

The HYADES, who in appearance are somewhat similar to the Oceanides, are cloudy divinities, and, from the fact of their being invariably accompanied by rain, are represented as incessantly weeping.

The MELIADES were the nymphs who presided over fruit-trees.

Before concluding this subject, attention should be drawn to the fact that, in more modern times, this beautiful idea of animating all nature in detail reappears under the various local traditions extant in different countries. Thus do the Oceanides and Nereides live again in the mermaids, whose existence is still believed in by mariners, whilst the flower and meadow nymphs assume the shape of those tiny elves and fairies, who were formerly believed to hold their midnight revels in every wood and on every common; indeed, even at the present day, the Irish peasantry, especially in the west, firmly believe in the existence of the fairies, or "good people," as they are called.

THE WINDS.

According to the oldest accounts, Æolus was a king of the Æolian Islands, to whom Zeus gave the command of the winds, which he kept shut up in a deep cave, and which he freed at his pleasure, or at the command of the gods.

In later times the above belief underwent a change, and the winds came to be regarded as distinct divinities, whose aspect accorded with the respective winds with which they were identified. They were depicted as winged youths in full vigour in the act of flying through the air.

The principal winds were: Boreas (the north wind), Eurus (the east wind), Zephyrus (the west wind), and Notus (the south wind), who were said to be the children of Eos and Astræus.

There are no myths of interest connected with these divinities. Zephyrus was united to Chloris (Flora), the goddess of flowers. Of Boreas it is related that while flying over the river Ilissus, he beheld on the banks Oreithyia, the charming daughter of Erechtheus, king of Athens, whom he carried off to his native Thrace, and there made her his bride. Boreas and Oreithyia were the parents of Zetes and Calais, afterwards famous in the expedition of the Argonauts.

There was an altar erected at Athens in honour of Boreas, in commemoration of his having destroyed the Persian fleet sent to attack the Greeks.

On the Acropolis at Athens there was a celebrated octagonal temple, built by Pericles, which was dedicated to the winds, and on its sides were their various representations. The ruins of this temple are still to be seen.

PAN (FAUNUS).

Pan was the god of fertility, and the special patron of shepherds and huntsmen; he presided over all rural occupations, was chief of the Satyrs, and head of all rural divinities.

According to the common belief, he was the son of Hermes and a wood nymph, and came into the world with horns sprouting from his forehead, a goat's beard and a crooked nose, pointed ears, and the tail and feet of a goat, and presented altogether so repulsive an appearance that, at the sight of him, his mother fled in dismay.

Hermes, however, took up his curious little offspring, wrapt him in a hare skin, and carried him in his arms to Olympus. The grotesque form and merry antics of the little stranger made him a great favourite with all the immortals, especially Dionysus; and they bestowed upon him the name of Pan (all), because he had delighted them *all*.

His favourite haunts were grottoes, and his delight was to wander in uncontrolled freedom over rocks and mountains, following his various pursuits, ever cheerful, and usually very noisy. He was a great lover of music, singing, dancing, and all pursuits which enhance the pleasures of life; and hence, in spite of his repulsive appearance, we see him surrounded with nymphs of the forests and dales, who love to dance round him to the cheerful music of his pipe, the syrinx. The myth concerning the origin of Pan's pipe is as follows:—Pan became enamoured of a beautiful nymph, called Syrinx, who, appalled at his terrible appearance, fled from the pertinacious attentions of her unwelcome suitor. He pursued her to the banks of the river Ladon, when, seeing his near approach, and feeling escape impossible, she called on the gods for assistance, who, in answer to her prayer, transformed her into a reed, just as Pan was about to seize her. Whilst the love-sick Pan was sighing and lamenting his unfortunate fate, the winds gently swayed the reeds, and produced a murmuring sound as of one complaining. Charmed with the soothing tones, he endeavoured to reproduce them himself, and after cutting seven of the reeds of unequal length, he joined them together, and succeeded in producing the pipe, which he called the syrinx, in memory of his lost love.

Pan was regarded by shepherds as their most valiant protector, who defended their flocks from the attacks of wolves. The shepherds of these early times, having no penfolds, were in the habit of gathering together their flocks in mountain caves, to protect them against the inclemency of the weather, and also to secure them at night against the attacks of wild animals; these caves, therefore, which were very numerous in the mountain districts of Arcadia, Bœotia, &c., were all consecrated to Pan.

As it is customary in all tropical climates to repose during the heat of the day, Pan is represented as greatly enjoying his afternoon sleep in the cool shelter of a tree or cave, and also as being highly displeased at any sound which disturbed his slumbers, for which reason the shepherds were always particularly careful to keep unbroken silence during these hours, whilst they themselves indulged in a quiet siesta.

Pan was equally beloved by huntsmen, being himself a great lover of the woods, which afforded to his cheerful and active disposition full scope, and in which he loved to range at will. He was regarded as the patron of the chase, and the rural sportsmen, returning from an unsuccessful day's sport, beat, in token of their displeasure, the wooden image of Pan, which always occupied a prominent place in their dwellings.

All sudden and unaccountable sounds which startle travellers in lonely spots, were attributed to Pan, who possessed a frightful and most discordant voice; hence the term *pan*ic terror, to indicate sudden fear. The Athenians ascribed their victory at Marathon to the alarm which he created among the Persians by his terrible voice.

Pan was gifted with the power of prophecy, which he is said to have imparted to Apollo, and he possessed a well-known and very ancient oracle in Arcadia, in which state he was more especially worshipped.

The artists of later times have somewhat toned down the original very unattractive conception of Pan, as above described, and merely represent him as a young man, hardened by the exposure to all weathers which a rural life involves, and bearing in his hand the shepherd's crook and syrinx—these being his usual attributes—whilst small horns project from his forehead. He is either undraped, or wears merely the light cloak called the chlamys.

The usual offerings to Pan were milk and honey in shepherds' bowls. Cows, lambs, and rams were also sacrificed to him.

After the introduction of Pan into the worship of Dionysus, we hear of a number of little Pans (Panisci), who are sometimes confounded with the Satyrs.

FAUNUS.

The Romans had an old Italian divinity called Faunus, who, as the god of shepherds, was identified with the Greek Pan, and represented in a similar manner.

Faunus is frequently called Inuus or the fertilizer, and

Lupercus or the one who wards off wolves. Like Pan, he possessed the gift of prophecy, and was the presiding spirit of the woods and fields; he also shared with his Greek proto-type the faculty of alarming travellers in solitary places. Bad dreams and evil apparitions were attributed to Faunus, and he was believed to enter houses stealthily at night for this purpose.

Fauna was the wife of Faunus, and participated in his functions.

THE SATYRS.

The Satyrs were a race of woodland spirits, who evidently personified the free, wild, and untrammelled life of the forest. Their appearance was both grotesque and repulsive; they had flat broad noses, pointed ears, and little horns sprouting from their foreheads, a rough shaggy skin, and small goat's tails. They led a life of pleasure and self-indulgence, followed the chase, revelled in every description of wild music and dancing, were terrible wine-bibbers, and addicted to the deep slumbers which follow heavy potations. They were no less dreaded by mortals than by the gentle woodland nymphs, who always avoided their coarse rough sports.

The Satyrs were conspicuous figures in the train of Dionysus, and, as we have seen, Silenus their chief was tutor to the wine god. The older Satyrs were called Silens, and are represented in antique sculpture, as more nearly approaching the human form.

In addition to the ordinary Satyrs, artists delighted in depicting little Satyrs, young imps, frolicking about the woods in a marvellous variety of droll attitudes. These little fellows greatly resemble their friends and companions, the Panisci.

In rural districts it was customary for the shepherds and peasants who attended the festivals of Dionysus, to dress themselves in the skins of goats and other animals, and, under this disguise, they permitted themselves all kinds of playful tricks and excesses, to which circumstance the conception of the Satyrs is by some authorities attributed.

In Rome the old Italian wood-divinities, the FAUNS, who had goats' feet and all other characteristics of the Satyrs greatly exaggerated, were identified with them.

PRIAPUS.

Priapus, the son of Dionysus and Aphrodite, was regarded as the god of fruitfulness, the protector of flocks, sheep, goats, bees, the fruit of the vine, and all garden produce.

His statues, which were set up in gardens and vine-yards, acted not only as objects of worship, but also as scarecrows, the appearance of this god being especially repulsive and unsightly. These statues were formed of wood or stone, and from the hips downwards were merely rude columns. They represent him as having a red and very ugly face; he bears in his hand a pruning knife, and his head is crowned with a wreath of vine and laurel. He usually carries fruit in his garments or a cornucopia in his hand, always, however, retaining his singularly revolting aspect. It is said that Hera, wishing to punish Aphrodite, sent her this misshapen and unsightly son, and that when he was born, his mother was so horrified at the sight of him, that she ordered him to be exposed on the mountains, where he was found by some shepherds, who, taking pity on him, saved his life.

This divinity was chiefly worshipped at Lampsacus, his birthplace. Asses were sacrificed to him, and he received the first-fruits of the fields and gardens, with a libation of milk and honey.

The worship of Priapus was introduced into Rome at the same time as that of Aphrodite, and was identified with a native Italian divinity named Mutunus.

ASCLEPIAS (ÆSCULAPIUS).

Asclepias, the god of the healing art, was the son of Apollo and the nymph Coronis. He was educated by the noble Centaur Chiron, who instructed him in all knowledge, but more especially in that of the properties of herbs. Asclepias searched out the hidden powers of plants, and discovered cures for the various diseases which afflict the human body. He brought his art to such perfection, that he not only succeeded in warding off death, but also restored the dead to life. It was popularly believed that he was materially assisted in his wonderful cures by the blood of the Medusa, given to him by Pallas-Athene.

It is well to observe that the shrines of this divinity, which were usually built in healthy places, on hills outside the town, or near wells which were believed to have healing powers, offered at the same time means of cure for the sick and suffering, thus combining religious with sanitary influences. It was the custom for the sufferer to sleep in the temple, when, if he had been earnest in his devotions, Asclepias appeared to him in a dream, and revealed the means to be employed for the cure of his malady. On the walls of these temples were hung tablets, inscribed by the different pilgrims with the particulars of their maladies, the remedies practised, and the cures worked by the god:—a custom undoubtedly productive of most beneficial results.

Groves, temples, and altars were dedicated to Asclepias in many parts of Greece, but Epidaurus, the chief seat of his worship,—where, indeed, it is said to have originated,—contained his principal temple, which served at the same time as a hospital.

The statue of Asclepias in the temple at Epidaurus was formed of ivory and gold, and represented him as an old man with a full beard, leaning on a staff round which a serpent is climbing. The serpent was the distinguishing symbol of this divinity, partly because these reptiles were greatly used by the ancients in the cure of diseases, and partly also because all the prudence and wisdom of the serpent were deemed indispensable to the judicious physician.

His usual attributes are a staff, a bowl, a bunch of herbs, a pineapple, a dog, and a serpent.

His children inherited, for the most part, the distinguished talents of their father. Two of his sons, Machaon and Podalirius, accompanied Agamemnon to the Trojan war, in which expedition they became renowned, not only as military heroes, but also as skilful physicians.

Their sisters, **HYGEIA** (health), and **PANACEA** (all-healing), had temples dedicated to them, and received divine honours. The function of Hygeia was to maintain the health of the community, which great blessing was supposed to be brought by her as a direct and beneficent gift from the gods.

ÆSCULAPIUS.

The worship of Æsculapius was introduced into Rome from Epidaurus, whence the statue of the god of healing was brought at the time of a great pestilence. Grateful for their deliverance from this plague, the Romans erected a temple in his honour, on an island near the mouth of the Tiber.

ROMAN DIVINITIES—

JANUS.

From the earliest ages Janus was regarded by the Romans with the utmost affection and veneration, as a divinity who ranked only second to Jupiter himself, and through whom all prayers and petitions were transmitted to the other gods.

He was believed to preside over the beginnings of all things, hence it was he who inaugurated the years, months, and seasons, and in course of time came to be considered as specially protecting the beginnings of all human enterprises. The great importance which the Romans attached to an auspicious commencement, as contributing to the ultimate success of an enterprise, accounts for the high estimation in which Janus was held as the god of beginnings.

This divinity would appear to have been the ancient sun-god of the Italian tribes, in which capacity he opens and closes the gates of heaven every morning and evening. Hence he was regarded as the door-keeper of heaven, and also as the presiding deity over all gates, entrances, &c., on earth.

The fact of his being the god of city gates, which were called Jani after him, is ascribed, however, to the following myth:—After the abduction of their women by the Romans, the Sabines, in revenge, invaded the Roman state, and were already about to enter the gates of the city, when suddenly a hot sulphur spring, which was believed to have been sent by Janus for their special preservation, gushed forth from the earth, and arrested the progress of the enemy.

In his character as guardian of gates and doors, he was also regarded as a protecting deity of the home, for which reason little shrines were erected to him over the doors of houses, which contained an image of the god, having two faces.

Janus possessed no temples in the ordinary acceptation of the word, but all the gates of cities were dedicated to him. Close to the Forum of Rome stood the so-called temple of Janus, which, however, was merely an arched passage, closed by massive gates. This temple was open only in time of war, as it was supposed that the god had then taken his departure with the Roman army, over whose welfare he personally presided. It is worthy of notice, as an evidence of the many wars in which the Romans were engaged, that the gates of this sanctuary were only closed three times during 700 years.

As the god who ushers in the new year, the first month was called after him, and on the 1st of January his most important festival was celebrated, on which occasion all entrances of public and private buildings were decorated with laurel branches and garlands of flowers.

His sacrifices, consisting of cakes, wine, and barley, were offered to him at the beginning of every month; and before sacrificing to the other gods his name was always invoked, and a libation poured out to him.

Janus is usually represented with two faces; in his special function as door-keeper of heaven he stands erect, bearing a key in one hand, and a rod or sceptre in the other.

It is supposed that Janus was the most ancient king of Italy, who, during his life, governed his subjects with such wisdom and moderation that, in gratitude for the benefits conferred upon them, his people deified him after death and placed him in the foremost rank among their divinities. We have already seen in the history of Cronus that Saturn, who was identified with the Greek Cronus (god of time), was the friend and colleague of Janus. Anxious to prove his gratitude to his benefactor, Cronus endowed him with the knowledge of past and future events, which enabled him to adopt the wisest measures for the welfare of his subjects, and it is on this account that Janus is represented with two faces looking in opposite directions, the one to the past, the other to the future.

FLORA.

Flora was the goddess of flowers, and was regarded as a beneficent power, who watched over and protected the early blossoms.

She was held in the highest estimation by the Romans, and a festival, called the Floralia, was celebrated in her honour from the 28th of April to the 1st of May. This festival was a season of universal merriment, in which flowers were used profusely in adorning houses, streets, &c., and were worn by young girls in their hair.

Flora, who typified the season of Spring, is generally represented as a lovely maiden, garlanded with flowers.

ROBIGUS.

In opposition to Flora we find an antagonistic divinity, called Robigus, a worker of evil, who delighted in the destruction of the tender herbs by mildew, and whose wrath could only be averted by prayers and sacrifices, when he was invoked under the title of Averuncus, or the Avertor.

The festival of Robigus (the Robigalia) was celebrated on the 25th of April.

POMONA.

Pomona was the goddess of orchards and fruit-trees, who, according to Ovid, cares not for woods or streams, but loves her gardens and the boughs that bear the thriving fruit.

Pomona, who typifies Autumn, is represented as a lovely maiden, laden with branches of fruit-trees.

VERTUMNUS.

Vertumnus was the god of garden and field produce. He personifies the change of seasons, and that process of transformation in nature by means of which the leaf-buds become developed into blossoms, and the blossoms into fruit.

The change of seasons is symbolized in a myth which represents Vertumnus as metamorphosing himself into a variety of different forms in order to gain the affection of Pomona, who so loved her vocation that she abjured all thoughts of marriage. He first appears to her as a ploughman, typifying Spring; then as a reaper, to represent Summer; afterwards as a vine-gatherer, to indicate Autumn; and finally as a gray-haired old woman, symbolical of the snows of Winter; but it was not until he assumed his true form, that of a beautiful youth, that he succeeded in his suit.

Vertumnus is generally represented crowned with wheat-sheaves, and bearing in his hand a cornucopia.

PALES.

Pales, a very ancient Italian divinity, is represented sometimes as a male, sometimes as a female power.

As a male divinity he is more particularly the god of shepherds and flocks.

As a female deity, Pales presides over husbandry and the fruitfulness of herds. Her festivals, the Palilia, were celebrated on the 21st of April, the day on which the city of Rome was founded. During this festival it was customary for shepherds to ignite a mass of straw, through which they rushed with their flocks, believing that this ordeal would purify them from sin.

The name Palatine, which originally signified a pastoral colony, is derived from this divinity. Her offerings were cakes and milk.

PICUS.

Picus, the son of Saturn and father of Faunus, was a woodland divinity, gifted with prophetic powers.

An ancient myth relates that Picus was a beautiful youth, united to a nymph called Canens. The sorceress Circe, infatuated by his beauty, endeavoured to secure his love, but he rejected her advances, and she, in revenge, changed him into a woodpecker, under which form he still retained his powers of prophecy.

Picus is represented as a youth, with a woodpecker perched upon his head, which bird became henceforth regarded as possessed of the power of prophecy.

PICUMNUS AND PILUMNUS.

Picumnus and Pilumnus were two household divinities of the Romans, who were the special presiding deities of new-born infants.

SILVANUS.

Silvanus was a woodland divinity, who, like Faunus, greatly resembled the Greek Pan. He was the presiding deity of plantations and forests, and specially protected the boundaries of fields.

Silvanus is represented as a hale old man, carrying a cypress-tree, for, according to Roman mythology, the transformation of the youth Cyparissus into the tree which bears his name was attributed to him.

His sacrifices consisted of milk, meat, wine, grapes, wheat-ears, and pigs.

TERMINUS.

Terminus was the god who presided over all boundaries and landmarks.

He was originally represented by a simple block of stone, which in later times became surmounted by a head of this divinity. Numa Pompilius, the great benefactor of his people, anxious to inculcate respect for the rights of property, specially enjoined the erection of these blocks of stone, as a durable monument to mark the line dividing one property from another. He also caused altars to be raised to Terminus, and instituted his festival (the Terminalia), which was celebrated on the 23rd of February.

Upon one occasion, when Tarquin wished to remove the altars of several deities, in order to build a new temple, it is said that Terminus and Juventas alone objected to being displaced. This obstinate refusal on their part was interpreted as a good omen, signifying that the city of Rome would never lose her boundaries, and would remain ever young and vigorous.

CONSUS.

Consus was the god of secret counsel.

The Romans believed that when an idea developed itself spontaneously within the mind of an individual, it was Consus who had prompted the suggestion. This applied, however, more particularly to plans which resulted satisfactorily.

An altar was erected to this divinity on the Circus Maximus, which was kept always covered, except during his festival, the Consualia, which was celebrated on the 18th of August.

LIBITINA.

Libitina was the goddess who presided over funerals. This divinity was identified with Venus, possibly because the ancients considered that the power of love extended even to the realms of death.

Her temple in Rome, which was erected by Servius Tullius, contained all the requisites for funerals, and these could either be bought or hired there. A register of all deaths which occurred in the city of Rome was kept in this temple, and in order to ascertain the rate of mortality, a piece of money was paid by command of Servius Tullius, on the demise of each person.

LAVERNA.

Laverna was the presiding goddess of thieves, and of all artifice and fraud. There was an altar erected to her near the Porta Lavernalis, which was called after her, and she possessed a sacred grove on the Via Salavia.

COMUS.

Comus was the presiding genius of banquets, festive scenes, revelry, and all joyous pleasures and reckless gaiety.

He is represented as a young man crowned with flowers, his face heated and flushed with wine, leaning against a post in a half-sleepy and drunken attitude, with a torch falling from his hand.

THE CAMENÆ.

The Camenæ were prophetic nymphs held in high veneration by the ancient Italians. They were four in number, the best known of whom are Carmenta and Egeria.

Carmenta was celebrated as being the mother of Evander,

who led an Arcadian colony into Italy, and founded a town on the river Tiber, which became afterwards incorporated with the city of Rome. Evander is said to have been the first who introduced Greek art and civilization into Italy, and also the worship of Greek divinities.

A temple was erected to Carmenta on the Capitoline Hill, and a festival, called the Carmentalia, was celebrated in her honour on the 11th of January.

Egeria is said to have initiated Numa Pompilius in the forms of religious worship, which he introduced among his people. She was regarded as the giver of life, and was therefore invoked by women before the birth of their children.

The Camenæ are frequently identified by Roman writers with the Muses.

GENII.

A comforting and assuring belief existed among the Romans, that each individual was accompanied through life, from the hour of his birth to that of his death, by a protecting spirit, called his genius, who prompted him to good and noble deeds, and acted towards him as a guardian angel, comforting him in sorrow, and guiding him throughout his earthly career.

In the course of time a second genius was believed to exist, of an evil nature, who, as the instigator of all wrong-doing, was ever at war with the beneficent genius; and on the issue of the conflict between these antagonistic influences, depended the fate of the individual. The genii were depicted as winged beings, greatly resembling our modern representations of guardian angels.

Every state, town, or city, (as well as every man), possessed its special genius. The sacrifices to the genii consisted of wine, cakes, and incense, which were offered to them on birthdays.

The genius which guided a woman was called, after the queen of heaven, Juno.

Among the Greeks, beings called Dæmons were regarded as exercising similar functions to those of the Roman genii. They were believed to be the spirits of the righteous race which existed in the Golden Age, who watched over mankind, carrying their prayers to the gods, and the gifts of the gods to them.

MANES.

LEMURES (LARVÆ) AND LARES.

The Manes were the spirits of the departed, and were of two kinds, viz., Lemures (or Larvæ) and Lares.

The Lemures were those Manes who haunted their former abodes on earth as evil spirits, appearing at night under awful forms and hideous shapes, greatly to the alarm of their friends and relatives. They were so feared that a festival, called the Lemuralia, was celebrated in order to propitiate them.

It appears extremely probable that the superstitions with regard to ghosts, haunted houses, &c., which exist even at the present day, owe their origin to this very ancient pagan source.

The Lares Familiares were a much more pleasing conception. They were the spirits of the ancestors of each family, who exercised after death a protecting power over the well-being and prosperity of the family to which they had in life belonged. The place of honour beside the hearth was occupied by the statue of the Lar of the house, who was supposed to have been the founder of the family. This statue was the object of profound veneration, and was honoured on all occasions by every member of the family; a portion of each meal was laid before it, and it was believed to take an active part in all family affairs and domestic events, whether of a sad or joyful nature. Before starting on any expedition the master of the house saluted the statue of the Lar, and, on his return, a solemn thanksgiving was offered to this, the presiding deity of his hearth and home, in grateful acknowledgment of his protection; whereupon the statue was crowned with garlands of flowers, these being the favourite offerings to the Lares on all occasions of especial family rejoicing.

The first act of a bride on entering her new abode was to do homage to the Lar, in the belief that he would exercise over her a protecting influence and shield her from evil.

In addition to those above enumerated there were also public Lares, who were guardians of the state, highroads, country, and sea. Their temples were always open for any pious worshipper to enter, and on their altars public sacrifices were offered for the welfare of the state or city.

PENATES.

The Penates were deities selected by each family, and frequently by its individual members, as a special protector. Various causes led to this selection. If, for instance, a child were born on the festival of Vesta, it was thought that that deity would henceforward act as its special guardian. If a youth possessed great business talents he adopted Mercury as his tutelary deity; should he, on the other hand, develop a passion for music, Apollo was selected as his patron god, and so forth. These became regarded as the special divinities of the household, small images of them adorned the surroundings of the hearth, and honours similar to those paid to the Lares were accorded to them.

Just as there were public Lares so there were public Penates, which were worshipped by the Roman people under the form of two youthful warriors, who, in later times, were regarded as identical with Castor and Pollux. They are generally represented on horseback, with conical caps on their heads, and bearing long spears in their hands.

PUBLIC WORSHIP OF THE
ANCIENT GREEKS AND ROMANS—

TEMPLES.

In very remote times the Greeks had no shrines or sanctuaries devoted to public worship, but performed their devotions beneath the vast and boundless canopy of heaven, in the great temple of nature itself. Believing that their divinities throned above the clouds, pious worshippers naturally sought the highest available points, in order to place themselves in the closest communion possible with their gods; hence the summits of high mountains were selected for devotional purposes, and the more exalted the rank and importance of the divinity invoked, the more elevated was the site selected for his or her worship. But the inconvenience attending this mode of worship gradually suggested the idea of erecting edifices which would afford means of shelter from the inclemency of the weather.

These structures were, in the first instance, of the most simple form, and without decoration; but when, with the progress of civilization, the Greeks became a wealthy and powerful people, temples were built and adorned with the greatest splendour and magnificence, talent, labour, and wealth being lavished unsparingly on their erection and decoration; indeed so massively were they constructed, that some of them have, to a certain extent, withstood the ravages of time. The city of Athens especially contains numerous remains of these buildings of antiquity. On the Acropolis we may still behold, among other monuments of ancient art, the temple of Athene-Polias, and that of Theseus, the latter of which is the most entire ancient edifice in the world. In the island of Delos, also, are to be seen the ruins of the temples of Apollo and Artemis, both of which are in a wonderful state of preservation. These ruins are most valuable, being sufficiently complete to enable us to study, by their aid, the plan and character of the original structure.

Among the Lacedæmonians, however, we find no vestiges of these stately temples, for they were specially enjoined by a law of Lycurgus to serve the gods with as little outlay as possible. When the great lawgiver was asked the reason of this injunction, he replied that the Lacedæmonians, being a poor nation, might otherwise abstain altogether from the observance of their religious duties, and wisely added that magnificent edifices and costly sacrifices were not so pleasing to the gods, as the true piety and unfeigned devotion of their worshippers.

The most ancient temples known to us served a double purpose: they were not only consecrated to the service of the gods, but were at the same time venerable monuments in honour of the dead. Thus, for instance, the temple of Pallas-Athene, in the tower of the city of Larissa, served as the sepulchre of Acrisius, and the Acropolis at Athens received the ashes of Cecrops, founder of the city.

A temple was frequently dedicated to two or more gods, and was always built after the manner considered most acceptable to the particular divinities to whom it was consecrated; for just as trees, birds, and animals of every description were held to be sacred to certain deities, so almost every god had a form of building peculiar to himself, which was deemed more acceptable to him than any other. Thus the Doric style of architecture was sacred to Zeus, Ares, and Heracles; the Ionic to Apollo, Artemis, and Dionysus; and the Corinthian to Hestia.

In the porch of the temple stood a vessel of stone or brass, containing holy water (which had been consecrated by putting into it a burning torch, taken from the altar), with which all those admitted to take part in the sacrifices were besprinkled. In the inmost recess of the sanctuary was the most holy place, into which none but the priests were suffered to enter.

Temples in the country were usually surrounded with groves of trees. The solitude of these shady retreats naturally tended to inspire the worshipper with awe and reverence, added to which the delightful shade and coolness afforded by tall leafy trees is peculiarly grateful in hot countries. Indeed so general did this custom of building temples in groves become, that all places devoted to sacred purposes, even where no trees existed, were called groves. That this practice must be of very remote antiquity is proved by the Biblical injunction, having for its object the separation of the Jews from all idolatrous practices: "Thou shalt not plant thee a grove of trees near unto the altar of the Lord thy God."

STATUES.

The Greeks worshipped their gods without any visible representations of them until the time of Cecrops. The most ancient of these representations consisted of square blocks of stone, upon which the name of the deity intended to be represented was engraved. The first attempts at sculpture were rude stocks, with a head at one end and a shapeless trunk at the other, tapering slightly down to the feet, which, however, were not divided, the limbs being in no way defined. But the artists of later times devoted all their genius to the successful production of the highest ideals of their gods, some of which are preserved to this day, and are regarded as examples of purest art.

On a pedestal in the centre of the edifice stood the statue of the divinity to whom the temple was dedicated, surrounded by images of other gods, all of which were fenced off by rails.

ALTARS.

The altar in a Greek temple, which stood in the centre of the building and in front of the statue of the presiding deity, was generally of a circular form, and constructed of stone. It was customary to engrave upon it the name or distinguishing symbol of the divinity to whom it was dedicated; and it was held so sacred that if any malefactor fled to it his life was safe from his pursuers, and it was considered one of the greatest acts of sacrilege to force him from this asylum.

The most ancient altars were adorned with horns, which in former times were emblems of power and dignity, as wealth, and consequently importance, consisted among most primitive nations in flocks and herds.

In addition to those erected in places of public worship, altars were frequently raised in groves, on highways, or in the market-places of cities.

The gods of the lower world had no altars whatever, ditches or trenches being dug for the reception of the blood of the sacrifices offered to them.

PRIESTS.

In ancient times the priests were recognized as a special social caste, and were distinguished not only by their sacerdotal vestments, but also by their piety, wisdom, and blameless life. They were the chosen mediators between gods and men, and offered prayers and sacrifices in the name of the people, whom they also instructed as to what vows, gifts, and offerings would be most acceptable to the gods.

Every deity had a different order of priests consecrated to

his worship, and in every place a high-priest was appointed, whose duty it was to superintend the rest of his order, and also to carry out the more sacred rites and religious observances.

Priests and priestesses were permitted to marry, but not a second time; some, however, voluntarily adopted a life of celibacy.

SACRIFICES.

There is no doubt that a feeling of gratitude to the gods for their protecting care, and the abundance with which they were believed to bless mankind, has induced men of all nations and in all countries to feel a desire to sacrifice to their divinities some portion of the gifts so generously lavished upon them.

Among the Greeks, sacrifices were of various kinds. They consisted of *free-will offerings*, *propitiatory offerings*, &c.

Free-will offerings were grateful acknowledgments for benefits received, and usually consisted of the first-fruits of the field, or the finest of the flocks and herds, which were required to be without spot or blemish.

Propitiatory offerings were brought with the object of appeasing the anger of the gods.

In addition to those above enumerated, sacrifices were made, either with a view of obtaining success in an enterprise about to be undertaken, or in fulfilment of a vow, or at the command of an oracle.

Every sacrifice was accompanied by salt and also by a libation, which usually consisted of wine, the cup being always filled to the brim, indicating that the offering was made without stint. When sacrificing to the infernal gods the cup containing the libation was filled with blood.

The animals offered to the Olympian divinities were white, whilst those to the gods of the lower world were black. When a man offered a special sacrifice for himself or his family it partook of the nature of his occupation; thus a shepherd brought a sheep, a vine-grower his grapes, and so forth. But in the case of public sacrifices, the supposed individuality of the deity was always consulted. For instance, to Demeter a sow was offered, because that animal is apt to root up the seed-corn; to Dionysus a goat, on account of its being destructive to vineyards, &c.

The value of offerings depended greatly upon the position of the individual; it being regarded as a contempt of the gods for a rich man to bring a sordid offering, whilst from a poor man the smallest oblation was considered acceptable.

Hecatombs consisted of a hundred animals, and were offered by entire communities, or by wealthy individuals who either desired, or had obtained some special favour from the gods.

When a sacrifice was to be offered, a fire was kindled on the altar, into which wine and frankincense were poured, in order to increase the flame. In very ancient times, the victim was laid upon the altar and burned whole; but after the time of Prometheus portions only of the shoulders, thighs, entrails, &c., were sacrificed, the remainder becoming the perquisites of the priests.

The officiating priests wore a crown composed of the leaves of the tree sacred to the deity they invoked. Thus when sacrificing to Apollo the crowns were of laurel; when to Heracles, of poplar. This practice of wearing crowns was, at a later period, adopted by the general public at banquets and other festivities.

On occasions of special solemnity the horns of the victim were overlaid with gold, and the altars decked with flowers and sacred herbs.

The mode of conducting the sacrifices was as follows:—All things being prepared, a salt cake, the sacrificial knife, and the crowns, were placed in a small basket, and carried to the sanctuary by a young maiden, whereupon the victim was conducted into the temple, frequently to the accompaniment of music. If a small animal, it was driven loose to the altar; if a large one, it was led by a long trailing rope, in order to indicate that it was not an unwilling sacrifice.

When all were assembled, the priest, after walking in solemn state round the altar, besprinkled it with a mixture of meal and holy water, after which he also besprinkled the assembled worshippers, and exhorted them to join with him in prayer. The service being ended, the priest first tasted the libation, and after causing the congregation to do the like, poured the remainder between the horns of the victim, after which frankincense was strewn upon the altar, and a portion of the meal and water poured upon the animal, which was then killed. If by any chance the victim escaped the stroke, or became in any way restless, it was regarded as an evil omen; if, on the contrary, it expired without a struggle, it was considered auspicious.

At the sacrifices to the aërial divinities music was added, whilst dances were performed round the altar, and sacred hymns sung. These hymns were generally composed in honour of the gods, and contained an account of their famous actions, their clemency and beneficence, and the gifts conferred by them on mankind. In conclusion, the gods were invoked for a continuance of their favour, and when the service was ended a feast was held.

ORACLES.

The desire to penetrate the dark veil of futurity, and thereby to avert, if possible, threatened danger, has animated mankind in all ages of the world. Prophetic knowledge was sought by the Greeks at the mouth of oracles, whose predictions were interpreted to the people by priests, specially appointed for the purpose.

The most famous of these institutions was the oracle of Apollo at Delphi, which was held in general repute all over the world. People flocked from far and near to consult this wonderful mouth-piece of the gods, one month in the year being specially set apart for the purpose.

The priestess who delivered the oracles was called the Pythia, after the serpent Python, which was killed by Apollo. Having first bathed in the waters of the Castalian spring, she was conducted into the temple by the priests, and was seated on a sort of three-legged stool or table, called a tripod, which was placed over the mouth of a cave whence issued sulphurous vapours. Here she gradually became affected in a remarkable manner, and fell into an ecstatic condition, in which she uttered wild and extraordinary phrases, which were held to be the utterance of Apollo himself; these the priests interpreted to the people, but in most cases in so ambiguous a manner that the fulfilment of the prediction could not easily be disputed. During the ceremony, clouds of incense filled the temple, and hid the priestess from the view of the uninitiated, and at its conclusion she was reconducted, in a fainting condition, to her cell.

The following is a striking instance of the ambiguity of oracular predictions:—Crœsus, the rich king of Lydia, before going to war with Cyrus, king of Persia, consulted an oracle as to the probable success of the expedition. The reply he received was, that if he crossed a certain river he would destroy a great empire. Interpreting the response as being favourable to his design, Crœsus crossed the river, and encountered the Persian king, by whom he was entirely defeated; and his own empire being destroyed, the prediction of the oracle was said to have been fulfilled.

SOOTHSAYERS (Augurs).

In addition to the manifestation of the will of the gods by means of oracles, the Greeks also believed that certain men, called soothsayers, were gifted with the power of foretelling future events from dreams, from observing the flight of birds, the entrails of sacrificed animals, and even the direction of the flames and smoke from the altar, &c.

AUGURS.

The Roman soothsayers were called augurs, and played an important part in the history of the Romans, as no enterprise was ever undertaken without first consulting them with regard to its ultimate success.

FESTIVALS.

Festivals were instituted as seasons of rest, rejoicing, and thanksgiving, and also as anniversaries to commemorate events of national importance. The most ancient festivals were those held after the ingathering of the harvest or vintage, and were celebrated with rejoicings and merry-makings, which lasted many days, during which time the first-fruits of the fields were offered to the gods, accompanied by prayers and thanksgiving.

The festivals held in cities in honour of special divinities, or in commemoration of particular events, were conducted with an elaborate ceremonial. Gorgeous processions, games, chariot races, &c., were conspicuous features on these occasions, and dramatic performances, representing particu--lar episodes in the lives of the gods and heroes, frequently took place.

We subjoin a few of the most interesting of the Greek and Roman festivals.

GREEK FESTIVALS—

ELEUSINIAN MYSTERIES.

One of the most ancient and important among the festivals observed by the Greeks was that of the Eleusinian Mysteries, which was celebrated in honour of Demeter and Persephone. The name was derived from Eleusis, a town in Attica, where the Mysteries were first introduced by the goddess herself. They were divided into the Greater and Lesser Mysteries, and, according to the general account, were held every five years. The Greater, which were celebrated in honour of Demeter, and lasted nine days, were held in autumn; the Lesser, dedicated to Persephone (who at these festivals was affectionately called Cora, or the maiden), were held in spring.

It is supposed that the secrets taught to the initiated by the priests—the expounders of the Mysteries—were moral meanings, elucidated from the myths concerning Demeter and Persephone; but the most important belief inculcated was the doctrine of the immortality of the soul. That the lessons taught were of the highest moral character is universally admitted. "The souls of those who participated in them were filled with the sweetest hopes both as to this and the future world;" and it was a common saying among the Athenians: "In the Mysteries no one is sad."

The initiation into these solemn rites (which was originally the exclusive privilege of the Athenians) was accompanied with awe-inspiring ceremonies; and secrecy was so strictly enjoined that its violation was punished by death. At the conclusion of the initiation great rejoicings took place, chariot-races, wrestling matches, &c., were held, and solemn sacrifices offered.

The initiation into the Lesser Mysteries served as a preparation for the Greater.

THESMOPHORIA.

The Thesmophoria was another festival held in honour of Demeter, in her character as presiding over marriage and social institutions resulting from the spread of agriculture.

This festival was celebrated exclusively by women.

DIONYSIA.

A joyous spring festival was held in honour of Dionysus, in the month of March, and lasted several days.

This festival, which was called the Greater Dionysia, was celebrated with particular splendour at Athens, when strangers flocked from all parts of the world to take part in the ceremonies. The city was gaily decorated, the houses were garlanded with ivy-leaves, crowds perambulated the streets, everything wore its holiday garb, and wine was freely indulged in.

In the processions which took place during these festivities, the statue of Dionysus was carried, and men and women, crowned with ivy and bearing the thyrsus, were dressed in every description of grotesque costume, and played on drums, pipes, flutes, cymbals, &c. Some representing Silenus rode on asses, others wearing fawn-skins appeared as Pan or the Satyrs, and the whole multitude sang pæans in honour of the wine-god. Public shows, games, and sports took place, and the entire city was full of revelry.

What lent additional interest to these festivals was the custom of introducing new comedies and tragedies to the public, representations of which were given, and prizes awarded to those which elicited the greatest admiration.

The Lesser Dionysia were vintage festivals, celebrated in rural districts in the month of November, and were characterized by drinking, feasting, and joviality of all kinds.

In connection with some of the festivals in honour of Dionysus were certain mystic observances, into which only women, called Menades or Bacchantes, were initiated. Clad in fawn-skins, they assembled by night on the mountain sides, some carrying blazing torches, others thyrsi, and all animated with religious enthusiasm and frenzy. They shouted, clapped their hands, danced wildly, and worked themselves up to such a pitch of excitement and fury that in their mad frenzy they tore in pieces the animal brought as a sacrifice to Dionysus.

Under the name of Bacchanalia, these mystic rites were introduced into Rome, where men also were allowed to participate in them; but they were attended with such frightful excesses that the state authorities at length interfered and prohibited them.

PANATHENÆA.

The Panathenæa was a famous festival celebrated in Athens in honour of Athene-Polias, the guardian of the state. There were two festivals of this name, the Lesser and the Greater Panathenæa. The former was held annually, and the latter, which lasted several days, was celebrated every fourth year.

For the Greater Panathenæa a garment, embroidered with gold, called the Peplus, was specially woven by Athenian maidens, on which was represented the victory gained by Athene over the Giants. This garment was suspended to the mast of a ship which stood outside the city; and during the festival, which was characterized by a grand procession, the ship (with the Peplus on its mast) was impelled forward by means of invisible machinery, and formed the most conspicuous feature of the pageant. The whole population, bearing olive branches in their hands, took part in the procession; and amidst music and rejoicings this imposing pageant wended its way to the temple of Athene-Polias, where the Peplus was deposited on the statue of the goddess.

At this festival, Homer's poems were declaimed aloud, and poets also introduced their own works to the public. Musical contests, foot and horse races, and wrestling matches were held, and dances were performed by boys in armour.

Men who had deserved well of their country were presented at the festival with a crown of gold, and the name of the person so distinguished was announced publicly by a herald.

The victors in the races and athletic games received, as a prize, a vase of oil, supposed to have been extracted from the fruit of the sacred olive-tree of Athene.

DAPHNEPHORIA.

The Daphnephoria was celebrated at Thebes in honour of Apollo every ninth year.

The distinguishing feature of this festival was a procession to the temple of Apollo, in which a young priest (the Daphnephorus) of noble descent, splendidly attired and wearing a crown of gold, was preceded by a youth, carrying an emblematical representation of the sun, moon, stars, and days of the year, and followed by beautiful maidens bearing laurel branches, and singing hymns in honour of the god.

ROMAN FESTIVALS—

SATURNALIA.

The Saturnalia, a national festival held in December in honour of Saturn, was celebrated after the ingathering of the harvest, and lasted several days.

It was a time of universal rejoicing, cessation from labour, and merry-making. School children had holidays, friends sent presents to each other, the law-courts were closed, and no business was transacted.

Crowds of people from the surrounding country flocked to Rome for this festival attired in every variety of masquerade dress; practical jokes were given and received with the utmost good humour, shouts of exultation filled the air, all classes abandoned themselves to enjoyment, and unrestrained hilarity reigned supreme. Social distinctions were for a time suspended, or even reversed; and so heartily was the spirit of this festival entered into, that masters waited upon their slaves at banquets which they provided for them; the slaves being dressed upon these occasions in the garments of their masters.

There appears little doubt that the modern Carnival is a survival of the ancient Saturnalia.

CEREALIA.

This festival was celebrated in honour of Ceres. It was solemnized exclusively by women, who, dressed in white garments,
wandered about with torches in their hands, to represent the
search of the goddess for her daughter Proserpine.

During this festival, games were celebrated in the Circus
Maximus, to which none were admitted unless clothed in
white.

VESTALIA.

The Vestalia was a festival held in honour of Vesta on the 9th
of June, and was celebrated exclusively by women, who
walked barefooted in procession to the temple of the goddess.

The priestesses of Vesta, called Vestales or Vestal Virgins,
played a conspicuous part in these festivals. They were six in
number, and were chosen—between the ages of six and ten—
from the noblest families in Rome. Their term of office was
thirty years. During the first ten years, they were initiated in
their religious duties, during the second ten they performed
them, and during the third they instructed novices. Their
chief duty was to watch and feed the ever-burning flame on
the altar of Vesta, the extinction of which was regarded as a
national calamity of ominous import.

Great honours and privileges were accorded to them; the
best seats were reserved for their use at all public spectacles,
and even the consuls and prætors made way for them to pass.
If they met a criminal on his way to execution they had the
power to pardon him, provided it could be proved that the
meeting was accidental.

The Vestales were vowed to chastity, a violation of which
was visited by the frightful punishment of being buried alive.

PART II.
—LEGENDS.

CADMUS.

The following is the legendary account of the founding of Thebes:—

After the abduction of his daughter Europa by Zeus, Agenor, king of Phœnicia, unable to reconcile himself to her loss, despatched his son Cadmus in search of her, desiring him not to return without his sister.

For many years Cadmus pursued his search through various countries, but without success. Not daring to return home without her, he consulted the oracle of Apollo at Delphi; and the reply was that he must desist from his task, and take upon himself a new duty, *i.e.* that of founding a city, the site of which would be indicated to him by a heifer which had never borne the yoke, and which would lie down on the spot whereon the city was to be built.

Scarcely had Cadmus left the sacred fane, when he observed a heifer who bore no marks of servitude on her neck, walking slowly in front of him. He followed the animal for a considerable distance, until at length, on the site where Thebes afterwards stood, she looked towards heaven and, gently lowing, lay down in the long grass. Grateful for this mark of divine favour, Cadmus resolved to offer up the animal as a sacrifice, and accordingly sent his followers to fetch water for the libation from a neighbouring spring. This spring, which was sacred to Ares, was situated in a wood, and guarded by a fierce dragon, who, at the approach of the retainers of Cadmus, suddenly pounced upon them and killed them.

After waiting some time for the return of his servants Cadmus grew impatient, and hastily arming himself with his lance and spear, set out to seek them. On reaching the spot, the mangled remains of his unfortunate followers met his view, and near them he beheld the frightful monster, dripping with the blood of his victims. Seizing a huge rock, the hero hurled it with all his might upon the dragon; but protected by his tough black skin and steely scales as by a coat of mail, he remained unhurt. Cadmus now tried his lance, and with more success, for it pierced the side of the beast, who, furious with pain, sprang at his adversary, when Cadmus, leaping aside, succeeded in fixing the point of his spear within his jaws, which final stroke put an end to the encounter.

While Cadmus stood surveying his vanquished foe Pallas-Athene appeared to him, and commanded him to sow the teeth of the dead dragon in the ground. He obeyed; and out of the furrows there arose a band of armed men, who at once commenced to fight with each other, until all except five were killed. These last surviving warriors made peace with each other, and it was with their assistance that Cadmus now built the famous city of Thebes. In later times the noblest Theban families proudly claimed their descent from these mighty earth-born warriors.

Ares was furious with rage when he discovered that Cadmus had slain his dragon, and would have killed him had not Zeus interfered, and induced him to mitigate his punishment to that of servitude for the term of eight years. At the end of that time the god of war became reconciled to Cadmus, and, in token of his forgiveness, bestowed upon him the hand of his daughter Harmonia in marriage. Their nuptials were almost as celebrated as those of Peleus and Thetis. All the gods honoured them with their presence, and offered rich gifts and congratulations. Cadmus himself presented his lovely bride with a splendid necklace fashioned by Hephæstus, which, however, after the death of Harmonia, always proved fatal to its possessor.

The children of Cadmus and Harmonia were one son, Polydorus, and four daughters, Autonoe, Ino, Semele, and Agave.

For many years the founder of Thebes reigned happily, but at length a conspiracy was formed against him, and he was deprived of his throne by his grandson Pentheus. Accompanied by his faithful wife Harmonia, he retired into Illyria, and after death they were both changed by Zeus into serpents, and transferred to Elysium.

PERSEUS.

Perseus, one of the most renowned of the legendary heroes of antiquity, was the son of Zeus and Danaë, daughter of Acrisius, king of Argos.

An oracle having foretold to Acrisius that a son of Danaë would be the cause of his death, he imprisoned her in a tower of brass in order to keep her secluded from the world. Zeus, however, descended through the roof of the tower in the form of a shower of gold, and the lovely Danaë became his bride.

For four years Acrisius remained in ignorance of this union, but one evening as he chanced to pass by the brazen chamber, he heard the cry of a young child proceeding from within, which led to the discovery of his daughter's marriage with Zeus. Enraged at finding all his precautions unavailing, Acrisius commanded the mother and child to be placed in a chest and thrown into the sea.

But it was not the will of Zeus that they should perish. He directed Poseidon to calm the troubled waters, and caused the chest to float safely to the island of Seriphus. Dictys, brother of Polydectes, king of the island, was fishing on the sea-shore when he saw the chest stranded on the beach; and pitying the helpless condition of its unhappy occupants, he conducted them to the palace of the king, where they were treated with the greatest kindness.

Polydectes eventually became united to Danaë, and bestowed upon Perseus an education befitting a hero. When he saw his stepson develop into a noble and manly youth he endeavoured to instil into his mind a desire to signalize himself by the achievement of some great and heroic deed, and after mature deliberation it was decided that the slaying of the Gorgon, Medusa, would bring him the greatest renown.

For the successful accomplishment of his object it was necessary for him to be provided with a pair of winged sandals, a magic wallet, and the helmet of Aïdes, which rendered the wearer invisible, all of which were in the keeping of the Nymphs, the place of whose abode was known only to the Grææ. Perseus started on his expedition, and, guided by Hermes and Pallas-Athene, arrived, after a long journey, in the far-off region, on the borders of Oceanus, where dwelt the Græææ, daughters of Phorcys and Ceto. He at once applied to them for the necessary information, and on their refusing to grant it he deprived them of their single eye and tooth, which he only restored to them when they gave him full directions with regard to his route. He then proceeded to the abode of the Nymphs, from whom he obtained the objects indispensable for his purpose.

Equipped with the magic helmet and wallet, and armed with a sickle, the gift of Hermes, he attached to his feet the winged sandals, and flew to the abode of the Gorgons, whom he found fast asleep. Now as Perseus had been warned by his celestial guides that whoever looked upon these weird sisters would be transformed into stone, he stood with averted face before the sleepers, and caught on his bright metal shield their triple image. Then, guided by Pallas-Athene, he cut off the head of the Medusa, which he placed in his wallet. No sooner had he done so than from the headless trunk there sprang forth the winged steed Pegasus, and Chrysaor, the father of the winged giant Geryon. He now hastened to elude the pursuit of the two surviving sisters, who, aroused from their slumbers, eagerly rushed to avenge the death of their sister.

His invisible helmet and winged sandals here stood him in good stead; for the former concealed him from the view of the Gorgons, whilst the latter bore him swiftly over land and sea, far beyond the reach of pursuit. In passing over the burning plains of Libya the drops of blood from the head of the Medusa oozed through the wallet, and falling on the hot sands below produced a brood of many-coloured snakes, which spread all over the country.

Perseus continued his flight until he reached the kingdom of Atlas, of whom he begged rest and shelter. But as this king possessed a valuable orchard, in which every tree bore golden fruit, he was fearful lest the slayer of the Medusa might destroy the dragon which guarded it, and then rob him of his treasures. He therefore refused to grant the hospitality which the hero demanded, whereupon Perseus, exasperated at the churlish repulse, produced from his wallet the head of the Medusa, and holding it towards the king, transformed him into a stony mountain. Beard and hair erected themselves into forests; shoulders, hands, and limbs became huge rocks, and the head grew up into a craggy peak which reached into the clouds.

Perseus then resumed his travels. His winged sandals bore him over deserts and mountains, until he arrived at Æthiopia, the kingdom of King Cepheus. Here he found the country inundated with disastrous floods, towns and villages destroyed, and everywhere signs of desolation and ruin. On a projecting cliff close to the shore he beheld a lovely maiden chained to a rock. This was Andromeda, the king's daughter. Her mother Cassiopea, having boasted that her beauty surpassed that of the Nereides, the angry sea-nymphs appealed to Poseidon to avenge their wrongs, whereupon the sea-god devastated the country with a terrible inundation, which brought with it a huge monster who devoured all that came in his way.

In their distress the unfortunate Æthiopians applied to the oracle of Jupiter-Ammon, in the Libyan desert, and obtained the response, that only by the sacrifice of the king's daughter to the monster could the country and people be saved.

Cepheus, who was tenderly attached to his child, at first refused to listen to this dreadful proposal; but overcome at length by the prayers and solicitations of his unhappy subjects, the heart-broken father gave up his child for the welfare of his country. Andromeda was accordingly chained to a rock on the sea-shore to serve as a prey to the monster, whilst her unhappy parents bewailed her sad fate on the beach below.

On being informed of the meaning of this tragic scene, Perseus proposed to Cepheus to slay the dragon, on condition that the lovely victim should become his bride. Overjoyed at the prospect of Andromeda's release, the king gladly acceded to the stipulation, and Perseus hastened to the rock, to breathe words of hope and comfort to the trembling maiden. Then assuming once more the helmet of Aïdes, he mounted into the air, and awaited the approach of the monster.

Presently the sea opened, and the shark's head of the gigantic beast of the deep raised itself above the waves. Lashing his tail furiously from side to side, he leaped forward to seize his victim; but the gallant hero, watching his opportunity, suddenly darted down, and producing the head of the Medusa from his wallet, held it before the eyes of the dragon, whose hideous body became gradually transformed into a huge black rock, which remained for ever a silent witness of the miraculous deliverance of Andromeda. Perseus then led the maiden to her now happy parents, who, anxious to evince their gratitude to her deliverer ordered immediate preparations to be made for the nuptial feast. But the young hero was not to bear away his lovely bride uncontested; for in the midst of the banquet, Phineus, the king's brother, to whom Andromeda had previously been betrothed, returned to claim his bride. Followed by a band of armed warriors he forced his way into the hall, and a desperate encounter took place between the rivals, which might have terminated fatally for Perseus, had he not suddenly bethought himself of the Medusa's head. Calling to his friends to avert their faces, he drew it from his wallet, and held it before Phineus and his formidable body-guard, whereupon they all stiffened into stone.

Perseus now took leave of the Æthiopian king, and, accompanied by his beautiful bride, returned to Seriphus, where a joyful meeting took place between Danaë and her son. He then sent a messenger to his grandfather, informing him that he intended returning to Argos; but Acrisius, fearing the fulfilment of the oracular prediction, fled for protection to his friend Teutemias, king of Larissa. Anxious to induce the aged monarch to return to Argos, Perseus followed him thither. But here a strange fatality occurred. Whilst taking part in some funereal games, celebrated in honour of the king's father, Perseus, by an unfortunate throw of the discus, accidentally struck his grandfather, and thereby was the innocent cause of his death.

After celebrating the funereal rites of Acrisius with due solemnity, Perseus returned to Argos; but feeling loath to occupy the throne of one whose death he had caused, he exchanged kingdoms with Megapenthes, king of Tiryns, and in course of time founded the cities of Mycenæ and Midea.

The head of the Medusa he presented to his divine patroness, Pallas-Athene, who placed it in the centre of her shield.

Many great heroes were descended from Perseus and Andromeda, foremost among whom was Heracles, whose mother, Alcmene, was their granddaughter.

Heroic honours were paid to Perseus, not only throughout Argos, but also at Athens and in the island of Seriphus.

ION.

Ion was the son of Crëusa (the beauteous daughter of Erechtheus, king of Athens) and the sun-god Phœbus-Apollo, to whom she was united without the knowledge of her father.

Fearing the anger of Erechtheus, Crëusa placed her new-born babe in a little wicker basket, and hanging some golden charms round his neck, invoked for him the protection of the gods, and concealed him in a lonely cave. Apollo, pitying his deserted child, sent Hermes to convey him to Delphi, where he deposited his charge on the steps of the temple. Next morning the Delphic priestess discovered the infant, and was so charmed by his engaging appearance that she adopted him as her own son. The young child was carefully tended and reared by his kind foster-mother, and was brought up in the service of the temple, where he was intrusted with some of the minor duties of the holy edifice.

And now to return to Crëusa. During a war with the Eubœans, in which the latter were signally defeated, Xuthus, son of Æolus, greatly distinguished himself on the side of the Athenians, and as a reward for his valuable services, the hand of Crëusa, the king's daughter, was bestowed upon him in marriage. Their union, however, was not blest with children, and as this was a source of great grief to both of them, they repaired to Delphi in order to consult the oracle. The response was, that Xuthus should regard the first person who met him on leaving the sanctuary as his son. Now it happened that Ion, the young guardian of the temple, was the first to greet his view, and when Xuthus beheld the beautiful youth, he gladly welcomed him as his son, declaring that the gods had sent him to be a blessing and comfort to his old age. Crëusa, however, who concluded that the youth was the offspring of a secret marriage on the part of her husband, was filled with suspicion and jealousy; when an old servant, observing her grief, begged her to be comforted, assuring her that the cause of her distress should be speedily removed.

When, upon the occasion of the public adoption of his son, Xuthus gave a grand banquet, the old servant of Crëusa contrived to mix a strong poison in the wine of the unsuspecting Ion. But the youth—according to the pious custom of the ancients, of offering a libation to the gods before partaking of any repast—poured upon the ground a portion of the wine before putting it to his lips, when suddenly, as if by a miracle, a dove flew into the banquet-hall, and sipped of the wine of the libation; whereupon the poor little creature began to quiver in every limb, and in a few moments expired.

Ion's suspicions at once fell upon the obsequious servant of Crëusa, who with such officious attention had filled his cup. He violently seized the old man, and accused him of his murderous intentions. Unprepared for this sudden attack he admitted his guilt, but pointed to the wife of Xuthus as the instigator of the crime. Ion was about to avenge himself upon Crëusa, when, by means of the divine intervention of Apollo, his foster-mother, the Delphic priestess appeared on the scene, and explained the true relationship which existed between Crëusa and Ion. In order to set all doubts at rest, she produced the charms which she had found round the neck of the infant, and also the wicker basket in which he had been conveyed to Delphi.

Mother and son now became reconciled to each other, and Crëusa revealed to Ion the secret of his divine origin. The priestess of Delphi foretold that he would become the father of a great nation, called after him the Ionians, and also that Xuthus and Crëusa would have a son called Dorus, who would be the progenitor of the Dorian people, both of which predictions were in due time verified.

DÆDALUS and ICARUS.

Dædalus, a descendant of Erechtheus, was an Athenian architect, sculptor, and mechanician. He was the first to introduce the art of sculpture in its higher development, for before his time statues were merely rude representations, having the limbs altogether undefined.

But great as was his genius, still greater was his vanity, and he could brook no rival. Now his nephew and pupil, Talus, exhibited great talent, having invented both the saw and the compass, and Dædalus, fearing lest he might overshadow his own fame, secretly killed him by throwing him down from the citadel of Pallas-Athene. The murder being discovered, Dædalus was summoned before the court of the Areopagus and condemned to death; but he made his escape to the island of Crete, where he was received by king Minos in a manner worthy of his great reputation.

Dædalus constructed for the king the world-renowned labyrinth, which was an immense building, full of intricate passages, intersecting each other in such a manner, that even Dædalus himself is said, upon one occasion, to have nearly lost his way in it; and it was in this building the king placed the Minotaur, a monster with the head and shoulders of a bull and the body of a man.

In the course of time the great artist became weary of his long exile, more especially as the king, under the guise of friendship, kept him almost a prisoner. He therefore resolved to make his escape, and for this purpose ingeniously contrived wings for himself and his young son Icarus, whom he diligently trained how to use them. Having awaited a favourable opportunity, father and son commenced their flight, and were well on their way when Icarus, pleased with the novel sensation, forgot altogether his father's oft-repeated injunction not to approach too near the sun. The consequence was that the wax, by means of which his wings were attached, melted, and he fell into the sea and was drowned. The body of the unfortunate Icarus was washed up by the tide, and was buried by the bereaved father on an island which he called after his son, Icaria.

After this sad event, Dædalus winged his flight to the island of Sicily, where he met with a kind welcome from king Cocalus, for whom he constructed several important public works. But no sooner did Minos receive the intelligence that his great architect had found an asylum with Cocalus than he sailed over to Sicily with a large army, and sent messengers to the Sicilian king demanding the surrender of his guest. Cocalus feigned compliance and invited Minos to his palace, where he was treacherously put to death in a warm bath. The body of their king was brought to Agrigent by the Cretans, where it was buried with great pomp, and over his tomb a temple to Aphrodite was erected.

Dædalus passed the remainder of his life tranquilly in the island of Sicily, where he occupied himself in the construction of various beautiful works of art.

THE ARGONAUTS.

Aeson, king of Iolcus, was forced to fly from his dominions, which had been usurped by his younger brother, Pelias, and with difficulty succeeded in saving the life of his young son, Jason, who was at that time only ten years of age. He intrusted him to the care of the Centaur Chiron, by whom he was carefully trained in company with other noble youths, who, like himself, afterwards signalized themselves by their bravery and heroic exploits. For ten years Jason remained in the cave of the Centaur, by whom he was instructed in all useful and warlike arts. But as he approached manhood he became filled with an unconquerable desire to regain his paternal inheritance. He therefore took leave of his kind friend and preceptor, and set out for Iolcus to demand from his uncle Pelias the kingdom which he had so unjustly usurped.

In the course of his journey he came to a broad and foaming river, on the banks of which he perceived an old woman, who implored him to help her across. At first he hesitated, knowing that even alone he would find some difficulty in stemming the fierce torrent; but, pitying her forlorn condition, he raised her in his arms, and succeeded, with a great effort, in reaching the opposite shore. But as soon as her feet had touched the earth she became transformed into a beautiful woman, who, looking kindly at the bewildered youth, informed him that she was the goddess Hera, and that she would henceforth guide and protect him throughout his career. She then disappeared, and, full of hope and courage at this divine manifestation, Jason pursued his journey. He now perceived that in crossing the river he had lost one of his sandals, but as it could not be recovered he was obliged to proceed without it.

On his arrival at Iolcus he found his uncle in the market-place, offering up a public sacrifice to Poseidon. When the king had concluded his offering, his eye fell upon the distinguished stranger, whose manly beauty and heroic bearing had already attracted the attention of his people. Observing that one foot was unshod, he was reminded of an oracular prediction which foretold to him the loss of his kingdom by a man wearing only one sandal. He, however, disguised his fears, conversed kindly with the youth, and drew from him his name and errand. Then pretending to be highly pleased with his nephew, Pelias entertained him sumptuously for five days, during which time all was festivity and rejoicing. On the sixth, Jason appeared before his uncle, and with manly firmness demanded from him the throne and kingdom which were his by right. Pelias, dissembling his true feelings, smilingly consented to grant his request, provided that, in return, Jason would undertake an expedition for him, which his advanced age prevented him from accomplishing himself. He informed his nephew that the shade of Phryxus had appeared to him in his dreams, and entreated him to bring back from Colchis his mortal remains and the Golden Fleece; and added that if Jason succeeded in obtaining for him these sacred relics, throne, kingdom, and sceptre should be his.

STORY OF THE GOLDEN FLEECE.

Athamas, king of Bœotia, had married Nephele, a cloud-nymph, and their children were Helle and Phryxus. The restless and wandering nature of Nephele, however, soon wearied her husband, who, being a mortal, had little sympathy with his ethereal consort; so he divorced her, and married the beautiful but wicked Ino (sister of Semele), who hated her step-children, and even planned their destruction. But the watchful Nephele contrived to circumvent her cruel designs, and succeeded in getting the children out of the palace. She then placed them both on the back of a winged ram, with a fleece of pure gold, which had been given to her by Hermes; and on this wonderful animal brother and sister rode through the air over land and sea; but on the way Helle, becoming seized with giddiness, fell into the sea (called after her the Hellespont) and was drowned.

Phryxus arrived safely at Colchis, where he was hospitably received by king Aëtes, who gave him one of his daughters in marriage. In gratitude to Zeus for the protection accorded him during his flight, Phryxus sacrificed to him the golden ram, whilst the fleece he presented to Aëtes, who nailed it up in the Grove of Ares, and dedicated it to the god of War. An oracle having declared that the life of Aëtes depended on the safe-keeping of the fleece, he carefully guarded the entrance to the grove by placing before it an immense dragon, which never slept.

Building and Launch of the Argo.—We will now return to Jason, who eagerly undertook the perilous expedition proposed to him by his uncle, who, well aware of the dangers attending such an enterprise, hoped by this means to rid himself for ever of the unwelcome intruder.

Jason accordingly began to arrange his plans without delay, and invited the young heroes whose friendship he had formed whilst under the care of Chiron, to join him in the perilous expedition. None refused the invitation, all feeling honoured at being allowed the privilege of taking part in so noble and heroic an undertaking.

Jason now applied to Argos, one of the cleverest ship-builders of his time, who, under the guidance of Pallas-Athene, built for him a splendid fifty-oared galley, which was called the Argo, after the builder. In the upper deck of the vessel the goddess had imbedded a board from the speaking oak of the oracle of Zeus at Dodona, which ever retained its powers of prophecy. The exterior of the ship was ornamented with magnificent carvings, and the whole vessel was so strongly built that it defied the power of the winds and waves, and was, nevertheless, so light that the heroes, when necessary, were able to carry it on their shoulders. When the vessel was completed, the Argonauts (so called after their ship) assembled, and their places were distributed by lot.

Jason was appointed commander-in-chief of the expedition, Tiphys acted as steersman, Lynceus as pilot. In the bow of the vessel sat the renowned hero Heracles; in the stern, Peleus (father of Achilles) and Telamon (the father of Ajax the Great). In the inner space were Castor and Pollux, Neleus (the father of Nestor), Admetus (the husband of Alcestes), Meleager (the slayer of the Calydonian boar), Orpheus (the renowned singer), Menoctius (the father of Patroclus), Theseus (afterwards king of Athens) and his friend Pirithöus (the son of Ixion), Hylas (the adopted son of Heracles), Euphemus (the son of Poseidon), Oileus (father of Ajax the Lesser), Zetes and Calais (the winged sons of Boreas), Idmon the Seer (the son of Apollo), Mopsus (the Thessalian prophet), &c. &c.

Before their departure Jason offered a solemn sacrifice

to Poseidon and all the other sea-deities; he also invoked the protection of Zeus and the Fates, and then, Mopsus having taken the auguries, and found them auspicious, the heroes stepped on board. And now a favourable breeze having sprung up, they take their allotted places, the anchor is weighed, and the ship glides like a bird out of the harbour into the waters of the great sea.

Arrival at Lemnos.—The Argo, with her brave crew of fifty heroes, was soon out of sight, and the sea-breeze only wafted to the shore a faint echo of the sweet strains of Orpheus.

For a time all went smoothly, but the vessel was soon driven, by stress of weather, to take refuge in a harbour in the island of Lemnos. This island was inhabited by women only, who, the year before, in a fit of mad jealousy, had killed all the male population of the island, with the exception of the father of their queen, Hypsipyle. As the protection of their island now devolved upon themselves they were always on the look-out for danger. When, therefore, they sighted the Argo from afar they armed themselves and rushed to the shore, determined to repel any invasion of their territory.

On arriving in port the Argonauts, astonished at beholding an armed crowd of women, despatched a herald in one of their boats, bearing the staff of peace and friendship. Hypsipyle, the queen, proposed that food and presents should be sent to the strangers, in order to prevent their landing; but her old nurse, who stood beside her, suggested that this would be a good opportunity to provide themselves with noble husbands, who would act as their defenders, and thus put an end to their constant fears. Hypsipyle listened attentively to the advice of her nurse, and after some consultation, decided to invite the strangers into the city. Robed in his purple mantle, the gift of Pallas-Athene, Jason, accompanied by some of his companions, stepped on shore, where he was met by a deputation consisting of the most beautiful of the Lemnian women, and, as commander of the expedition, was invited into the palace of the queen.

When he appeared before Hypsipyle, she was so struck with his godlike and heroic presence that she presented him with her father's sceptre, and invited him to seat himself on the throne beside her. Jason thereupon took up his residence in the royal castle, whilst his companions scattered themselves through the town, spending their time in feasting and pleasure. Heracles, with a few chosen comrades, alone remained on board.

From day to day their departure was delayed, and the Argonauts, in their new life of dissipation, had almost forgotten the object of the expedition, when Heracles suddenly appeared amongst them, and at last recalled them to a sense of their duty.

Giants and Doliones.—The Argonauts now pursued their voyage, till contrary winds drove them towards an island, inhabited by the Doliones, whose king Cyzicus received them with great kindness and hospitality. The Doliones were descendants of Poseidon, who protected them against the frequent attacks of their fierce and formidable neighbours, the earth-born Giants—monsters with six arms.

Whilst his companions were attending a banquet given by king Cyzicus, Heracles, who, as usual, had remained behind to guard the ship, observed that these Giants were busy blocking up the harbour with huge rocks. He at once realized the danger, and, attacking them with his arrows, succeeded in considerably thinning their numbers; then, assisted by the heroes, who at length came to his aid, he effectually destroyed the remainder.

The Argo now steered out of the harbour and set sail; but in consequence of a severe storm which arose at night, was driven back once more to the shores of the kindly Doliones. Unfortunately, however, owing to the darkness of the night, the inhabitants failed to recognize their former guests, and, mistaking them for enemies, commenced to attack them. Those who had so recently parted as friends were now engaged in mortal combat, and in the battle which ensued, Jason himself pierced to the heart his friend king Cyzicus; whereupon the Doliones, being deprived of their leader, fled to their city and closed the gates. When morning dawned, and both sides perceived their error, they were filled with the deepest sorrow and remorse; and for three days the heroes remained with the Doliones, celebrating the funereal rites of the slain, with every demonstration of mourning and solemnity.

Heracles left behind.—The Argonauts once more set sail, and after a stormy voyage arrived at Mysia, where they were hospitably received by the inhabitants, who spread before them plentiful banquets and sumptuously regaled them.

While his friends were feasting, Heracles, who had declined to join them, went into the forest to seek a fir-tree which he required for an oar, and was missed by his adopted son Hylas, who set out to seek him. When the youth arrived at a spring, in the most secluded part of the forest, the nymph of the fountain was so struck by his beauty that she drew him down beneath the waters, and he was seen no more. Polyphemus, one of the heroes, who happened to be also in the forest, heard his cry for help, and on meeting Heracles informed him of the circumstance. They at once set out in search of the missing youth, no traces of whom were to be found, and whilst they were engaged looking for him, the Argo set sail and left them behind.

The ship had proceeded some distance before the absence of Heracles was observed. Some of the heroes were in favour of returning for him, others wished to proceed on their journey, when, in the midst of the dispute, the sea-god Glaucus arose from the waves, and informed them that it was the will of Zeus that Heracles, having another mission to perform, should remain behind. The Argonauts continued their voyage without their companions; Heracles returned to Argos, whilst Polyphemus remained with the Mysians, where he founded a city and became its king.

Contest with Amycus.—Next morning the Argo touched at the country of the Bebrycians, whose king Amycus was a famous pugilist, and permitted no strangers to leave his shores without matching their strength with his. When the heroes, therefore, demanded permission to land, they were informed that they could only do so provided that one of their number should engage in a boxing-match with the king. Pollux, who was the best pugilist in Greece, was selected as their champion, and a contest took place, which, after a tremendous struggle, proved fatal to Amycus, who had hitherto been victorious in all similar encounters.

Phineus and the Harpies.—They now proceeded towards Bithynia, where reigned the blind old prophet-king Phineus, son of Agenor. Phineus had been punished by the gods with premature old age and blindness for having abused the gift of prophecy. He was also tormented by the Harpies, who swooped down upon his food, which they either devoured or so defiled as to render it unfit to be eaten. This poor old man, trembling with the weakness of age, and faint with hunger, appeared before the Argonauts, and implored their assistance against his fiendish tormentors, whereupon Zetes and Calais, the winged sons of Boreas, recognizing in him the husband of their sister Cleopatra, affectionately embraced him, and promised to rescue him from his painful position.

The heroes prepared a banquet on the sea-shore, to which they invited Phineus; but no sooner had he taken his place, than the Harpies appeared and devoured all the viands. Zetes and Calais now rose up into the air, drove the Harpies away, and were pursuing them with drawn swords, when Iris, the swift-footed messenger of the gods, appeared, and desired them to desist from their work of vengeance, promising that Phineus should be no longer molested.

Freed at length from his tormentors the old man sat down and enjoyed a plentiful repast with his kind friends the

Argonauts, who now informed him of the object of their voyage. In gratitude for his deliverance Phineus gave them much useful information concerning their journey, and not only warned them of the manifold dangers awaiting them, but also instructed them how they might be overcome.

Passage of the Symplegades.—After a fortnight's sojourn in Bithynia the Argonauts once more set sail, but had not proceeded far on their course, when they heard a fearful and tremendous crash. This was caused by the meeting of two great rocky islands, called the Symplegades, which floated about in the sea, and constantly met and separated.

Before leaving Bithynia, the blind old seer, Phineus, had informed them that they would be compelled to pass between these terrible rocks, and he instructed them how to do so with safety. As they now approached the scene of danger they remembered his advice, and acted upon it. Typhus, the steersman, stood at the helm, whilst Euphemus held in his hand a dove ready to be let loose; for Phineus had told them that if the dove ventured to fly through, they might safely follow. Euphemus now despatched the bird, which passed swiftly through the islands, yet not without losing some of the feathers of her tail, so speedily did they reunite. Seizing the moment when the rocks once more separated, the Argonauts worked at their oars with all their might, and achieved the perilous passage in safety.

After the miraculous passage of the Argo, the Symplegades became permanently united, and attached to the bottom of the sea.

The Stymphalides.—The Argo pursued her course along the southern coast of the Pontus, and arrived at the island of Aretias, which was inhabited by birds, who, as they flew through the air, discharged from their wings feathers sharp as arrows.

As the ship was gliding along, Oileus was wounded by one of these birds, whereupon the Argonauts held a council, and by the advice of Amphidamas, an experienced hero, all put on their helmets, and held up their glittering shields, uttering, at the same time, such fearful cries that the birds flew away in terror, and the Argonauts were enabled to land with safety on the island.

Here they found four shipwrecked youths, who proved to be the sons of Phryxus, and were greeted by Jason as his cousins. On ascertaining the object of the expedition they volunteered to accompany the Argo, and to show the heroes the way to Colchis. They also informed them that the Golden Fleece was guarded by a fearful dragon, that king Aëtes was extremely cruel, and, as the son of Apollo, was possessed of superhuman strength.

Arrival at Colchis.—Taking with them the four new-comers they journeyed on, and soon came in sight of the snow-capped peaks of the Caucasus, when, towards evening, the loud flapping of wings was heard overhead. It was the giant eagle of Prometheus on his way to torture the noble and long-suffering Titan, whose fearful groans soon afterwards fell upon their ears. That night they reached their journey's end, and anchored in the smooth waters of the river Phases. On the left bank of this river they beheld Ceuta, the capital of Colchis; and on their right a wide field, and the sacred grove of Ares, where the Golden Fleece, suspended from a magnificent oak-tree, was glittering in the sun. Jason now filled a golden cup with wine, and offered a libation to mother-earth, the gods of the country, and the shades of those of the heroes who had died on the voyage.

Next morning a council was held, in which it was decided, that before resorting to forcible measures kind and conciliatory overtures should first be made to king Aëtes in order to induce him to resign the Golden Fleece. It was arranged that Jason, with a few chosen companions, should proceed to the royal castle, leaving the remainder of the crew to guard the Argo. Accompanied, therefore, by Telamon and

Augeas, and the four sons of Phryxus, he set out for the palace.

When they arrived in sight of the castle they were struck by the vastness and massiveness of the building, at the entrance to which sparkling fountains played in the midst of luxuriant and park-like gardens. Here the king's daughters, Chalciope and Medea, who were walking in the grounds of the palace, met them. The former, to her great joy, recognized in the youths who accompanied the hero her own long-lost sons, whom she had mourned as dead, whilst the young and lovely Medea was struck with the noble and manly form of Jason.

The news of the return of the sons of Phryxus soon spread through the palace, and brought Aëtes himself to the scene, whereupon the strangers were presented to him, and were invited to a banquet which the king ordered to be prepared in their honour. All the most beautiful ladies of the court were present at this entertainment; but in the eyes of Jason none could compare with the king's daughter, the young and lovely Medea.

When the banquet was ended, Jason related to the king his various adventures, and also the object of his expedition, with the circumstances which had led to his undertaking it. Aëtes listened, in silent indignation, to this recital, and then burst out into a torrent of invectives against the Argonauts and his grand-children, declaring that the Fleece was his rightful property, and that on no consideration would he consent to relinquish it. Jason, however, with mild and persuasive words, contrived so far to conciliate him, that he was induced to promise that if the heroes could succeed in demonstrating their divine origin by the performance of some task requiring superhuman power, the Fleece should be theirs.

The task proposed by Aëtes to Jason was that he should yoke the two brazen-footed, fire-breathing oxen of the king (which had been made for him by Hephæstus) to his ponderous iron plough. Having done this he must till with them the stony field of Ares, and then sow in the furrows the poisonous teeth of a dragon, from which armed men would arise. These he must destroy to a man, or he himself would perish at their hands.

When Jason heard what was expected of him, his heart for a moment sank within him; but he determined, nevertheless, not to flinch from his task, but to trust to the assistance of the gods, and to his own courage and energy.

Jason ploughs the Field of Ares.—Accompanied by his two friends, Telamon and Augeas, and also by Argus, the son of Chalciope, Jason returned to the vessel for the purpose of holding a consultation as to the best means of accomplishing these perilous feats.

Argus explained to Jason all the difficulties of the superhuman task which lay before him, and pronounced it as his opinion that the only means by which success was possible was to enlist the assistance of the Princess Medea, who was a priestess of Hecate, and a great enchantress. His suggestion meeting with approval, he returned to the palace, and by the aid of his mother an interview was arranged between Jason and Medea, which took place, at an early hour next morning, in the temple of Hecate.

A confession of mutual attachment took place, and Medea, trembling for her lover's safety, presented him with a magic salve, which possessed the property of rendering any person anointed with it invulnerable for the space of one day against fire and steel, and invincible against any adversary however powerful. With this salve she instructed him to anoint his spear and shield on the day of his great undertaking. She further added that when, after having ploughed the field and sown the teeth, armed men should arise from the furrows, he must on no account lose heart, but remember to throw among them a huge rock, over the possession of which they would fight among themselves, and their attention being thus diverted he would find it an easy task to destroy them. Overwhelmed with gratitude, Jason thanked her, in the most earnest manner, for her wise counsel and timely aid; at the same time he offered her his hand, and promised her he would not return to Greece without taking her with him as his wife.

Next morning Aëtes, in all the pomp of state, surrounded by his family and the members of his court, repaired to a spot whence a full view of the approaching spectacle could be obtained. Soon Jason appeared in the field of Ares, looking as noble and majestic as the god of war himself. In a distant part of the field the brazen yokes and the massive plough met his view, but as yet the dread animals themselves were nowhere to be seen. He was about to go in quest of them, when they suddenly rushed out from a subterranean cave, breathing flames of fire, and enveloped in a thick smoke.

The friends of Jason trembled; but the undaunted hero, relying on the magic powers with which he was imbued by Medea, seized the oxen, one after the other, by the horns, and forced them to the yoke. Near the plough was a helmet full of dragon's teeth, which he sowed as he ploughed the field, whilst with sharp pricks from his lance he compelled the monstrous creatures to draw the plough over the stony ground, which was thus speedily tilled.

While Jason was engaged sowing the dragon's teeth in the deep furrows of the field, he kept a cautious look-out lest the germinating giant brood might grow too quickly for him, and as soon as the four acres of land had been tilled he unyoked the oxen, and succeeded in frightening them so effectually with his weapons, that they rushed back in terror to their subterranean stables. Meanwhile armed men had sprung up out of the furrows, and the whole field now bristled with lances; but Jason, remembering the instructions of Medea, seized an immense rock and hurled it into the midst of these earth-born warriors, who immediately began to attack each other. Jason then rushed furiously upon them, and after a terrible struggle not one of the giants remained alive.

Furious at seeing his murderous schemes thus defeated,

Aëtes not only perfidiously refused to give Jason the Fleece which he had so bravely earned, but, in his anger, determined to destroy all the Argonauts, and to burn their vessel.

Jason secures the Golden Fleece.—Becoming aware of the treacherous designs of her father, Medea at once took measures to baffle them. In the darkness of night she went on board the Argo, and warned the heroes of their approaching danger. She then advised Jason to accompany her without loss of time to the sacred grove, in order to possess himself of the long-coveted treasure. They set out together, and Medea, followed by Jason, led the way, and advanced boldly into the grove. The tall oak-tree was soon discovered, from the topmost boughs of which hung the beautiful Golden Fleece. At the foot of this tree, keeping his ever-wakeful watch, lay the dreadful, sleepless dragon, who at sight of them bounded forward, opening his huge jaws.

Medea now called into play her magic powers, and quietly approaching the monster, threw over him a few drops of a potion, which soon took effect, and sent him into a deep sleep; whereupon Jason, seizing the opportunity, climbed the tree and secured the Fleece. Their perilous task being now accomplished, Jason and Medea quitted the grove, and hastened on board the Argo, which immediately put to sea.

Murder of Absyrtus.—Meanwhile Aëtes, having discovered the loss of his daughter and the Golden Fleece, despatched a large fleet, under the command of his son Absyrtus, in pursuit of the fugitives. After some days' sail they arrived at an island at the mouth of the river Ister, where they found the Argo at anchor, and surrounded her with their numerous ships. They then despatched a herald on board of her, demanding the surrender of Medea and the Fleece.

Medea now consulted Jason, and, with his consent, carried out the following stratagem. She sent a message to her brother Absyrtus, to the effect that she had been carried off against her will, and promised that if he would meet her, in the darkness of night, in the temple of Artemis, she would assist him in regaining possession of the Golden Fleece. Relying on the good faith of his sister, Absyrtus fell into the snare, and duly appeared at the appointed trysting-place; and whilst Medea kept her brother engaged in conversation, Jason rushed forward and slew him. Then, according to a preconcerted signal, he held aloft a lighted torch, whereupon the Argonauts attacked the Colchians, put them to flight, and entirely defeated them.

The Argonauts now returned to their ship, when the prophetic board from the Dodonean oak thus addressed them: "The cruel murder of Absyrtus was witnessed by the Erinyes, and you will not escape the wrath of Zeus until the goddess Circe has purified you from your crime. Let Castor and Pollux pray to the gods that you may be enabled to find the abode of the sorceress." In obedience to the voice, the twin-brothers invoked divine assistance, and the heroes set out in search of the isle of Circe.

They arrive at the Island of Circe.—The good ship Argo sped on her way, and, after passing safely through the foaming waters of the river Eridanus, at length arrived in the harbour of the island of Circe, where she cast anchor.

Commanding his companions to remain on board, Jason landed with Medea, and conducted her to the palace of the sorceress. The goddess of charms and magic arts received them kindly, and invited them to be seated; but instead of doing so they assumed a supplicating attitude, and humbly besought her protection. They then informed her of the dreadful crime which they had committed, and implored her to purify them from it. This Circe promised to do. She forthwith commanded her attendant Naiads to kindle the fire on the altar, and to prepare everything necessary for the performance of the mystic rites, after which a dog was sacrificed, and the sacred cakes were burned. Having thus duly purified the criminals, she severely reprimanded them for the horrible murder of which they had been guilty; whereupon Medea, with veiled head, and weeping bitterly, was reconducted by Jason to the Argo.

Further Adventures of the Argonauts.—Having left the island of Circe they were wafted by gentle zephyrs towards the abode of the Sirens, whose enticing strains soon fell upon their ears. The Argonauts, powerfully affected by the melody, were making ready to land, when Orpheus perceived the danger, and, to the accompaniment of his magic lyre, commenced one of his enchanting songs, which so completely absorbed his listeners that they passed the island in safety; but not before Butes, one of their number, lured by the seductive music of the Sirens, had sprung from the vessel into the waves below. Aphrodite, however, in pity for his youth, landed him gently on the island of Libibaon before the Sirens could reach him, and there he remained for many years.

And now the Argonauts approached new dangers, for on one side of them seethed and foamed the whirlpool of Charybdis, whilst on the other towered the mighty rock whence the monster Scylla swooped down upon unfortunate mariners; but here the goddess Hera came to their assistance, and sent to them the sea-nymph Thetis, who guided them safely through these dangerous straits.

The Argo next arrived at the island of the Phæaces, where they were hospitably entertained by King Alcinous and his queen Arete. But the banquet prepared for them by their kind host was unexpectedly interrupted by the appearance of a large army of Colchians, sent by Aëtes to demand the restoration of his daughter.

Medea threw herself at the feet of the queen, and implored her to save her from the anger of her father, and Arete, in her kindness of heart, promised her her protection. Next morning, in an assembly of the people at which the Colchians were invited to be present, the latter were informed that as Medea was the lawful wife of Jason they could not consent to deliver her up; whereupon the Colchians, seeing that the resolution of the king was not to be shaken, and fearing to face the anger of Aëtes should they return to Colchis without her, sought permission of Alcinous to settle in his kingdom, which request was accorded them.

After these events the Argonauts once more set sail, and steered for Iolcus; but, in the course of a terrible and fearful night, a mighty storm arose, and in the morning they found themselves stranded on the treacherous quicksands of Syrtes, on the shores of Libya. Here all was a waste and barren desert, untenanted by any living creature, save the venomous snakes which had sprung from the blood of the Medusa when borne by Perseus over these arid plains.

They had already passed several days in this abode of desolation, beneath the rays of the scorching sun, and had abandoned themselves to the deepest despair, when the Libyan queen, who was a prophetess of divine origin, appeared to Jason, and informed him that a sea-horse would be sent by the gods to act as his guide.

Scarcely had she departed when a gigantic hippocamp was seen in the distance, making its way towards the Argo. Jason now related to his companions the particulars of his interview with the Libyan prophetess, and after some deliberation it was decided to carry the Argo on their shoulders, and to follow wherever the sea-horse should lead them. They then commenced a long and weary journey through the desert, and at last, after twelve days of severe toil and terrible suffering, the welcome sight of the sea greeted their view. In gratitude for having been saved from their manifold dangers they offered up sacrifices to the gods, and launched their ship once more into the deep waters of the ocean.

Arrival at Crete.—With heartfelt joy and gladness they proceeded on their homeward voyage, and after some days arrived at the island of Crete, where they purposed to furnish themselves with fresh provisions and water. Their landing, however, was opposed by a terrible giant who guarded the island against all intruders. This giant, whose name was Talus, was the last of the Brazen race, and being formed of brass, was invulnerable, except in his right ankle, where there was a sinew of flesh and a vein of blood. As he saw the Argo nearing the coast, he hurled huge rocks at her, which would inevitably have sunk the vessel had not the crew beat a hasty retreat. Although sadly in want of food and water, the Argonauts had decided to proceed on their journey rather than face so powerful an opponent, when Medea came forward and assured them that if they would trust to her she would destroy the giant.

Enveloped in the folds of a rich purple mantle, she stepped on deck, and after invoking the aid of the Fates, uttered a magic incantation, which had the effect of throwing Talus into a deep sleep. He stretched himself at full length upon the ground, and in doing so grazed his vulnerable ankle against the point of a sharp rock, whereupon a mighty stream of blood gushed forth from the wound. Awakened by the pain, he tried to rise, but in vain, and with a mighty groan of anguish the giant fell dead, and his enormous body rolled heavily over into the deep. The heroes being now able to land, provisioned their vessel, after which they resumed their homeward voyage.

Arrival at Iolcus.—After a terrible night of storm and darkness they passed the island of Ægina, and at length reached in safety the port of Iolcus, where the recital of their numerous adventures and hair-breadth escapes was listened to with wondering admiration by their fellow-countrymen.

The Argo was consecrated to Poseidon, and was carefully preserved for many generations till no vestige of it remained, when it was placed in the heavens as a brilliant constellation.

On his arrival at Iolcus, Jason conducted his beautiful bride to the palace of his uncle Pelias, taking with him the

Golden Fleece, for the sake of which this perilous expedition had been undertaken. But the old king, who had never expected that Jason would return alive, basely refused to fulfil his part of the compact, and declined to abdicate the throne.

Indignant at the wrongs of her husband, Medea avenged them in a most shocking manner. She made friends with the daughters of the king, and feigned great interest in all their concerns. Having gained their confidence, she informed them, that among her numerous magic arts, she possessed the power of restoring to the aged all the vigour and strength of youth, and in order to give them a convincing proof of the truth of her assertion, she cut up an old ram, which she boiled in a cauldron, whereupon, after uttering various mystic incantations, there came forth from the vessel a beautiful young lamb. She then assured them, that in a similar manner they could restore to their old father his former youthful frame and vigour. The fond and credulous daughters of Pelias lent an all too willing ear to the wicked sorceress, and thus the old king perished at the hands of his innocent children.

Death of Jason.—Medea and Jason now fled to Corinth, where at length they found, for a time, peace and tranquillity, their happiness being completed by the birth of three children.

As time passed on, however, and Medea began to lose the beauty which had won the love of her husband, he grew weary of her, and became attracted by the youthful charms of Glauce, the beautiful daughter of Creon, king of Corinth. Jason had obtained her father's consent to their union, and the wedding-day was already fixed, before he disclosed to Medea the treachery which he meditated against her. He used all his persuasive powers in order to induce her to consent to his union with Glauce, assuring her that his affection had in no way diminished, but that for the sake of the advantages which would thereby accrue to their children, he had decided on forming this alliance with the royal house. Though justly enraged at his deceitful conduct, Medea dissembled her wrath, and, feigning to be satisfied with this explanation, sent, as a wedding-gift to her rival, a magnificent robe of cloth-of-gold. This robe was imbued with a deadly poison which penetrated to the flesh and bone of the wearer, and burned them as though with a consuming fire. Pleased with the beauty and costliness of the garment, the unsuspecting Glauce lost no time in donning it; but no sooner had she done so than the fell poison began to take effect. In vain she tried to tear the robe away; it defied all efforts to be removed, and after horrible and protracted sufferings, she expired.

Maddened at the loss of her husband's love Medea next put to death her three sons, and when Jason, thirsting for revenge, left the chamber of his dead bride, and flew to his own house in search of Medea, the ghastly spectacle of his murdered children met his view. He rushed frantically to seek the murderess, but nowhere could she be found. At length, hearing a sound above his head, he looked up, and beheld Medea gliding through the air in a golden chariot drawn by dragons.

In a fit of despair Jason threw himself on his own sword, and perished on the threshold of his desolate and deserted home.

PELOPS.

Pelops, the son of the cruel Tantalus, was a pious and virtuous prince. After his father was banished into Tartarus, a war ensued between Pelops and the king of Troy, in which the former was vanquished and forced to fly from his dominions in Phrygia. He emigrated into Greece, where, at the court of Œnomaus, king of Elis, he beheld Hippodamia, the king's daughter, whose beauty won his heart. But an oracle having foretold to Œnomaus that he would die on the day of his daughter's marriage, he threw every obstacle in the way of her suitors, and declared that he would only give her to him who succeeded in vanquishing him in a chariot race, but that all unsuccessful competitors should suffer death at his hands.

The conditions of the contest were as follows:—The race was to be run from a given point at Pisa to the altar of Poseidon at Corinth; the suitor was allowed to start on his course whilst Œnomaus performed his sacrifice to Zeus, and only on its completion did the king mount his chariot, guided by the skilful Myrtilus, and drawn by his two famous horses, Phylla and Harpinna, who surpassed in swiftness the winds themselves. In this manner many a gallant young prince had perished; for although a considerable start was given to all competitors, still Œnomaus, with his swift team, always overtook them before they reached the goal, and killed them with his spear. But the love of Pelops for Hippodamia overcame all fears, and, undeterred by the terrible fate of his predecessors, he announced himself to Œnomaus as a suitor for the hand of his daughter.

On the eve of the race, Pelops repaired to the sea-shore and earnestly implored Poseidon to assist him in his perilous undertaking. The sea-god heard his prayer, and sent him out of the deep a chariot drawn by two winged horses.

When Pelops appeared on the course, the king at once recognized the horses of Poseidon; but, nothing daunted, he relied on his own supernatural team, and the contest was allowed to proceed.

Whilst the king was offering his sacrifice to Zeus Pelops set out on the race, and had nearly reached the goal, when, turning round, he beheld Œnomaus, spear in hand, who, with his magic steeds, had nearly overtaken him. But in this emergency Poseidon came to the aid of the son of Tantalus. He caused the wheels of the royal chariot to fly off, whereupon the king was thrown out violently, and killed on the spot, just as Pelops arrived at the altar of Poseidon.

As the hero was about to return to Pisa to claim his bride, he beheld, in the distance, flames issuing from the royal castle, which at that instant had been struck by lightning. With his winged horses he flew to rescue his lovely bride, and succeeded in extricating her uninjured from the burning building. They soon afterwards became united, and Pelops reigned in Pisa for many years in great splendour.

HERACLES (HERCULES).

Heracles, the most renowned hero of antiquity, was the son of Zeus and Alcmene, and the great grandson of Perseus.

At the time of his birth Alcmene was living at Thebes with her husband Amphitryon, and thus the infant Heracles was born in the palace of his stepfather.

Aware of the animosity with which Hera persecuted all those who rivalled her in the affections of Zeus, Alcmene, fearful lest this hatred should be visited on her innocent child, intrusted him, soon after his birth, to the care of a faithful servant, with instructions to expose him in a certain field, and there leave him, feeling assured that the divine offspring of Zeus would not long remain without the protection of the gods.

Soon after the child had been thus abandoned, Hera and Pallas-Athene happened to pass by the field, and were attracted by its cries. Athene pityingly took up the infant in her arms, and prevailed upon the queen of heaven to put it to her breast; but no sooner had she done so, than the child, causing her pain, she angrily threw him to the ground, and left the spot. Athene, moved with compassion, carried him to Alcmene, and entreated her kind offices on behalf of the poor little foundling. Alcmene at once recognized her child, and joyfully accepted the charge.

Soon afterwards Hera, to her extreme annoyance, discovered whom she had nursed, and became filled with jealous rage. She now sent two venomous snakes into the chamber of Alcmene, which crept, unperceived by the nurses, to the cradle of the sleeping child. He awoke with a cry, and grasping a snake in each hand, strangled them both. Alcmene and her attendants, whom the cry of the child had awakened, rushed to the cradle, where, to their astonishment and terror, they beheld the two reptiles dead in the hands of the infant Heracles. Amphitryon was also attracted to the chamber by the commotion, and when he beheld this astounding proof of supernatural strength, he declared that the child must have been sent to him as a special gift from Zeus. He accordingly consulted the famous seer Tiresias, who now informed him of the divine origin of his stepson, and prognosticated for him a great and distinguished future.

When Amphitryon heard the noble destiny which awaited the child intrusted to his care, he resolved to educate him in a manner worthy of his future career. At a suitable age he himself taught him how to guide a chariot; Eurytus, how to handle the bow; Autolycus, dexterity in wrestling and boxing; and Castor, the art of armed warfare; whilst Linus, the son of Apollo, instructed him in music and letters.

Heracles was an apt pupil; but undue harshness was intolerable to his high spirit, and old Linus, who was not the gentlest of teachers, one day corrected him with blows, whereupon the boy angrily took up his lyre, and, with one stroke of his powerful arm, killed his tutor on the spot.

Apprehensive lest the ungovernable temper of the youth might again involve him in similar acts of violence, Amphitryon sent him into the country, where he placed him under the charge of one of his most trusted herdsmen. Here, as he grew up to manhood, his extraordinary stature and strength became the wonder and admiration of all beholders. His aim, whether with spear, lance, or bow, was unerring, and at the age of eighteen he was considered to be the strongest as well as the most beautiful youth in all Greece.

The Choice of Heracles.—Heracles felt that the time had now arrived when it became necessary to decide for himself how to make use of the extraordinary powers with which he had been endowed by the gods; and in order to meditate in solitude on this all-important subject, he repaired to a lonely and secluded spot in the heart of the forest.

Here two females of great beauty appeared to him. One was Vice, the other Virtue. The former was full of artificial wiles and fascinating arts, her face painted and her dress gaudy and attractive; whilst the latter was of noble bearing and modest mien, her robes of spotless purity.

Vice stepped forward and thus addressed him: "If you will walk in my paths, and make me your friend, your life shall be one round of pleasure and enjoyment. You shall taste of every delight which can be procured on earth; the choicest viands, the most delicious wines, the most luxuriant of couches shall be ever at your disposal; and all this without any exertion on your part, either physical or mental."

Virtue now spoke in her turn: "If you will follow me and be my friend, I promise you the reward of a good conscience, and the love and respect of your fellowmen. I cannot undertake to smooth your path with roses, or to give you a life of idleness and pleasure; for you must know that the gods grant no good and desirable thing that is not earned by labour; and as you sow, so must you reap."

Heracles listened patiently and attentively to both speakers, and then, after mature deliberation, decided to follow in the paths of virtue, and henceforth to honour the gods, and to devote his life to the service of his country.

Full of these noble resolves he sought once more his rural home, where he was informed that on Mount Cithæron, at the foot of which the herds of Amphitryon were grazing, a ferocious lion had fixed his lair, and was committing such frightful ravages among the flocks and herds that he had become the scourge and terror of the whole neighbourhood. Heracles at once armed himself and ascended the mountain, where he soon caught sight of the lion, and rushing at him with his sword succeeded in killing him. The hide of the animal he wore ever afterwards over his shoulders, and the head served him as a helmet.

As he was returning from this, his first exploit, he met the heralds of Erginus, king of the Minyans, who were proceeding to Thebes to demand their annual tribute of 100 oxen. Indignant at this humiliation of his native city, Heracles mutilated the heralds, and sent them back, with ropes round their necks, to their royal master.

Erginus was so incensed at the ill-treatment of his messengers that he collected an army and appeared before the gates of Thebes, demanding the surrender of Heracles. Creon, who was at this time king of Thebes, fearing the consequences of a refusal, was about to yield, when the hero, with the assistance of Amphitryon and a band of brave youths, advanced against the Minyans.

Heracles took possession of a narrow defile through which the enemy were compelled to pass, and as they entered the pass the Thebans fell upon them, killed their king Erginus, and completely routed them. In this engagement Amphitryon, the kind friend and foster-father of Heracles, lost his life. The hero now advanced upon Orchomenus, the capital of the Minyans, where he burned the royal castle and sacked the town.

After this signal victory all Greece rang with the fame of the young hero, and Creon, in gratitude for his great services, bestowed upon him his daughter Megara in marriage. The Olympian gods testified their appreciation of his valour by sending him presents; Hermes gave him a sword, Phœbus-Apollo a bundle of arrows, Hephæstus a golden quiver, and Athene a coat of leather.

Heracles and Eurystheus.—And now it will be necessary to retrace our steps. Just before the birth of Heracles, Zeus, in an assembly of the gods, exultingly declared that the child who should be born on that day to the house of Perseus should rule over all his race. When Hera heard her lord's boastful announcement she knew well that it was for the child of the hated Alcmene that this brilliant destiny was designed; and in order to rob the son of her rival of his rights, she called to her aid the goddess Eilithyia, who retarded the birth of Heracles, and caused his cousin Eurystheus (another grandson of Perseus) to precede him into the world. And thus, as the word of the mighty Zeus was irrevocable, Heracles became the subject and servant of his cousin Eurystheus.

When, after his splendid victory over Erginus, the fame of Heracles spread throughout Greece, Eurystheus (who had become king of Mycenæ), jealous of the reputation of the young hero, asserted his rights, and commanded him to undertake for him various difficult tasks. But the proud spirit of the hero rebelled against this humiliation, and he was about to refuse compliance, when Zeus appeared to him and desired him not to rebel against the Fates. Heracles now repaired to Delphi in order to consult the oracle, and received the answer that after performing ten tasks for his cousin Eurystheus his servitude would be at an end.

Soon afterwards Heracles fell into a state of the deepest melancholy, and through the influence of his inveterate enemy, the goddess Hera, this despondency developed into raving madness, in which condition he killed his own children. When he at length regained his reason he was so horrified and grieved at what he had done, that he shut himself up in his chamber and avoided all intercourse with men. But in his loneliness and seclusion the conviction that work would be the best means of procuring oblivion of the past decided him to enter, without delay, upon the tasks appointed him by Eurystheus.

1. The Nemean Lion.—His first task was to bring to Eurystheus the skin of the much-dreaded Nemean lion, which ravaged the territory between Cleone and Nemea, and whose hide was invulnerable against any mortal weapon.

Heracles proceeded to the forest of Nemea, where, having

discovered the lion's lair, he attempted to pierce him with his arrows; but finding these of no avail he felled him to the ground with his club, and before the animal had time to recover from the terrible blow, Heracles seized him by the neck and, with a mighty effort, succeeded in strangling him. He then made himself a coat of mail of the skin, and a new helmet of the head of the animal. Thus attired, he so alarmed Eurystheus by appearing suddenly before him, that the king concealed himself in his palace, and henceforth forbade Heracles to enter his presence, but commanded him to receive his behests, for the future, through his messenger Copreus.

2. The Hydra.—His second task was to slay the Hydra, a monster serpent (the offspring of Typhon and Echidna), bristling with nine heads, one of which was immortal. This monster infested the neighbourhood of Lerna, where she committed great depredations among the herds.

Heracles, accompanied by his nephew Iolaus, set out in a chariot for the marsh of Lerna, in the slimy waters of which he found her. He commenced the attack by assailing her with his fierce arrows, in order to force her to leave her lair, from which she at length emerged, and sought refuge in a wood on a neighbouring hill. Heracles now rushed forward and endeavoured to crush her heads by means of well-directed blows from his tremendous club; but no sooner was one head destroyed than it was immediately replaced by two others. He next seized the monster in his powerful grasp; but at this juncture a giant crab came to the assistance of the Hydra and commenced biting the feet of her assailant. Heracles destroyed this new adversary with his club, and now called upon his nephew to come to his aid. At his command Iolaus set fire to the neighbouring trees, and, with a burning branch, seared the necks of the monster as Heracles cut them off, thus effectually preventing the growth of more. Heracles next struck off the immortal head, which he buried by the road-side, and placed over it a heavy stone. Into the poisonous blood of the monster he then dipped his arrows, which ever afterwards rendered wounds inflicted by them incurable.

3. The Horned Hind.—The third labour of Heracles was to bring the horned hind Cerunitis alive to Mycenæ. This animal, which was sacred to Artemis, had golden antlers and hoofs of brass.

Not wishing to wound the hind Heracles patiently pursued her through many countries for a whole year, and overtook her at last on the banks of the river Ladon; but even there he was compelled, in order to secure her, to wound her with one of his arrows, after which he lifted her on his shoulders and carried her through Arcadia. On his way he met Artemis with her brother Phœbus-Apollo, when the goddess angrily reproved him for wounding her favourite hind; but Heracles succeeded in appeasing her displeasure, whereupon she permitted him to take the animal alive to Mycenæ.

4. The Erymantian Boar.—The fourth task imposed upon Heracles by Eurystheus was to bring alive to Mycenæ the Erymantian boar, which had laid waste the region of Erymantia, and was the scourge of the surrounding neighbourhood.

On his way thither he craved food and shelter of a Centaur named Pholus, who received him with generous hospitality, setting before him a good and plentiful repast. When Heracles expressed his surprise that at such a well-furnished board wine should be wanting, his host explained that the wine-cellar was the common property of all the Centaurs, and that it was against the rules for a cask to be broached, except all were present to partake of it. By dint of persuasion, however, Heracles prevailed on his kind host to make an exception in his favour; but the powerful, luscious odour of the good old wine soon spread over the mountains, and brought large numbers of Centaurs to the spot, all armed with huge rocks and fir-trees. Heracles drove them back with fire-brands, and then, following up his victory, pursued them with his arrows as far as Malea, where they took refuge in the cave of the kind old Centaur Chiron. Unfortunately, however, as Heracles was shooting at them with his poisoned darts, one of these pierced the knee of Chiron. When Heracles discovered that it was the friend of his early days that he had wounded, he was overcome with sorrow and regret. He at once extracted the arrow, and anointed the wound with a salve, the virtue of which had been taught him by Chiron himself. But all his efforts were unavailing. The wound, imbued with the deadly poison of the Hydra, was incurable, and so great was the agony of Chiron that, at the intercession of Heracles, death was sent him by the gods; for otherwise, being immortal, he would have been doomed to endless suffering.

Pholus, who had so kindly entertained Heracles, also perished by means of one of these arrows, which he had extracted from the body of a dead Centaur. While he was quietly examining it, astonished that so small and insignificant an object should be productive of such serious results, the arrow fell upon his foot and fatally wounded him. Full of grief at this untoward event, Heracles buried him with due honours, and then set out to chase the boar.

With loud shouts and terrible cries he first drove him out of the thickets into the deep snow-drifts which covered the summit of the mountain, and then, having at length wearied him with his incessant pursuit, he captured the exhausted animal, bound him with a rope, and brought him alive to Mycenæ.

5. Cleansing the Stables of Augeas.—After slaying the Erymantian boar Eurystheus commanded Heracles to cleanse in one day the stables of Augeas.

Augeas was a king of Elis who was very rich in herds. Three thousand of his cattle he kept near the royal palace in an inclosure where the refuse had accumulated for many years.

When Heracles presented himself before the king, and offered to cleanse his stables in one day, provided he should receive in return a tenth part of the herds, Augeas, thinking the feat impossible, accepted his offer in the presence of his son Phyleus.

Near the palace were the two rivers Peneus and Alpheus, the streams of which Heracles conducted into the stables by means of a trench which he dug for this purpose, and as the waters rushed through the shed, they swept away with them the whole mass of accumulated filth.

But when Augeas heard that this was one of the labours imposed by Eurystheus, he refused the promised guerdon. Heracles brought the matter before a court, and called Phyleus as a witness to the justice of his claim, whereupon Augeas, without waiting for the delivery of the verdict, angrily banished Heracles and his son from his dominions.

6. The Stymphalides.—The sixth task was to chase away the Stymphalides, which were immense birds of prey who, as we have seen (in the legend of the Argonauts), shot from their wings feathers sharp as arrows. The home of these birds was on the shore of the lake Stymphalis, in Arcadia (after which they were called), where they caused great destruction among men and cattle.

On approaching the lake, Heracles observed great numbers of them; and, while hesitating how to commence the attack, he suddenly felt a hand on his shoulder. Looking round he beheld the majestic form of Pallas-Athene, who held in her hand a gigantic pair of brazen clappers made by Hephæstus, with which she presented him; whereupon he ascended to the summit of a neighbouring hill, and commenced to rattle them violently. The shrill noise of these instruments was so intolerable to the birds that they rose into the air in terror, upon which he aimed at them with his arrows, destroying them in great numbers, whilst such as escaped his darts flew away, never to return.

7. The Cretan Bull.—The seventh labour of Heracles was to capture the Cretan bull.

Minos, king of Crete, having vowed to sacrifice to Poseidon any animal which should first appear out of the sea, the god caused a magnificent bull to emerge from the waves in order to test the sincerity of the Cretan king, who, in making this vow, had alleged that he possessed no animal, among his own herds, worthy the acceptance of the mighty sea-god. Charmed with the splendid animal sent by Poseidon, and eager to possess it, Minos placed it among his herds, and substituted as a sacrifice one of his own bulls. Hereupon Poseidon, in order to punish the cupidity of Minos, caused the animal to become mad, and commit such great havoc in the island as to endanger the safety of the inhabitants. When Heracles, therefore, arrived in Crete for the purpose of capturing the bull, Minos, far from opposing his design, gladly gave him permission to do so.

The hero not only succeeded in securing the animal, but tamed him so effectually that he rode on his back right across the sea as far as the Peloponnesus. He now delivered him up to Eurystheus, who at once set him at liberty, after which he became as ferocious and wild as before, roamed all over Greece into Arcadia, and was eventually killed by Theseus on the plains of Marathon.

8. The Mares of Diomedes.—The eighth labour of Heracles was to bring to Eurystheus the mares of Diomedes, a son of Ares, and king of the Bistonians, a warlike Thracian tribe. This king possessed a breed of wild horses of tremendous size and strength, whose food consisted of human flesh, and all strangers who had the misfortune to enter the country were made prisoners and flung before the horses, who devoured them.

When Heracles arrived he first captured the cruel Diomedes himself, and then threw him before his own mares, who, after devouring their master, became perfectly tame and tractable. They were then led by Heracles to the sea-shore, when the Bistonians, enraged at the loss of their king, rushed after the hero and attacked him. He now gave the animals in charge of his friend Abderus, and made such a furious onslaught on his assailants that they turned and fled.

But on his return from this encounter he found, to his great grief, that the mares had torn his friend in pieces and devoured him. After celebrating due funereal rites to the unfortunate Abderus, Heracles built a city in his honour, which he named after him. He then returned to Tiryns, where he delivered up the mares to Eurystheus, who set them loose on Mount Olympus, where they became the prey of wild beasts.

It was after the performance of this task that Heracles joined the Argonauts in their expedition to gain possession of the Golden Fleece, and was left behind at Chios, as already narrated. During his wanderings he undertook his ninth labour, which was to bring to Eurystheus the girdle of Hippolyte, queen of the Amazons.

9. The Girdle of Hippolyte.—The Amazons, who dwelt on the shores of the Black Sea, near the river Thermodon, were a nation of warlike women, renowned for their strength, courage, and great skill in horsemanship. Their queen, Hippolyte, had received from her father, Ares, a beautiful girdle, which she always wore as a sign of her royal power and authority, and it was this girdle which Heracles was required to place in the hands of Eurystheus, who designed it as a gift for his daughter Admete.

Foreseeing that this would be a task of no ordinary difficulty the hero called to his aid a select band of brave companions, with whom he embarked for the Amazonian town Themiscyra. Here they were met by queen Hippolyte, who was so impressed by the extraordinary stature and noble bearing of Heracles that, on learning his errand, she at once consented to present him with the coveted girdle. But Hera, his implacable enemy, assuming the form of an Amazon, spread the report in the town that a stranger was about to carry off their queen. The Amazons at once flew to arms and mounted their horses, whereupon a battle ensued, in which many of their bravest warriors were killed or wounded. Among the latter was their most skilful leader, Melanippe, whom Heracles afterwards restored to Hippolyte, receiving the girdle in exchange.

On his voyage home the hero stopped at Troy, where a new adventure awaited him.

During the time that Apollo and Poseidon were condemned by Zeus to a temporary servitude on earth, they built for king Laomedon the famous walls of Troy, afterwards so renowned in history; but when their work was completed the king treacherously refused to give them the reward due to them. The incensed deities now combined to punish the offender. Apollo sent a pestilence which decimated the people, and Poseidon a flood, which bore with it a marine monster, who swallowed in his huge jaws all that came within his reach.

In his distress Laomedon consulted an oracle, and was informed that only by the sacrifice of his own daughter Hesione could the anger of the gods be appeased. Yielding at length to the urgent appeals of his people he consented to make the sacrifice, and on the arrival of Heracles the maiden was already chained to a rock in readiness to be devoured by the monster.

When Laomedon beheld the renowned hero, whose marvellous feats of strength and courage had become the wonder and admiration of all mankind, he earnestly implored him to save his daughter from her impending fate, and to rid the country of the monster, holding out to him as a reward the horses which Zeus had presented to his grandfather Tros in compensation for robbing him of his son Ganymede.

Heracles unhesitatingly accepted the offer, and when the monster appeared, opening his terrible jaws to receive his prey, the hero, sword in hand, attacked and slew him. But the perfidious monarch once more broke faith, and Heracles, vowing future vengeance, departed for Mycenæ, where he presented the girdle to Eurystheus.

10. The Oxen of Geryones.—The tenth labour of Heracles was the capture of the magnificent oxen belonging to the giant Geryon or Geryones, who dwelt on the island of Erythia in the bay of Gadria (Cadiz). This giant, who was the son of Chrysaor, had three bodies with three heads, six hands, and six feet. He possessed a herd of splendid cattle, which were famous for their size, beauty, and rich red colour. They were guarded by another giant named Eurytion, and a two-headed dog called Orthrus, the offspring of Typhon and Echidna.

In choosing for him a task so replete with danger, Eurystheus was in hopes that he might rid himself for ever of his hated cousin. But the indomitable courage of the hero rose with the prospect of this difficult and dangerous undertaking.

After a long and wearisome journey he at last arrived at the western coast of Africa, where, as a monument of his perilous expedition, he erected the famous "Pillars of Hercules," one of which he placed on each side of the Straits of Gibraltar. Here he found the intense heat so insufferable that he angrily raised his bow towards heaven, and threatened to shoot the sun-god. But Helios, far from being incensed at his audacity, was so struck with admiration at his daring that he lent to him the golden boat with which he accomplished his nocturnal transit from West to East, and thus Heracles crossed over safely to the island of Erythia.

No sooner had he landed than Eurytion, accompanied by his savage dog Orthrus, fiercely attacked him; but Heracles, with a superhuman effort, slew the dog and then his master. Hereupon he collected the herd, and was proceeding to the sea-shore when Geryones himself met him, and a desperate encounter took place, in which the giant perished.

Heracles then drove the cattle into the sea, and seizing one of the oxen by the horns, swam with them over to the opposite coast of Iberia (Spain). Then driving his magnificent prize before him through Gaul, Italy, Illyria, and Thrace, he at length arrived, after many perilous adventures and hair-breadth escapes, at Mycenæ, where he delivered them up to Eurystheus, who sacrificed them to Hera.

Heracles had now executed his ten tasks, which had been accomplished in the space of eight years; but Eurystheus refused to include the slaying of the Hydra and the cleansing of the stables of Augeas among the number, alleging as a reason that the one had been performed by the assistance of Iolaus, and that the other had been executed for hire. He therefore insisted on Heracles substituting two more labours in their place.

11. The Apples of the Hesperides.—The eleventh task imposed by Eurystheus was to bring him the golden apples of the Hesperides, which grew on a tree presented by Gæa to Hera, on the occasion of her marriage with Zeus. This sacred tree was guarded by four maidens, daughters of Night, called the Hesperides, who were assisted in their task by a terrible hundred-headed dragon. This dragon never slept, and out of its hundred throats came a constant hissing sound, which effectually warned off all intruders. But what rendered the undertaking still more difficult was the complete ignorance of the hero as to the locality of the garden, and he was forced, in consequence, to make many fruitless journeys and to undergo many trials before he could find it.

He first travelled through Thessaly and arrived at the river Echedorus, where he met the giant Cycnus, the son of Ares and Pyrene, who challenged him to single combat. In this encounter Heracles completely vanquished his opponent, who was killed in the contest; but now a mightier adversary appeared on the scene, for the war-god himself came to avenge his son. A terrible struggle ensued, which had lasted some time, when Zeus interfered between the brothers, and put an end to the strife by hurling a thunderbolt between them.

Heracles proceeded on his journey, and reached the banks of the river Eridanus, where dwelt the Nymphs, daughters of Zeus and Themis. On seeking advice from them as to his route, they directed him to the old sea-god Nereus, who alone knew the way to the Garden of the Hesperides. Heracles found him asleep, and seizing the opportunity, held him so firmly in his powerful grasp that he could not possibly escape, so that notwithstanding his various metamorphoses he was at last compelled to give the information required. The hero then crossed over to Libya, where he engaged in a wrestling-match with king Anteos, son of Poseidon and Gæa, which terminated fatally for his antagonist.

From thence he proceeded to Egypt, where reigned Busiris, another son of Poseidon, who (acting on the advice given by an oracle during a time of great scarcity) sacrificed all strangers to Zeus. When Heracles arrived he was seized and dragged to the altar; but the powerful demi-god burst asunder his bonds, and then slew Busiris and his son.

Resuming his journey he now wandered on through Arabia until he arrived at Mount Caucasus, where Prometheus groaned in unceasing agony. It was at this time that Heracles (as already related) shot the eagle which had so long tortured the noble and devoted friend of mankind. Full of gratitude for his deliverance, Prometheus instructed him how to find his way to that remote region in the far West where Atlas supported the heavens on his shoulders, near which lay the Garden of the Hesperides. He also warned Heracles not to attempt to secure the precious fruit himself, but to assume for a time the duties of Atlas, and to despatch him for the apples.

On arriving at his destination Heracles followed the advice of Prometheus. Atlas, who willingly entered into the arrangement, contrived to put the dragon to sleep, and then, having cunningly outwitted the Hesperides, carried off three of the golden apples, which he now brought to Heracles. But when the latter was prepared to relinquish his burden, Atlas, having once tasted the delights of freedom, declined to resume his post, and announced his intention of being himself the bearer of the apples to Eurystheus, leaving Heracles to fill his place. To this proposal the hero feigned assent, merely begging that Atlas would be kind enough to support the heavens for a few moments whilst he contrived a pad for his head. Atlas good-naturedly threw down the apples and once more resumed his load, upon which Heracles bade him adieu, and departed.

When Heracles conveyed the golden apples to Eurystheus the latter presented them to the hero, whereupon Heracles placed the sacred fruit on the altar of Pallas-Athene, who restored them to the garden of the Hesperides.

12. Cerberus.—The twelfth and last labour which Eurystheus imposed on Heracles was to bring up Cerberus from the lower world, believing that all his heroic powers would be unavailing in the Realm of Shades, and that in this, his last and most perilous undertaking, the hero must at length succumb and perish.

Cerberus was a monster dog with three heads, out of whose awful jaws dripped poison; the hair of his head and back was formed of venomous snakes, and his body terminated in the tail of a dragon.

After being initiated into the Eleusinian Mysteries, and obtaining from the priests certain information necessary for the accomplishment of his task, Heracles set out for Tænarum in Lacolia, where there was an opening which led to the under-world. Conducted by Hermes, he commenced his descent into the awful gulf, where myriads of shades soon began to appear, all of whom fled in terror at his approach, Meleager and Medusa alone excepted. About to strike the latter with his sword, Hermes interfered and stayed his hand, reminding him that she was but a shadow, and that consequently no weapon could avail against her.

Arrived before the gates of Hades he found Theseus and

Pirithöus, who had been fixed to an enchanted rock by Aïdes for their presumption in endeavouring to carry off Persephone. When they saw Heracles they implored him to set them free. The hero succeeded in delivering Theseus, but when he endeavoured to liberate Pirithöus, the earth shook so violently beneath him that he was compelled to relinquish his task.

Proceeding further Heracles recognized Ascalaphus, who, as we have seen in the history of Demeter, had revealed the fact that Persephone had swallowed the seeds of a pomegranate offered to her by her husband, which bound her to Aïdes for ever. Ascalaphus was groaning beneath a huge rock which Demeter in her anger had hurled upon him, and which Heracles now removed, releasing the sufferer.

Before the gates of his palace stood Aïdes the mighty ruler of the lower world, and barred his entrance; but Heracles, aiming at him with one of his unerring darts, shot him in the shoulder, so that for the first time the god experienced the agony of mortal suffering. Heracles then demanded of him permission to take Cerberus to the upper-world, and to this Aïdes consented on condition that he should secure him unarmed. Protected by his breastplate and lion's skin Heracles went in search of the monster, whom he found at the mouth of the river Acheron. Undismayed by the hideous barking which proceeded from his three heads, he seized the throat with one hand and the legs with the other, and although the dragon which served him as a tail bit him severely, he did not relinquish his grasp. In this manner he conducted him to the upper-world, through an opening near Troezen in Argolia.

When Eurystheus beheld Cerberus he stood aghast, and despairing of ever getting rid of his hated rival, he returned the hell-hound to the hero, who restored him to Aïdes, and with this last task the subjection of Heracles to Eurystheus terminated.

Murder of Iphitus.—Free at last Heracles now returned to Thebes; and it being impossible for him to live happily with

Megara in consequence of his having murdered her children he, with her own consent, gave her in marriage to his nephew Iolaus. Heracles himself sought the hand of Iole, daughter of Eurytus, king of Œchalia, who had instructed him when a boy in the use of the bow. Hearing that this king had promised to give his daughter to him who could surpass himself and his three sons in shooting with the bow, Heracles lost no time in presenting himself as a competitor. He soon proved that he was no unworthy pupil of Eurytus, for he signally defeated all his opponents. But although the king treated him with marked respect and honour he refused, nevertheless, to give him the hand of his daughter, fearing for her a similar fate to that which had befallen Megara. Iphitus, the eldest son of Eurytus, alone espoused the cause of Heracles, and essayed to induce his father to give his consent to the marriage; but all to no purpose, and at length, stung to the quick at his rejection, the hero angrily took his departure.

Soon afterwards the oxen of the king were stolen by the notorious thief Autolycus, and Heracles was suspected by Eurytus of having committed the theft. But Iphitus loyally defended his absent friend, and proposed to seek out Heracles, and with his assistance to go in search of the missing cattle.

The hero warmly welcomed his staunch young friend, and entered cordially into his plan. They at once set out on their expedition; but their search proved altogether unsuccessful. When they approached the city of Tiryns they mounted a tower in hopes of discovering the missing herd in the surrounding country; but as they stood on the topmost summit of the building, Heracles became suddenly seized with one of his former attacks of madness, and mistaking his friend Iphitus for an enemy, hurled him down into the plain below, and he was killed on the spot.

Heracles now set forth on a weary pilgrimage, begging in vain that some one would purify him from the murder of Iphitus. It was during these wanderings that he arrived at the palace of his friend Admetus, whose beautiful and heroic wife (Alcestes) he restored to her husband after a terrible struggle with Death, as already related.

Soon after this event Heracles was struck with a fearful disease, and betook himself to the temple of Delphi, hoping to obtain from the oracle the means of relief. The priestess, however, refused him a response on the ground of his having murdered Iphitus, whereupon the angry hero seized upon the tripod, which he carried off, declaring that he would construct an oracle for himself. Apollo, who witnessed the sacrilege, came down to defend his sanctuary, and a violent struggle ensued. Zeus once more interfered, and, flashing his lightnings between his two favourite sons, ended the combat. The Pythia now vouchsafed an answer to the prayer of the hero, and commanded him, in expiation of his crime, to allow himself to be sold by Hermes for three years as a slave, the purchase-money to be given to Eurytus in compensation for the loss of his son.

Heracles becomes the Slave of Omphale.—Heracles bowed in submission to the divine will, and was conducted by Hermes to Omphale, queen of Lydia. The three talents which she paid for him were given to Eurytus, who, however, declined to accept the money, which was handed over to the children of Iphitus.

Heracles now regained his former vigour. He rid the territory of Omphale of the robbers which infested it and performed for her various other services requiring strength and courage. It was about this time that he took part in the Calydonian boar-hunt, details of which have already been given.

When Omphale learned that her slave was none other than the renowned Heracles himself she at once gave him his liberty, and offered him her hand and kingdom. In her palace Heracles abandoned himself to all the enervating luxuries of an oriental life, and so completely was the great hero enthralled by the fascination which his mistress exercised over him, that whilst she playfully donned his lion's skin and helmet, he, attired in female garments, sat at her feet spinning wool, and beguiling the time by the relation of his past adventures.

But when at length, his term of bondage having expired, he became master of his own actions, the manly and energetic spirit of the hero reasserted itself, and tearing himself away from the palace of the Mæonian queen, he determined to carry out the revenge he had so long meditated against the treacherous Laomedon and the faithless Augeas.

Heracles executes vengeance on Laomedon and Augeas.— Gathering round him some of his old brave companions-in-arms, Heracles collected a fleet of vessels and set sail for Troy, where he landed, took the city by storm, and killed Laomedon, who thus met at length the retribution he had so richly deserved.

To Telamon, one of his bravest followers, he gave Hesione, the daughter of the king, in marriage. When Heracles gave her permission to release one of the prisoners of war she chose her own brother Podarces, whereupon she was informed that as he was already a prisoner of war she would be compelled to ransom him. On hearing this Hesione took off her golden diadem, which she joyfully handed to the hero. Owing to this circumstance Podarces henceforth bore the name of Priamus (or Priam), which signifies the "ransomed one."

Heracles now marched against Augeas to execute his vengeance on him also for his perfidious conduct. He stormed the city of Elis and put to death Augeas and his sons, sparing only his brave advocate and staunch defender Phyleus, on whom he bestowed the vacant throne of his father.

Heracles and Deianeira.—Heracles now proceeded to Calydon, where he wooed the beautiful Deianeira, daughter of Œneus, king of Ætolia; but he encountered a formidable rival in Achelous, the river-god, and it was agreed that their claims should be decided by single combat. Trusting to his power of assuming various forms at will, Achelous felt confident of success; but this availed him nothing, for having at last transformed himself into a bull, his mighty adversary broke off one of his horns, and compelled him to acknowledge himself defeated.

After passing three happy years with Deianeira an unfortunate accident occurred, which for a time marred their felicity. Heracles was one day present at a banquet given by Œneus, when, by a sudden swing of his hand, he had the misfortune to strike on the head a youth of noble birth, who, according to the custom of the ancients, was serving the guests at table, and so violent was the blow that it caused his death. The father of the unfortunate youth, who had witnessed the occurrence, saw that it was the result of accident, and therefore absolved the hero from blame. But Heracles resolved to act according to the law of the land, banished himself from the country, and bidding farewell to his father-in-law, set out for Trachin to visit his friend King Ceyx, taking with him his wife Deianeira, and his young son Hyllus.

In the course of their journey they arrived at the river Evenus, over which the Centaur Nessus was in the habit of carrying travellers for hire. Heracles, with his little son in his arms, forded the stream unaided, intrusting his wife to the care of the Centaur, who, charmed with the beauty of his fair burden, attempted to carry her off. But her cries were heard by her husband, who without hesitation shot Nessus through the heart with one of his poisoned arrows. Now the dying Centaur was thirsting for revenge. He called Deianeira to his side, and directed her to secure some of the blood which flowed from his wound, assuring her that if, when in danger of losing her husband's affection, she used it in the manner indicated by him, it would act as a charm, and prevent her from being supplanted by a rival. Heracles and Deianeira now pursued their journey, and after several adventures at length arrived at their destination.

Death of Heracles.—The last expedition undertaken by the great hero was against Eurytus, king of Œchalia, to revenge himself upon this king and his sons for having refused to bestow upon him the hand of Iole, after having fairly won the maiden. Having collected a large army Heracles set out for Eubœa in order to besiege Œchalia, its capital. Success crowned his arms. He stormed the citadel, slew the king and his three sons, reduced the town to ashes, and carried away captive the young and beautiful Iole.

Returning from his victorious expedition, Heracles halted at Cenœus in order to offer a sacrifice to Zeus, and sent to Deianeira to Trachin for a sacrificial robe. Deianeira having been informed that the fair Iole was in the train of Heracles was fearful lest her youthful charms might supplant her in the affection of her husband, and calling to mind the advice of the dying Centaur, she determined to test the efficacy of the love-charm which he had given to her. Taking out the phial which she had carefully preserved, she imbued the robe with a portion of the liquid which it contained, and then sent it to Heracles.

The victorious hero clothed himself with the garment, and was about to perform the sacrifice, when the hot flames rising from the altar heated the poison with which it was imbued, and soon every fibre of his body was penetrated by the deadly venom. The unfortunate hero, suffering the most fearful tortures, endeavoured to tear off the robe, but it adhered so closely to the skin that all his efforts to remove it only increased his agonies.

In this pitiable condition he was conveyed to Trachin, where Deianeira, on beholding the terrible suffering of which she was the innocent cause, was overcome with grief and remorse, and hanged herself in despair. The dying hero called his son Hyllus to his side, and desired him to make Iole his wife, and then ordering his followers to erect a funeral pyre, he mounted it and implored the by-standers to set fire to it, and thus in mercy to terminate his insufferable torments. But no one had the courage to obey him, until at last his friend and companion Philoctetes, yielding to his piteous appeal, lighted the pile, and received in return the bow and arrows of the hero.

Soon flames on flames ascended, and amidst vivid flashes of lightning, accompanied by awful peals of thunder, Pallas-Athene descended in a cloud, and bore her favourite hero in a chariot to Olympus.

Heracles became admitted among the immortals; and Hera, in token of her reconciliation, bestowed upon him the hand of her beautiful daughter Hebe, the goddess of eternal youth.

BELLEROPHON.

Bellerophon, or Bellerophontes, was the son of Glaucus, king of Corinth, and grandson of Sisyphus. In consequence of an unpremeditated murder Bellerophon fled to Tiryns, where he was kindly received by King Prœtus, who purified him from his crime. Antea, the wife of Prœtus, was so charmed with the comely youth that she fell in love with him; but Bellerophon did not return her affection, and she, in revenge, slandered him to the king by a gross misrepresentation of the facts.

The first impulse of Prœtus, when informed of the conduct of Bellerophon, was to kill him; but the youth, with his gentle and winning manners, had so endeared himself to his host that he felt it impossible to take his life with his own hands. He therefore sent him to his father-in-law, Iobates, king of Lycia, with a kind of letter or tablet which contained mysterious signs, indicating his desire that the bearer of the missive should be put to death. But the gods watched over the true and loyal youth, and inclined the heart of Iobates, who was an amiable prince, towards his guest. Judging by his appearance that he was of noble birth, he entertained him, according to the hospitable custom of the Greeks, in the most princely manner for nine days, and not until the morning of the tenth did he inquire his name and errand.

Bellerophon now presented to him the letter intrusted

to him by Prœtus. Iobates, who had become greatly attached to the youth, was horror-struck at its contents. Nevertheless he concluded that Prœtus must have good reasons for his conduct, and that probably Bellerophon had committed a crime which deserved death. But as he could not make up his mind to murder the guest he had grown to esteem, he decided to despatch him upon dangerous enterprises, in which he would in all probability lose his life.

He first sent him to kill the Chimæra, a monster which was at this time devastating the country. The fore part of its body was that of a lion, the centre of a goat, and the hind part of a dragon; whilst out of its jaws issued flames of fire.

Before starting on this difficult task Bellerophon invoked the protection of the gods, and in answer to his prayer they despatched to his aid the immortal-winged horse Pegasus, the offspring of Poseidon and Medusa. But the divine animal would not suffer himself to be caught, and at last, worn out with his fruitless exertions, Bellerophon fell into a deep sleep beside the sacred spring Pirene. Here Pallas-Athene appeared to him in a dream, and presented him with a magic bridle for the purpose of capturing the divine steed. On awaking Bellerophon instinctively put out his hand to grasp it, when, to his amazement, there lay beside him the bridle of his dream, whilst Pegasus was quietly drinking at the fountain close by. Seizing him by the mane Bellerophon threw the bridle over his head, and succeeded in mounting him without further difficulty; then rising with him into the air he slew the Chimæra with his arrows.

Iobates next sent him on an expedition against the Solymans, a fierce neighbouring tribe with whom he was at enmity. Bellerophon succeeded in vanquishing them, and was then despatched against the much-dreaded Amazons; but greatly to the astonishment of Iobates the hero again returned victorious.

Finally, Iobates placed a number of the bravest Lycians in ambush for the purpose of destroying him, but not one returned alive, for Bellerophon bravely defended himself and slew them all. Convinced at length that Bellerophon, far from deserving death, was the special favourite of the gods, who had evidently protected him throughout his perilous exploits, the king now ceased his persecutions.

Iobates admitted him to a share in the government, and gave him his daughter in marriage. But Bellerophon having attained the summit of earthly prosperity became intoxicated with pride and vanity, and incurred the displeasure of the gods by endeavouring to mount to heaven on his winged horse, for the purpose of gratifying his idle curiosity. Zeus punished him for his impiety by sending a gadfly to sting the horse, who became so restive that he threw his rider, who was precipitated to the earth. Filled with remorse at having offended the gods Bellerophon fell a prey to the deepest melancholy, and wandered about for the remainder of his life in the loneliest and most desolate places.

After death he was honoured in Corinth as a hero, and an altar was erected to him in the grove of Poseidon.

THESEUS.

Aegeus, king of Athens, being twice married, and having no children, was so desirous of an heir to his throne that he made a pilgrimage to Delphi in order to consult the oracle. But the response being ambiguous, he repaired to Troezen to consult his wise friend Pittheus, who reigned over that city, by whose advice he contracted a secret marriage with his friend's daughter Aethra.

After passing some time with his bride, Aegeus prepared to take his departure for his own dominions; but before doing so he led Aethra to the sea-shore, where, after depositing his sword and sandals under a huge rock, he thus addressed her: "Should the gods bless our union with a son, do not reveal to him the name and rank of his father until he is old enough to possess the strength requisite for moving this stone. Then send him to my palace at Athens bearing these tokens of his identity."

A son was born to Aethra, whom she called Theseus, and who was carefully trained and educated by his grandfather Pittheus. When he had developed into a strong and manly youth his mother conducted him to the spot where the rock had been placed by Aegeus, and at her command he rolled away the stone, and took possession of the sword and sandals which had lain there for sixteen years, and which she now desired him to convey to his father Aegeus, king of Athens.

His mother and grandfather were anxious that the youth should travel by the safe sea route, the road between Troezen and Athens being at this time infested with robbers of great ferocity and enormous strength. But feeling within himself the spirit of a hero, Theseus resolved to emulate the deeds of Heracles, with whose fame all Greece resounded, and therefore chose the more dangerous journey by land, as calculated to afford him an opportunity of distinguishing himself by feats of valour.

His first adventure occurred at Epidaurus, where he met Periphetes, a son of Hephæstus, who was armed with an iron club, with which he killed all travellers. Having received from his grandfather a full description of this savage, Theseus at once recognized him, and rushing upon him with his sword, succeeded after a desperate encounter in killing him. He appropriated the club as a trophy of his victory, and proceeded on his journey without hinderance until he arrived at the Isthmus of Corinth.

Here the people warned him to beware of Sinnis the robber, who forced all travellers to bend with him one of the branches of a tall pine-tree. Having dragged it to the ground, the cruel Sinnis suddenly released his hold, whereupon the bough rebounding high up into the air, the unfortunate victim was dashed to the ground and killed. When Theseus beheld Sinnis advancing towards him he steadily awaited his approach;

then seizing his powerful club, he killed the inhuman wretch with one blow.

Passing through the woody district of Crommyon Theseus next slew a wild and dangerous sow which had long ravaged the country.

He then continued his journey and approached the borders of Megara, where, on a narrow path overhanging the sea, dwelt the wicked Scyron, another terror to travellers. It was his custom to compel all strangers who passed his abode to wash his feet, during which operation he kicked them over the rock into the sea. Theseus boldly attacked the giant, overcame him, and then flung his body over the cliff where so many of his victims had perished.

Theseus now journeyed on to Eleusis, where he found another adversary in the person of King Cercyon, who forced all comers to wrestle with him, and killed those whom he vanquished; but Theseus overcame the mighty wrestler and slew him.

Near Eleusis, on the banks of the river Cephissus, Theseus met with a new adventure. Here lived the giant Damastes, called Procrustes or the Stretcher, who had two iron beds, one being long and the other short, into which he forced all strangers; In the short one he placed the tall men, whose limbs he cut to the size of the bed, whilst to the short ones he assigned the large bed, stretching them out to fit it; and thus he left his victims to expire in the most cruel torments. Theseus freed the country from this inhuman monster by serving him as he had done his unfortunate victims.

The hero now continued his journey, and at length reached Athens without meeting with any further adventures. When he arrived at his destination he found his father a helpless tool in the hands of the sorceress Medea, whom he had married after her departure from Corinth. Knowing, by means of her supernatural powers, that Theseus was the king's son, and fearing that her influence might be weakened by his presence, she poisoned the mind of the old king against the stranger, whom she represented as being a spy. It was accordingly arranged that Theseus should be invited to a banquet, and a strong poison mixed with his wine.

Now Theseus had resolved to reveal himself at this feast to the father whom he yearned to embrace. Before tasting the wine he put his plan into execution, and drew out his sword so that the eyes of the king might rest upon it. When Aegeus beheld once more the well-known weapon which he had so often wielded, he knew that it was his son who stood before him. He warmly embraced him, presented him as his heir to his courtiers and subjects, and then, no longer able to endure the sight of Medea, he banished her for ever from his dominions.

When Theseus was acknowledged as the rightful heir to the throne he was opposed by the fifty sons of Pallas, the king's brother, who had confidently expected that on the demise of the old king the government of the country would devolve upon them. They therefore resolved to put Theseus to death; but their plans becoming known to him, he surprised them as they lay in ambush awaiting his approach, and destroyed them all.

Fearing, however, lest the Athenians might entertain a prejudice against him on account of his extermination of their fellow-citizens, the Pallantids, Theseus resolved to perform some signal service for the state, which should gain for him the hearts of the people. He accordingly decided to rid the country of the famous bull of Marathon, which had become a terror to the cultivators of the land. He captured the animal and brought him in chains to Athens, where, after publicly exhibiting him to the astonished multitude, he solemnly sacrificed him to Apollo.

The next enterprise undertaken by Theseus far surpassed all his other feats of heroic daring, and secured to him the universal admiration and gratitude of his fellow-citizens. This was the slaying of the Minotaur, which put an end for ever to the shameful tribute of seven youths and seven maidens which was exacted from the Athenians every nine years.

The origin of this barbarous tribute was as follows: Androgeos, the youthful son of Minos, king of Crete, having been treacherously murdered by the Athenians, his father, anxious to avenge the death of his son, declared war against their king Aegeus, and conquered Athens and the villages in its vicinity. The conqueror henceforth compelled the Athenians to send to him every nine years a tribute of seven youths and seven maidens of the noblest families of the land, who became the prey of the Minotaur, a monster, half-man, half-bull, whose lair was in the wonderful labyrinth, constructed by Dædalus for the Cretan king.

When Theseus informed his father of his heroic determination, he was overwhelmed with grief, and endeavoured, by every means in his power, to shake his son's resolution, but, confident of success, Theseus assured his father that he would slay the Minotaur and return home victorious.

It was customary for the vessel bearing its unhappy freight of human victims to use on this voyage black sails only; but Theseus promised his father that, should he return in safety, he would hoist white ones in their place.

Before leaving Athens Theseus, by the advice of an oracle, chose Aphrodite as his guardian and protectress, and accordingly offered up a sacrifice to her. When he arrived in the presence of king Minos, the goddess of Love inspired Ariadne, the beautiful daughter of the king, with an ardent attachment for the noble young hero. During a secret interview, in which a mutual confession of affection took place, Ariadne furnished him with a sharp sword and a clue of thread, the end of which she desired him to fasten at the entrance to the labyrinth and to continue to unwind it till he reached the lair of the Minotaur. Full of hope as to the successful issue of his undertaking, Theseus took leave of the kind maiden, after expressing his gratitude for her timely aid.

At the head of his companions he was now conducted by Minos to the entrance of the labyrinth. Strictly adhering to the injunctions of the fair Ariadne he succeeded in finding the Minotaur, whom, after a fierce and violent struggle, he defeated and killed; then carefully feeling his way, by means of the clue of thread, he led his companions safely out of the labyrinth. They then fled to their ship, taking with them the lovely maiden to whose affection for their deliverer they owed their safety.

Arrived at the island of Naxos, Theseus had a dream, in which Dionysus, the wine-god, appeared to him, and informed him that the Fates had decreed that Ariadne should be his bride, at the same time menacing the hero with all kinds of misfortunes should he refuse to resign her. Now Theseus, having been taught from his youth to reverence the gods, feared to disobey the wishes of Dionysus. He accordingly took a sad farewell of the beautiful maiden who so tenderly loved him, and left her on the lonely island, where she was found and wooed by the wine-god.

Theseus and his companions felt keenly the loss of their benefactress, and in their grief at parting with her, forgot that the ship still bore the black sails with which she had left the Attic coast. As she neared the port of Athens, Aegeus, who was anxiously awaiting the return of his son on the beach, caught sight of the vessel with its black sails, and concluding that his gallant son had perished, threw himself in despair into the sea.

With the unanimous approval of the Athenians, Theseus now ascended the vacant throne, and soon proved himself to be not only a valiant hero but also a wise prince and prudent legislator. Athens was at this time but a small city surrounded by a number of villages, each of which possessed its own separate form of government; but by means of kind and concil-iatory measures Theseus induced the heads of these different communities to resign their sovereignty, and to intrust the administration of public affairs to a court which should sit constantly at Athens, and exercise jurisdiction over all the inhabitants of Attica. The result of these judicious measures was, that the Athenians became a united and powerful people, and that numbers of strangers and foreigners flocked to Athens, which became a flourishing maritime port and a commercial centre of great importance.

Theseus renewed the Isthmian Games, and also instituted numerous festivals, the principal of which was the Panathenæa, held in honour of Athene-Polias.

It is related that Theseus upon one occasion arrived during a voyage at the Amazonian coast. Anxious to ascertain the object of his visit, the Amazons sent Hippolyte, one of their number, with presents to the stranger; but no sooner did the fair herald set foot on board his vessel than Theseus set sail and carried her off to Athens, where he made her his queen. Enraged at this indignity the Amazons determined to be revenged. Some time afterwards, when the whole affair would appear to have been forgotten, they seized the opportunity when the city of Athens was in a defenceless condition and landed an army in Attica. So sudden was their attack that they had penetrated into the very heart of the city before the Athenians could organize their forces; but Theseus expeditiously collected his troops and commenced such a furious onslaught upon the invaders that, after a desperate encounter, they were driven from the city. Peace was then concluded, whereupon the Amazons evacuated the country. During this engagement Hippolyte, forgetful of her origin, fought valiantly by the side of her husband against her own kinsfolk, and perished on the field of battle.

It was soon after this sad event that Theseus joined the world-renowned Calydonian Boar-hunt, in which he took a leading part. He also formed one of the brave band who shared in the perils of the Argonautic expedition.

The remarkable friendship which existed between Theseus and Pirithöus originated under such peculiar circumstances that it is worthy of mention.

Hearing upon one occasion that his herds, pasturing in the plains of Marathon, had been carried off by Pirithöus, Theseus collected together an armed force and sallied forth to punish the plunderer. But, when the two heroes met face to face, both were seized with an impulse of sympathetic admiration for each other. Pirithöus, holding out his hand in token of peace, exclaimed, "What satisfaction shall I render thee, oh Theseus? Be thou thyself the judge." Theseus seized the proffered hand and replied, "I ask nought save thy friendship;" whereupon the heroes embraced each other and swore eternal fidelity.

When, soon afterwards, Pirithöus became united to Hippodamia, a Thessalian princess, he invited Theseus to the wedding-feast, which was also attended, among other guests, by a large number of Centaurs, who were friends of Pirithöus. Towards the end of the banquet Eurytion, a young Centaur, heated and flushed with wine, seized the lovely bride and sought by force to carry her off. The other Centaurs, following his example, each endeavoured to capture a maiden. Pirithöus and his followers, aided by Theseus, who rendered most valuable assistance, attacked the Centaurs, and after a violent hand-to-hand struggle in which many perished, forced them to relinquish their prey.

After the death of Hippolyte Theseus sought the hand of Phædra, the sister of his former bride Ariadne, to whom he became united. For some years they lived happily together, and their union was blessed by the birth of two sons. During this time Hippolytus, the son of the Amazonian queen, had been absent from home, having been placed under the care of the king's uncles in order to be educated. When, having grown to manhood, he now returned to his father's palace, his young stepmother, Phædra, fell violently in love with him; but Hippolytus failed to return her affection, and treated her with contempt and indifference. Filled with rage and despair at his coldness Phædra put an end to her existence; and when she was discovered by her husband she held in her hand a letter, accusing Hippolytus of being the cause of her death, and of having conspired against the honour of the king.

Now Poseidon had upon one occasion promised to grant Theseus whatever request he should demand; he therefore called upon the sea-god to destroy Hippolytus, whom he cursed in the most solemn manner. The father's awful malediction fell but too soon upon his innocent son; for, as the latter was driving his chariot along the sea-shore, between Troezen and Athens, a monster, sent by Poseidon, rose out of the deep, and so frightened the horses that they became altogether unmanageable. As they rushed on in their mad career the chariot was dashed to pieces, and the unfortunate youth, whose feet had become entangled in the reins, was dragged along until life was nearly extinct.

In this condition he was found by the unhappy Theseus, who, having ascertained the true facts of the case from an old servant of Phædra, had hastened to prevent the catastrophe. But he arrived too late, and was only able to soothe the last moments of his dying son by acknowledging the sad mistake which he had committed, and declaring his firm belief in his honour and innocence.

After these events Theseus was persuaded by his friend Pirithöus, who had also about this time lost his young wife, Hippodamia, to join him in a journey through Greece, with the object of carrying off by force the most beautiful maidens whom they should chance to meet.

Arrived at Sparta they beheld, in the temple of Artemis, Helen, the daughter of Zeus and Leda, who was engaged in performing sacred dances in honour of the goddess. Although the maiden was only nine years old the fame of her beauty, which was destined to play so important a part in the history of Greece, had already spread far and wide. Theseus and Pirithöus forcibly abducted her, and then having cast lots for her, she fell to Theseus, who placed her under the charge of his mother Æthra.

Pirithöus now requested Theseus to assist him in his ambitious scheme of descending to the lower world and carrying off Persephone, the queen of Hades. Though fully alive to the perils of the undertaking Theseus would not forsake his friend, and together they sought the gloomy realm of Shades. But Aïdes had been forewarned of their approach, and scarcely had the two friends set foot within his dominions when, by his orders, they were seized, bound with chains, and secured to an enchanted rock at the entrance of Hades. Here the two friends languished for many years, until Heracles passed by in his search for Cerberus, when he released Theseus; but in obedience to an injunction of the gods, left Pirithöus to endure for ever the punishment of his too daring ambition.

While Theseus was imprisoned in the under world Castor and Pollux, the brothers of Helen, invaded Athens, and demanded the restoration of their young sister. Seeing his country threatened with the horrors of warfare, an Athenian citizen named Academus, who knew of Helen's place of conceal-ment, repaired to the camp of the Dioscuri, and informed them where they would find her. Æthra at once resigned her charge, whereupon the brothers took leave of Athens, and, accompanied by Helen, returned to their native country.

But the prolonged absence of Theseus gave rise to other troubles of a more serious character. Thinking the opportunity favourable for a revolt, a faction, headed by Menesthius, a descendant of Erechtheus, arrogated to themselves supreme power, and seized the reins of government.

Returned to Athens, Theseus at once took active meas-ures to quell the insubordination which existed on all sides. He expelled Menesthius from office, rigorously punished the ringleaders of the revolt, and placed himself once more upon the throne. But his hold upon the people was gone. His former services were all forgotten, and, finding at length that dissen-sions and revolts were rife, he voluntarily abdicated the throne, and retired to his estates in the island of Scyros. Here

Lycomedes, king of the island, feigned to receive him with the utmost friendship; but being, as it is supposed, in league with Menesthius, he led the old king to the summit of a high rock, under pretence of showing him his estates, and treacherously killed him by pushing him over the cliff.

Many centuries after his death, by the command of the oracle of Delphi, Cimon, the father of Miltiades, at the conclusion of the Persian war, brought the remains of Theseus, the great benefactor of Athens, to that city, and in his honour a temple was erected, which exists to the present day, and serves as a museum of art.

ŒDIPUS.

Laius, king of Thebes, the son of Labdacus, and a direct descendant of Cadmus, was married to Jocaste, the daughter of a noble Theban. An oracle having foretold that he would perish by the hand of his own son, he determined to destroy the infant to whom Jocaste had just given birth. With the consent of his wife, whose affection for her husband overcame her love for her child, he pierced the feet of the babe, bound them together, and handed the infant over to a servant, with instructions to expose him on Mount Cithæron to perish. But instead of obeying this cruel command, the servant intrusted him to a shepherd who was tending the flocks of Polybus, king of Corinth, and then returned to Laius and Jocaste, and informed them that their orders had been obeyed. The parents were satisfied with the intelligence, and quieted their conscience by the reflection that they had thus prevented their son from committing the crime of parricide.

Meanwhile the shepherd of king Polybus had unbound the feet of the infant, and in consequence of their being much swollen he called him Œdipus, or Swollen-foot. He then carried him to the king, his master, who, pitying the poor little waif, enlisted for him the kind offices of his wife, Merope. Œdipus was adopted by the king and queen as their own son, and grew up in the belief that they were his parents, until one day a Corinthian noble taunted him at a banquet with not being the son of the king. Stung at this reproach the youth appealed to Merope, but receiving an equivocal, though kindly answer, he repaired to Delphi to consult the oracle. The Pythia vouchsafed no reply to his inquiry, but informed him, to his horror, that he was fated to kill his father and to marry his own mother.

Filled with dismay, for he was tenderly attached to Polybus and Merope, Œdipus determined not to return to Corinth, and took instead the road leading to Bœotia. On his way a chariot passed him, in which sat an old man with two servants, who rudely pushed the pedestrian out of the path. In the scuffle which ensued Œdipus struck the old man with his heavy stick, and he fell back dead on the seat of the chariot. Struck with dismay at the unpremeditated murder which he had committed, the youth fled, and left the spot without learning that the old man whom he had killed was his father, Laius, king of Thebes.

Not long after this occurrence the Sphinx (full details of whom have already been given) was sent by the goddess Hera as a punishment to the Thebans. Stationed on a rocky height just outside the city, she propounded to the passers by riddles which she had been taught by the Muses, and whoever failed to solve them was torn in pieces and devoured by the monster, and in this manner great numbers of the inhabitants of Thebes had perished.

Now on the death of the old king Laius, Creon, the brother of the widowed queen, had seized the reins of government and mounted the vacant throne; and when at length his own son fell a victim to the Sphinx, he resolved at all costs to rid the country of this fearful scourge. He accordingly issued a proclamation, that the kingdom and the hand of his sister Jocaste should be awarded to him who should succeed in solving one of the riddles of the Sphinx, it having been foretold by an oracle that only then would the country be freed from the monster.

Just as this proclamation was being made in the streets of Thebes Œdipus, with his pilgrim's staff in his hand, entered the city. Tempted by the prospect of so magnificent a reward he repaired to the rock, and boldly requested the Sphinx to propound to him one of her riddles. She proposed to him one which she deemed impossible of solution, but Œdipus at once solved it; whereupon the Sphinx, full of rage and despair, precipitated herself into the abyss and perished. Œdipus received the promised reward. He became king of Thebes and the husband of Jocaste, the widow of his father, king Laius.

For many years Œdipus enjoyed the greatest happiness and tranquillity. Four children were born to him—two sons, Eteocles and Polynices, and two daughters, Antigone and Ismene. But at last the gods afflicted the country with a grievous pestilence, which made terrible havoc among the people. In their distress they entreated the help of the king, who was regarded by his subjects as a special favourite of the gods. Œdipus consulted an oracle, and the response was that the pestilence would continue to rage until the land was purified of the blood of king Laius, whose murderer was living unpunished at Thebes.

The king now invoked the most solemn imprecations on the head of the murderer, and offered a reward for any information concerning him. He then sent for the blind old seer Tiresias, and implored him, by means of his prophetic powers, to reveal to him the author of the crime. Tiresias at first hesitated, but yielding to the earnest solicitations of the king, the old prophet thus addressed him: "Thou thyself art the murderer of the old king Laius, who was thy father; and thou art wedded to his widow, thine own mother." In order to convince Œdipus of the truth of his words, he brought forward the old servant who had exposed him as a babe on Mount Cithæron, and the shepherd who had conveyed him to king Polybus. Horrified at this awful revelation Œdipus, in a fit of despair, deprived himself of sight, and the unfortunate Jocaste, unable to survive her disgrace, hanged herself.

Accompanied by his faithful and devoted daughter Antigone, Œdipus quitted Thebes and became a miserable and homeless outcast, begging his bread from place to place. At length, after a long and painful pilgrimage, he found a place of refuge in the grove of the Eumenides (at Colonus, near Athens), where his last moments were soothed and tended by the care and devotion of the faithful Antigone.

THE SEVEN AGAINST THEBES.

After the voluntary abdication of Œdipus, his two sons, Eteocles and Polynices, took possession of the crown and reigned over the city of Thebes. But Eteocles, being an ambitious prince, soon seized the reins of government himself, and expelled his brother from the throne.

Polynices now repaired to Argos, where he arrived in the dead of night. Outside the gates of the royal palace he encountered Tydeus, the son of Œneus, king of Calydon. Having accidentally killed a relative in the chase, Tydeus was also a fugitive; but being mistaken by Polynices in the darkness for an enemy, a quarrel ensued, which might have ended fatally, had not king Adrastus, aroused by the clamour, appeared on the scene and parted the combatants.

By the light of the torches borne by his attendants Adrastus observed, to his surprise, that on the shield of Polynices a lion was depicted, and on that of Tydeus a boar. The former bore this insignia in honour of the renowned hero Heracles, the latter in memory of the famous Calydonian boar-hunt. This circumstance reminded the king of an extraordinary oracular prediction concerning his two beautiful daughters, Argia and Deipyle, which was to the effect that he would give them in marriage to a lion and a boar. Hailing with delight what he regarded as an auspicious solution of the mysterious prophecy, he invited the strangers into his palace; and when he heard their history, and had convinced

263

himself that they were of noble birth, he bestowed upon Polynices his beautiful daughter Argia, and upon Tydeus the fair Deipyle, promising at the same time that he would assist both his sons-in-law to regain their rightful patrimony.

The first care of Adrastus was to aid Polynices in regaining possession of his lawful share in the government of Thebes. He accordingly invited the most powerful chiefs in his kingdom to join in the expedition, all of whom readily obeyed the call with the exception of the king's brother-in-law, Amphiaraus, the seer. As he foresaw a disastrous termination to the enterprise, and knew that not one of the heroes, save Adrastus himself, would return alive, he earnestly dissuaded the king from carrying out his project, and declined to take any part in the undertaking. But Adrastus, seconded by Polynices and Tydeus, was obstinately bent on the achievement of his purpose, and Amphiaraus, in order to escape from their importunities, concealed himself in a hiding-place known only to his wife Eriphyle.

Now on the occasion of the marriage of Amphiaraus it had been agreed, that if he ever differed in opinion with the king, his wife should decide the question. As the presence of Amphiaraus was indispensable to the success of the under-taking, and, moreover, as Adrastus would not enter upon it without "the eye of the army," as he called his brother-in-law, Polynices, bent on securing his services, determined to bribe Eriphyle to use her influence with her husband and to decide the question in accordance with his wishes. He bethought himself of the beautiful necklace of Harmonia, wife of Cadmus, which he had brought with him in his flight from Thebes. Without loss of time he presented himself before the wife of Amphiaraus, and held up to her admiring gaze the glittering bauble, promising that if she revealed the hiding-place of her husband and induced him to join the expedition, the necklace should be hers. Eriphyle, unable to withstand the tempting bait, accepted the bribe, and thus Amphiaraus was compelled to join the army. But before leaving his home he extorted a solemn promise from his son Alcmæon that, should he perish on the field of battle, he would avenge his death on his mother, the perfidious Eriphyle.

Seven leaders were now chosen, each at the head of a separate detachment of troops. These were Adrastus the king, his two brothers Hippomedon and Parthenopæus, Capaneus his nephew, Polynices and Tydeus, and Amphiaraus.

When the army was collected they set out for Nemea, which was at this time governed by king Lycurgus. Here the Argives, being short of water, halted on the outskirts of a forest in order to search for a spring, when they saw a majestic and beautiful woman seated on the trunk of a tree, nursing an infant. They concluded from her noble and queenly appearance that she must be a goddess, but were informed by her that she was Hypsipile, queen of the Lemnians, who had been carried away captive by pirates, and sold as a slave to king Lycurgus, and that she was now acting as nurse to his infant son. When the warriors told her that they were in search of water, she laid the child down in the grass, and led them to a secret spring in the forest, with which she alone was acquainted. But on their return they found, to their grief, that the unfortunate babe had been killed during their absence, by a serpent. They slew the reptile, and then collecting the remains of the infant, they buried them with funereal honours and proceeded on their way.

The warlike host now appeared before the walls of Thebes, and each leader placed himself before one of the seven gates of the city in readiness for the attack. Eteocles, in conjunction with Creon, had made due preparations to repel the invaders, and had stationed troops, under the command of trusty leaders, to guard each of the gates. Then, according to the practice of the ancients of consulting sooth-sayers before entering upon any undertaking, the blind old seer Tiresias was sent for, who, after carefully taking the auguries from the flight of birds, declared that all efforts to defend the city would prove unavailing, unless the youngest descendant of the house of Cadmus would offer himself as a voluntary sacrifice for the good of the state.

When Creon heard the words of the seer his first thought was of his favourite son Menœceus, the youngest scion of the royal house, who was present at the interview. He therefore earnestly implored him to leave the city, and to repair for safety to Delphi. But the gallant youth heroically resolved to sacrifice his life for the benefit of his country, and after taking leave of his old father, mounted the city walls, and plunging a dagger into his heart, perished in the sight of the contending hosts.

Adrastus now gave his troops the word of command to storm the city, and they rushed forward to the attack with great valour. The battle raged long and furiously, and after heavy losses on both sides the Argives were routed and put to flight.

After the lapse of some days they reorganized their forces, and again appeared before the gates of Thebes, when Eteocles, grieved to think that there should be such a terrible loss of life on his account, sent a herald into the opposite camp, with a proposition that the fate of the campaign should be decided by single combat between himself and his brother Polynices. The challenge was readily accepted, and in the duel which took place outside the city walls, in the sight of the rival forces, Eteocles and Polynices were both fatally wounded and expired on the field of battle.

Both sides now claimed the day, and the result was that hostilities recommenced, and soon the battle raged with greater fury than ever. But victory at last declared itself for the Thebans. In their flight the Argives lost all their leaders, Adrastus excepted, who owed his safety to the fleetness of his horse Arion.

By the death of the brothers, Creon became once more king of Thebes, and in order to show his abhorrence of the conduct of Polynices in fighting against his country, he strictly forbade any one to bury either his remains or those of his allies. But the faithful Antigone, who had returned to Thebes on the death of her father, could not endure that the body of her brother should remain unburied. She therefore bravely disregarded the orders of the king, and endeavoured to give sepulture to the remains of Polynices.

When Creon discovered that his commands had been set at defiance, he inhumanly condemned the devoted maiden to be entombed alive in a subterranean vault. But retribution was at hand. His son, Hæmon, who was betrothed to Antigone, having contrived to effect an entrance into the vault, was horrified to find that Antigone had hanged herself by her veil. Feeling that life without her would be intolerable, he threw himself in despair on his own sword, and after solemnly invoking the malediction of the gods on the head of his father, expired beside the dead body of his betrothed.

Hardly had the news of the tragic fate of his son reached the king, before another messenger appeared, bearing the tidings that his wife Eurydice, on hearing of the death of Hæmon, had put an end to her existence, and thus the king found himself in his old age both widowed and childless.

Nor did he succeed in the execution of his vindictive designs; for Adrastus, who, after his flight from Thebes, had taken refuge at Athens, induced Theseus to lead an army against the Thebans, to compel them to restore the dead bodies of the Argive warriors to their friends, in order that they might perform due funereal rites in honour of the slain. This undertaking was successfully accomplished, and the remains of the fallen heroes were interred with due honours.

THE EPIGONI.

Ten years after these events the sons of the slain heroes, who were called Epigoni, or descendants, resolved to avenge the death of their fathers, and with this object entered upon a new expedition against the city of Thebes.

By the advice of the Delphic oracle the command was intrusted to Alcmæon, the son of Amphiaraus; but remembering the injunction of his father he hesitated to accept this post before executing vengeance on his mother Eriphyle. Thersander, however, the son of Polynices, adopting similar tactics to those of his father, bribed Eriphyle with the beautiful veil of Harmonia, bequeathed to him by Polynices, to induce her son Alcmæon and his brother Amphilochus to join in this second war against Thebes.

Now the mother of Alcmæon was gifted with that rare fascination which renders its possessor irresistible to all who may chance to come within its influence; nor was her own son able to withstand her blandishments. Yielding therefore to her wily representations he accepted the command of the troops, and at the head of a large and powerful army advanced upon Thebes.

Before the gates of the city Alcmæon encountered the Thebans under the command of Laodamas, the son of Eteocles. A fierce battle ensued, in which the Theban leader, after performing prodigies of valour, perished by the hand of Alcmæon.

After losing their chief and the flower of their army, the Thebans retreated behind the city walls, and the enemy now pressed them hard on every side. In their distress they appealed to the blind old seer Tiresias, who was over a hundred years old. With trembling lips and in broken accents, he informed them that they could only save their lives by abandoning their native city with their wives and families. Upon this they despatched ambassadors into the enemy's camp; and whilst these were protracting negotiations during the night, the Thebans, with their wives and children, evacuated the city. Next morning the Argives entered Thebes and plundered it, placing Thersander, the son of Polynices (who was a descendant of Cadmus), on the throne which his father had so vainly contested.

ALCMÆON AND THE NECKLACE.

When Alcmæon returned from his expedition against the Thebans he determined to fulfil the last injunction of his father Amphiaraus, who had desired him to be revenged on his mother Eriphyle for her perfidy in accepting a bribe to betray him. This resolution was further strengthened by the discovery that his unprincipled mother had urged him also to join the expedition in return for the much-coveted veil of Harmonia. He therefore put her to death; and taking with him the ill-fated necklace and veil, abandoned for ever the home of his fathers.

But the gods, who could not suffer so unnatural a crime to go unpunished, afflicted him with madness, and sent one of the Furies to pursue him unceasingly. In this unhappy condition he wandered about from place to place, until at last having reached Psophis in Arcadia, Phegeus, king of the country, not only purified him of his crime, but also bestowed upon him the hand of his daughter Arsinoë, to whom Alcmæon presented the necklace and veil, which had already been the cause of so much unhappiness.

Though now released from his mental affliction, the curse which hung over him was not entirely removed, and on his account the country of his adoption was visited with a severe drought. On consulting the oracle of Delphi he was informed that any land which offered him shelter would be cursed by the gods, and that the malediction would continue to follow him till he came to a country which was not in existence at the time he had murdered his mother. Bereft of hope, and resolved no longer to cast the shadow of his dark fate over those he loved, Alcmæon took a tender leave of his wife and little son, and became once more an outcast and wanderer.

Arrived after a long and painful pilgrimage at the river Achelous, he discovered, to his unspeakable joy, a beautiful and fertile island, which had but lately emerged from beneath the water. Here he took up his abode; and in this haven of rest he was at length freed from his sufferings, and finally purified of his crime by the river-god Achelous. But in his new-found home where prosperity smiled upon him, Alcmæon soon forgot the loving wife and child he had left behind, and wooed Calirrhoë, the beautiful daughter of the river-god, who became united to him in marriage.

For many years Alcmæon and Calirrhoë lived happily together, and two sons were born to them. But unfortunately for the peace of her husband, the daughter of Achelous had heard of the celebrated necklace and veil of Harmonia, and became seized with a violent desire to become the possessor of these precious treasures.

Now the necklace and veil were in the safe-keeping of Arsinoë; but as Alcmæon had carefully concealed the fact of his former marriage from his young wife, he informed her, when no longer able to combat her importunities, that he had concealed them in a cave in his native country, and promised to hasten thither and procure them for her. He accordingly took leave of Calirrhoë and his children, and proceeded to Psophis, where he presented himself before his deserted wife and her father, king Phegeus. To them he excused his absence by the fact of his having suffered from a fresh attack of madness, and added that an oracle had foretold to him that his malady would only be cured when he had deposited the necklace and veil of Harmonia in the temple of Apollo at Delphi. Arsinoë, deceived by his artful representations, unhesitatingly restored to him his bridal gifts, whereupon Alcmæon set out on his homeward journey, well satisfied with the successful issue of his expedition.

But the fatal necklace and veil were doomed to bring ruin and disaster to all who possessed them. During his sojourn at the court of king Phegeus, one of the servants who had accompanied Alcmæon betrayed the secret of his union with the daughter of the river-god; and when the king informed his sons of his treacherous conduct, they determined to avenge the wrongs of their sister Arsinoë. They accordingly concealed themselves at a point of the road which Alcmæon was compelled to pass, and as he neared the spot they suddenly emerged from their place of ambush, fell upon him and despatched him.

When Arsinoë, who still loved her faithless husband, heard of the murder, she bitterly reproached her brothers for the crime which they had perpetrated, at which they were so incensed, that they placed her in a chest, and conveyed her to Agapenor, son of Ancæus, at Tegea. Here they accused her of the murder of which they themselves were guilty, and she suffered a painful death.

Calirrhoë, on learning the sad fate of Alcmæon, implored Zeus that her infant sons might grow at once to manhood, and avenge the death of their father. The ruler of Olympus heard the petition of the bereaved wife, and, in answer to her prayer, the children of yesterday became transformed into bearded men, full of strength and courage, and thirsting for revenge.

Hastening to Tegea, they there encountered the sons of Phegeus, who were about to repair to Delphi, in order to deposit the necklace and veil in the sanctuary of Apollo; and before the brothers had time to defend themselves, the stalwart sons of Calirrhoë rushed upon them and slew them. They then proceeded to Psophis, where they killed king Phegeus and his wife, after which they returned to their mother with the necklace and veil, which, by the command of her father Achelous, were deposited as sacred offerings in the temple of Apollo at Delphi.

THE HERACLIDÆ.

After the apotheosis of Heracles, his children were so cruelly persecuted by Eurystheus, that they fled for protection to king Ceyx at Trachin, accompanied by the aged Iolaus, the nephew and life-long friend of their father, who constituted himself their guide and protector. But on Eurystheus demanding the surrender of the fugitives, the Heraclidæ, knowing that the small force at the disposal of king Ceyx would be altogether inadequate to protect them against the powerful king of Argos, abandoned his territory, and sought refuge at Athens, where they were hospitably received by king Demophoön, the son of the great hero Theseus. He warmly espoused their cause, and determined to protect them at all costs against Eurystheus, who had despatched a numerous force in pursuit of them.

When the Athenians had made all necessary preparations to repel the invaders, an oracle announced that the sacrifice of a maiden of noble birth was necessary to ensure to them victory; whereupon Macaria, the beautiful daughter of Heracles and Deianira, magnanimously offered herself as a sacrifice, and, surrounded by the noblest matrons and maidens of Athens, voluntarily devoted herself to death.

While these events were transpiring in Athens, Hyllus, the eldest son of Heracles and Deianira, had advanced with a large army to the assistance of his brothers, and having sent a messenger to the king announcing his arrival, Demophoön, with his army, joined his forces.

In the thick of the battle which ensued, Iolaus, following a sudden impulse, borrowed the chariot of Hyllus, and earnestly entreated Zeus and Hebe to restore to him, for this one day only, the vigour and strength of his youth. His prayer was heard. A thick cloud descended from heaven and enveloped the chariot, and when it disappeared, Iolaus, in the full plenitude of manly vigour, stood revealed before the astonished gaze of the combatants. He then led on his valiant band of warriors, and soon the enemy was in headlong flight; and Eurystheus, who was taken prisoner, was put to death by the command of king Demophoön.

After gratefully acknowledging the timely aid of the Athenians, Hyllus, accompanied by the faithful Iolaus and his brothers, took leave of king Demophoön, and proceeded to invade the Peloponnesus, which they regarded as their lawful patrimony; for, according to the will of Zeus, it should have been the rightful possession of their father, the great hero Heracles, had not Hera maliciously defeated his plans by causing his cousin Eurystheus to precede him into the world.

For the space of twelve months the Heraclidæ contrived to maintain themselves in the Peloponnesus; but at the expiration of that time a pestilence broke out, which spread over the entire peninsula, and compelled the Heraclidæ to evacuate the country and return to Attica, where for a time they settled.

After the lapse of three years Hyllus resolved on making another effort to obtain his paternal inheritance. Before setting out on the expedition, however, he consulted the oracle of Delphi, and the response was, that he must wait for the third fruit before the enterprise would prove successful. Interpreting this ambiguous reply to signify the third summer, Hyllus controlled his impatience for three years, when, having collected a powerful army, he once more entered the Peloponnesus.

At the isthmus of Corinth he was opposed by Atreus, the son of Pelops, who at the death of Eurystheus had inherited the kingdom. In order to save bloodshed, Hyllus offered to decide his claims by single combat, the conditions being, that if he were victorious, he and his brothers should obtain undisputed possession of their rights; but if defeated, the Heraclidæ were to desist for fifty years from attempting to press their claim.

The challenge was accepted by Echemon, king of Tegea, and Hyllus lost his life in the encounter, whereupon the sons of Heracles, in virtue of their agreement, abandoned the Peloponnesus and retired to Marathon.

Hyllus was succeeded by his son Cleodæus, who, at the expiration of the appointed time, collected a large army and invaded the Peloponnesus; but he was not more successful than his father had been, and perished there with all his forces.

Twenty years later his son Aristomachus consulted an oracle, which promised him victory if he went by way of the defile. The Heraclidæ once more set out, but were again defeated, and Aristomachus shared the fate of his father and grandfather, and fell on the field of battle.

When, at the expiration of thirty years, the sons of Aristomachus, Temenus, Cresphontes, and Aristodemus again consulted the oracle, the answer was still the same; but this time the following explanation accompanied the response: the third fruit signified the third generation, to which they themselves belonged, and not the third fruit of the earth; and by the defile was indicated, not the isthmus of Corinth, but the straits on the right of the isthmus.

Temenus lost no time in collecting an army and building ships of war; but just as all was ready and the fleet about to sail, Aristodemus, the youngest of the brothers, was struck by lightning. To add to their misfortunes, Hippolytes, a descendant of Heracles, who had joined in the expedition, killed a soothsayer whom he mistook for a spy, and the gods, in their displeasure, sent violent tempests, by means of which the entire fleet was destroyed, whilst famine and pestilence decimated the ranks of the army.

The oracle, on being again consulted, advised that Hippolytes, being the offender, should be banished from the country for ten years, and that the command of the troops should be delegated to a man having three eyes. A search was at once instituted by the Heraclidæ for a man answering to this description, who was found at length in the person of Oxylus, a descendant of the Ætolian race of kings. In obedience to the command of the oracle, Hippolytes was banished, an army and fleet once more equipped, and Oxylus elected commander-in-chief.

And now success at length crowned the efforts of the long-suffering descendants of the great hero. They obtained possession of the Peloponnesus, which was divided among them by lot. Argos fell to Temenus, Lacedæmon to Aristodemus, and Messene to Cresphontes. In gratitude for the services of their able leader, Oxylus, the kingdom of Elis, was conferred upon him by the Heraclidæ.

THE SIEGE OF TROY.

Troy or Ilion was the capital of a kingdom in Asia Minor, situated near the Hellespont, and founded by Ilus, son of Tros. At the time of the famous Trojan war this city was under the government of Priam, a direct descendant of Ilus. Priam was married to Hecuba, daughter of Dymas, king of Thrace; and among the most celebrated of their children were the renowned and valiant Hector, the prophetess Cassandra, and Paris, the cause of the Trojan war.

Before the birth of her second son Paris, Hecuba dreamt that she had given birth to a flaming brand, which was interpreted by Æsacus the seer (a son of Priam by a former marriage) to signify that she would bear a son who would cause the destruction of the city of Troy. Anxious to prevent the fulfilment of the prophecy, Hecuba caused her new-born babe to be exposed on Mount Ida to perish; but being found by some kind-hearted shepherds, the child was reared by them, and grew up unconscious of his noble birth.

As the boy approached manhood he became remarkable, not only for his wonderful beauty of form and feature, but also for his strength and courage, which he exercised in defending the flocks from the attacks of robbers and wild beasts; hence he was called Alexander, or helper of men. It was about this time that he settled the famous dispute concerning the golden apple, thrown by the goddess of Discord into the assembly of the gods. As we have already seen, he gave his decision in favour of Aphrodite; thus creating for himself two implacable enemies, for Hera and Athene never forgave the slight.

Paris became united to a beautiful nymph named Œnone, with whom he lived happily in the seclusion and tranquillity of a pastoral life; but to her deep grief this peaceful existence was not fated to be of long duration.

Hearing that some funereal games were about to be held in Troy in honour of a departed relative of the king, Paris resolved to visit the capital and take part in them himself. There he so greatly distinguished himself in a contest with his unknown brothers, Hector and Deiphobus, that the proud young princes, enraged that an obscure shepherd should snatch from them the prize of victory, were about to create a disturbance, when Cassandra, who had been a spectator of the proceedings, stepped forward, and announced to them that the humble peasant who had so signally defeated them was their own brother Paris. He was then conducted to the presence of his parents, who joyfully acknowledged him as their child; and amidst the festivities and rejoicings in honour of their new-found son the ominous prediction of the past was forgotten.

As a proof of his confidence, the king now intrusted Paris with a somewhat delicate mission. As we have already seen in the Legend of Heracles, that great hero conquered Troy, and after killing king Laomedon, carried away captive his beautiful daughter Hesione, whom he bestowed in marriage on his friend Telamon. But although she became princess of Salamis, and lived happily with her husband, her brother Priam never ceased to regret her loss, and the indignity which had been passed upon his house; and it was now proposed that Paris should be equipped with a numerous fleet, and proceed to Greece in order to demand the restoration of the king's sister.

Before setting out on this expedition, Paris was warned by Cassandra against bringing home a wife from Greece, and she predicted that if he disregarded her injunction he would bring inevitable ruin upon the city of Troy, and destruction to the house of Priam.

Under the command of Paris the fleet set sail, and arrived safely in Greece. Here the young Trojan prince first beheld Helen, the daughter of Zeus and Leda, and sister of the Dioscuri, who was the wife of Menelaus, king of Sparta, and the loveliest woman of her time. The most renowned heroes in Greece had sought the honour of her hand; but her stepfather, Tyndareus, king of Sparta, fearing that if he bestowed her in marriage on one of her numerous lovers he would make enemies of the rest, made it a stipulation that all suitors should solemnly swear to assist and defend the successful candidate, with all the means at their command, in any feud which might hereafter arise in connection with the marriage. He at length conferred the hand of Helen upon Menelaus, a warlike prince, devoted to martial exercises and the pleasures of the chase, to whom he resigned his throne and kingdom.

When Paris arrived at Sparta, and sought hospitality at the royal palace, he was kindly received by king Menelaus. At the banquet given in his honour, he charmed both host and hostess by his graceful manner and varied accomplishments, and specially ingratiated himself with the fair Helen, to whom he presented some rare and chaste trinkets of Asiatic manufacture.

Whilst Paris was still a guest at the court of the king of Sparta, the latter received an invitation from his friend Idomeneus, king of Crete, to join him in a hunting expedition; and Menelaus, being of an unsuspicious and easy temperament, accepted the invitation, leaving to Helen the duty of entertaining the distinguished stranger. Captivated by her surpassing loveliness, the Trojan prince forgot every sense of honour and duty, and resolved to rob his absent host of his beautiful wife. He accordingly collected his followers, and with their assistance stormed the royal castle, possessed himself of the rich treasures which it contained, and succeeded in carrying off its beautiful, and not altogether unwilling mistress.

They at once set sail, but were driven by stress of weather to the island of Crania, where they cast anchor; and it was not until some years had elapsed, during which time home and country were forgotten, that Paris and Helen proceeded to Troy.

Preparations for the War.—When Menelaus heard of the violation of his hearth and home he proceeded to Pylos, accompanied by his brother Agamemnon, in order to consult the wise old king Nestor, who was renowned for his great experience and state-craft. On hearing the facts of the case Nestor expressed it as his opinion that only by means of the combined efforts of all the states of Greece could Menelaus hope to regain Helen in defiance of so powerful a kingdom as that of Troy.

Menelaus and Agamemnon now raised the war-cry, which was unanimously responded to from one end of Greece to the other. Many of those who volunteered their services were former suitors of the fair Helen, and were therefore bound by their oath to support the cause of Menelaus; others joined from pure love of adventure, but one and all were deeply impressed with the disgrace which would attach to their country should such a crime be suffered to go unpunished. Thus a powerful army was collected in which few names of note were missing.

Only in the case of two great heroes, Odysseus (Ulysses) and Achilles, did Menelaus experience any difficulty.

Odysseus, famed for his wisdom and great astuteness, was at this time living happily in Ithaca with his fair young wife Penelope and his little son Telemachus, and was loath to leave his happy home for a perilous foreign expedition of uncertain duration. When therefore his services were solicited he feigned madness; but the shrewd Palamedes, a distinguished hero in the suite of Menelaus, detected and exposed the ruse, and thus Odysseus was forced to join in the war. But he never forgave the interference of Palamedes, and, as we shall see, eventually revenged himself upon him in a most cruel manner.

Achilles was the son of Peleus and the sea-goddess Thetis, who is said to have dipped her son, when a babe, in the river Styx, and thereby rendered him invulnerable, except in the right heel, by which she held him. When the boy was nine years old it was foretold to Thetis that he would either enjoy a long life of inglorious ease and inactivity, or that after a brief career of victory he would die the death of a hero. Naturally desirous of prolonging the life of her son, the fond mother devoutly hoped that the former fate might be allotted to him. With this view she conveyed him to the island of Scyros, in the Ægean Sea, where, disguised as a girl, he was brought up among the daughters of Lycomedes, king of the country.

Now that the presence of Achilles was required, owing to an oracular prediction that Troy could not be taken without him, Menelaus consulted Calchas the soothsayer, who revealed to him the place of his concealment. Odysseus was accordingly despatched to Scyros, where, by means of a clever device, he soon discovered which among the maidens was the object of his search. Disguising himself as a merchant, Odysseus obtained an introduction to the royal palace, where he offered to the king's daughters various trinkets for sale. The girls, with one exception, all examined his wares with unfeigned interest. Observing this circumstance Odysseus shrewdly concluded that the one who held aloof must be none other than the young Achilles himself. But in order further to test the correctness of his deduction, he now exhibited a beautiful set of warlike accoutrements, whilst, at a given signal, stirring strains of martial music were heard outside; whereupon Achilles, fired with warlike ardour, seized the weapons, and thus revealed his identity. He now joined the cause of the Greeks, accompanied at the request of his father by his kinsman Patroclus, and contributed to the expedition a large force of Thessalian troops, or Myrmidons, as they were called, and also fifty ships.

For ten long years Agamemnon and the other chiefs devoted all their energy and means in preparing for the expedition against Troy. But during these warlike preparations an attempt at a peaceful solution of the difficulty was not neglected. An embassy consisting of Menelaus, Odysseus, &c., was despatched to king Priam demanding the surrender of Helen; but though the embassy was received with the utmost pomp and ceremony, the demand was nevertheless rejected; upon which the ambassadors returned to Greece, and the order was given for the fleet to assemble at Aulis, in Bœotia.

Never before in the annals of Greece had so large an army been collected. A hundred thousand warriors were assembled at Aulis, and in its bay floated over a thousand ships, ready to convey them to the Trojan coast. The command of this mighty host was intrusted to Agamemnon, king of Argos, the most powerful of all the Greek princes.

Before the fleet set sail solemn sacrifices were offered to the gods on the sea-shore, when suddenly a serpent was seen to ascend a plane-tree, in which was a sparrow's nest containing nine young ones. The reptile first devoured the young birds and then their mother, after which it was turned by Zeus into stone. Calchas the soothsayer, on being consulted, interpreted the miracle to signify that the war with Troy would last for nine years, and that only in the tenth would the city be taken.

Departure of the Greek Fleet.—The fleet then set sail; but mistaking the Mysian coast for that of Troy, they landed troops and commenced to ravage the country. Telephus, king of the Mysians, who was a son of the great hero Heracles, opposed them with a large army, and succeeded in driving them back to their ships, but was himself wounded in the engagement by the spear of Achilles. Patroclus, who fought valiantly by the side of his kinsman, was also wounded in this battle; but Achilles, who was a pupil of Chiron, carefully bound up the wound, which he succeeded in healing; and from this incident dates the celebrated friendship which ever after existed between the two heroes, who even in death remained united.

The Greeks now returned to Aulis. Meanwhile, the wound of Telephus proving incurable, he consulted an oracle, and the response was, that he alone who had inflicted the wound possessed the power of curing it. Telephus accordingly proceeded to the Greek camp, where he was healed by Achilles, and, at the solicitation of Odysseus, consented to act as guide in the voyage to Troy.

Just as the expedition was about to start for the second

time, Agamemnon had the misfortune to kill a hind sacred
to Artemis, who, in her anger, sent continuous calms, which
prevented the fleet from setting sail. Calchas on being
consulted announced that the sacrifice of Iphigenia, the
daughter of Agamemnon, would alone appease the incensed
goddess. How Agamemnon at length overcame his feelings as
a father, and how Iphigenia was saved by Artemis herself, has
been already related in a previous chapter.

A fair wind having at length sprung up, the fleet once
more set sail. They first stopped at the island of Tenedos,
where the famous archer Philoctetes—who possessed the bow
and arrows of Heracles, given to him by the dying hero—was
bitten in the foot by a venomous snake. So unbearable was
the odour emitted by the wound, that, at the suggestion of
Odysseus, Philoctetes was conveyed to the island of Lesbos,
where, to his great chagrin, he was abandoned to his fate,
and the fleet proceeded on their journey to Troy.

Commencement of Hostilities.—Having received early intelligence of the impending invasion of their country, the Trojans
sought the assistance of the neighbouring states, who all gallantly
responded to their call for help, and thus ample preparations
were made to receive the enemy. King Priam being himself too
advanced in years for active service, the command of the army
devolved upon his eldest son, the brave and valiant Hector.

At the approach of the Greek fleet the Trojans appeared
on the coast in order to prevent their landing. But great hesitation prevailed among the troops as to who should be the first
to set foot on the enemy's soil, it having been predicted that
whoever did so would fall a sacrifice to the Fates. Protesilaus
of Phylace, however, nobly disregarding the ominous prediction, leaped on shore, and fell by the hand of Hector.

The Greeks then succeeded in effecting a landing, and in
the engagement which ensued the Trojans were signally
defeated, and driven to seek safety behind the walls of their

city. With Achilles at their head the Greeks now made a desperate attempt to take the city by storm, but were repulsed with terrible losses. After this defeat the invaders, foreseeing a long and wearisome campaign, drew up their ships on land, erected tents, huts, &c., and formed an intrenched camp on the coast.

Between the Greek camp and the city of Troy was a plain watered by the rivers Scamander and Simois, and it was on this plain, afterwards so renowned in history, that the ever memorable battles between the Greeks and Trojans were fought.

The impossibility of taking the city by storm was now recognized by the leaders of the Greek forces. The Trojans, on their side, being less numerous than the enemy, dared not venture on a great battle in the open field; hence the war dragged on for many weary years without any decisive engagement taking place.

It was about this time that Odysseus carried out his long meditated revenge against Palamedes. Palamedes was one of the wisest, most energetic, and most upright of all the Greek heroes, and it was in consequence of his unflagging zeal and wonderful eloquence that most of the chiefs had been induced to join the expedition. But the very qualities which endeared him to the hearts of his countrymen rendered him hateful in the eyes of his implacable enemy, Odysseus, who never forgave his having detected his scheme to avoid joining the army.

In order to effect the ruin of Palamedes, Odysseus concealed in his tent a vast sum of money. He next wrote a letter, purporting to be from king Priam to Palamedes, in which the former thanked the Greek hero effusively for the valuable information received from him, referring at the same time to a large sum of money which he had sent to him as a reward. This letter, which was found upon the person of a Phrygian prisoner, was read aloud in a council of the Greek princes. Palamedes was arraigned before the chiefs of the army and accused of betraying his country to the enemy, whereupon a search was instituted, and a large sum of money being found in his tent, he was pronounced guilty and sentenced to be stoned to death. Though fully aware of the base treachery practised against him, Palamedes offered not a word in self-defence, knowing but too well that, in the face of such damning evidence, the attempt to prove his innocence would be vain.

Defection of Achilles.—During the first year of the campaign the Greeks ravaged the surrounding country, and pillaged the neighbouring villages. Upon one of these foraging expeditions the city of Pedasus was sacked, and Agamemnon, as commander-in-chief, received as his share of the spoil the beautiful Chrysëis, daughter of Chryses, the priest of Apollo; whilst to Achilles was allotted another captive, the fair Brisëis. The following day Chryses, anxious to ransom his daughter, repaired to the Greek camp; but Agamemnon refused to accede to his proposal, and with rude and insulting words drove the old man away. Full of grief at the loss of his child Chryses called upon Apollo for vengeance on her captor. His prayer was heard, and the god sent a dreadful pestilence which raged for ten days in the camp of the Greeks. Achilles at length called together a council, and inquired of Calchas the sooth-sayer how to arrest this terrible visitation of the gods. The seer replied that Apollo, incensed at the insult offered to his priest, had sent the plague, and that only by the surrender of Chrysëis could his anger be appeased.

On hearing this Agamemnon agreed to resign the maiden; but being already embittered against Calchas for his prediction with regard to his own daughter Iphigenia, he now heaped insults upon the soothsayer and accused him of plotting against his interests. Achilles espoused the cause of Calchas, and a violent dispute arose, in which the son of Thetis would have killed his chief but for the timely interference of Pallas-Athene, who suddenly appeared beside him, unseen by the rest, and recalled him to a sense of the duty he owed to his commander. Agamemnon revenged himself on Achilles by depriving him of his beautiful captive, the fair Brisëis, who had become so attached to her kind and noble captor that she wept bitterly on being removed from his charge. Achilles, now fairly disgusted with the ungenerous conduct of his chief, withdrew himself to his tent, and obstinately declined to take further part in the war.

Heart-sore and dejected he repaired to the sea-shore, and there invoked the presence of his divine mother. In answer to his prayer Thetis emerged from beneath the waves, and comforted her gallant son with the assurance that she would entreat the mighty Zeus to avenge his wrongs by giving victory to the Trojans, so that the Greeks might learn to realize the great loss which they had sustained by his withdrawal from the army. The Trojans being informed by one of their spies of the defection of Achilles, became emboldened by the absence of this brave and intrepid leader, whom they feared above all the other Greek heroes; they accordingly sallied forth, and made a bold and eminently successful attack upon the Greeks, who, although they most bravely and obstinately defended their position, were completely routed, and driven back to their intrenchments, Agamemnon and most of the other Greek leaders being wounded in the engagement.

Encouraged by this marked and signal success the Trojans now commenced to besiege the Greeks in their own camp. At this juncture Agamemnon, seeing the danger which threatened the army, sunk for the moment all personal grievances, and despatched an embassy to Achilles consisting of many noble and distinguished chiefs, urgently entreating him to come to the assistance of his countrymen in this their hour of peril; promising that not only should the fair Brisëis be restored to him, but also that the hand of his own daughter should be bestowed on him in marriage, with seven towns as her dowry. But the obstinate determination of the proud hero was not to be moved; and though he listened courteously to the arguments and representations of the messengers of Agamemnon, his resolution to take no further part in the war remained unshaken.

In one of the engagements which took place soon afterwards, the Trojans, under the command of Hector, penetrated into the heart of the Greek camp, and had already commenced to burn their ships, when Patroclus, seeing the distress of his countrymen, earnestly besought Achilles to send him to the rescue at the head of the Myrmidons. The better nature of the hero prevailed, and he not only intrusted to his friend the command of his brave band of warriors, but lent him also his own suit of armour.

Patroclus having mounted the war-chariot of the hero, Achilles lifted on high a golden goblet and poured out a libation of wine to the gods, accompanied by an earnest petition for victory, and the safe return of his beloved comrade. As a parting injunction he warned Patroclus against advancing too far into the territory of the enemy, and entreated him to be content with rescuing the galleys.

At the head of the Myrmidons Patroclus now made a desperate attack upon the enemy, who, thinking that the invincible Achilles was himself in command of his battalions, became disheartened, and were put to flight. Patroclus followed up his victory and pursued the Trojans as far as the walls of their city, altogether forgetting in the excitement of battle the injunction of his friend Achilles. But his temerity cost the young hero his life, for he now encountered the mighty Hector himself, and fell by his hands. Hector stripped the armour from his dead foe, and would have dragged the body into the city had not Menelaus and Ajax the Greater rushed forward, and after a long and fierce struggle succeeded in rescuing it from desecration.

Death of Hector.—And now came the mournful task of informing Achilles of the fate of his friend. He wept bitterly over the dead body of his comrade, and solemnly vowed that the funereal rites should not be solemnized in his honour until he had slain Hector with his own hands, and captured twelve Trojans to be immolated on his funeral pyre. All other considerations vanished before the burning desire to avenge the death of his friend; and Achilles, now thoroughly aroused from his apathy, became reconciled to Agamemnon, and rejoined the Greek army. At the request of the goddess Thetis, Hephæstus forged for him a new suit of armour, which far surpassed in magnificence that of all the other heroes.

Thus gloriously arrayed he was soon seen striding along, calling the Greeks to arms. He now led the troops against the enemy, who were defeated and put to flight until, near the gates of the city, Achilles and Hector encountered each other. But here, for the first time throughout his whole career, the courage of the Trojan hero deserted him. At the near approach of his redoubtable antagonist he turned and fled for his life. Achilles pursued him; and thrice round the walls of the city was the terrible race run, in sight of the old king and queen, who had mounted the walls to watch the battle. Hector endeavoured, during each course, to reach the city gates, so that his comrades might open them to admit him or cover him with their missiles; but his adversary, seeing his design, forced him into the open plain, at the same time calling to his friends to hurl no spear upon his foe, but to leave to him the vengeance he had so long panted for. At length, wearied with the hot pursuit, Hector made a stand and challenged his foe to single combat. A desperate encounter took place, in which Hector succumbed to his powerful adversary at the Scæan gate; and with his last dying breath the Trojan hero foretold to his conqueror that he himself would soon perish on the same spot.

The infuriated victor bound the lifeless corpse of his fallen foe to his chariot, and dragged it three times round the city walls and thence to the Greek camp. Overwhelmed with horror at this terrible scene the aged parents of Hector uttered such heart-rending cries of anguish that they reached the ears of

Andromache, his faithful wife, who, rushing to the walls, beheld the dead body of her husband, bound to the conqueror's car.

Achilles now solemnized the funereal rites in honour of his friend Patroclus. The dead body of the hero was borne to the funeral pile by the Myrmidons in full panoply. His dogs and horses were then slain to accompany him, in case he should need them in the realm of shades; after which Achilles, in fulfilment of his savage vow, slaughtered twelve brave Trojan captives, who were laid on the funeral pyre, which was now lighted. When all was consumed the bones of Patroclus were carefully collected and inclosed in a golden urn. Then followed the funereal games, which consisted of chariot-races, fighting with the cestus (a sort of boxing-glove), wrestling matches, foot-races, and single combats with shield and spear, in all of which the most distinguished heroes took part, and contended for the prizes.

Penthesilea.—After the death of Hector, their great hope and bulwark, the Trojans did not venture beyond the walls of their city. But soon their hopes were revived by the appearance of a powerful army of Amazons under the command of their queen Penthesilea, a daughter of Ares, whose great ambition was to measure swords with the renowned Achilles himself, and to avenge the death of the valiant Hector.

Hostilities now recommenced in the open plain. Penthesilea led the Trojan host; the Greeks on their side being under the command of Achilles and Ajax. Whilst the latter succeeded in putting the enemy to flight, Achilles was challenged by Penthesilea to single combat. With heroic courage she went forth to the fight; but even the strongest men failed before the power of the great Achilles, and though a daughter of Ares, Penthesilea was but a woman. With generous chivalry the hero endeavoured to spare the brave and beautiful maiden-warrior, and only when his own life was in imminent danger did he make a serious effort to vanquish his enemy, when

Penthesilea shared the fate of all who ventured to oppose the spear of Achilles, and fell by his hand.

Feeling herself fatally wounded, she remembered the desecration of the dead body of Hector, and earnestly entreated the forbearance of the hero. But the petition was hardly necessary, for Achilles, full of compassion for his brave but unfortunate adversary, lifted her gently from the ground, and she expired in his arms.

On beholding the dead body of their leader in the possession of Achilles, the Amazons and Trojans prepared for a fresh attack in order to wrest it from his hands; but observing their purpose, Achilles stepped forward and loudly called upon them to halt. Then in a few well-chosen words he praised the great valour and intrepidity of the fallen queen, and expressed his willingness to resign the body at once.

The chivalrous conduct of Achilles was fully appreciated by both Greeks and Trojans. Thersites alone, a base and cowardly wretch, attributed unworthy motives to the gracious proceedings of the hero; and, not content with these insinuations, he savagely pierced with his lance the dead body of the Amazonian queen; whereupon Achilles, with one blow of his powerful arm, felled him to the ground, and killed him on the spot.

The well-merited death of Thersites excited no commiseration, but his kinsman Diomedes came forward and claimed compensation for the murder of his relative; and as Agamemnon, who, as commander-in-chief, might easily have settled the difficulty, refrained from interfering, the proud nature of Achilles resented the implied condemnation of his conduct, and he once more abandoned the Greek army and took ship for Lesbos. Odysseus, however, followed him to the island, and, with his usual tact, succeeded in inducing the hero to return to the camp.

Death of Achilles.—A new ally of the Trojans now appeared on the field in the person of Memnon, the Æthiopian, a son of Eos and Tithonus, who brought with him a powerful reinforcement of negroes. Memnon was the first opponent who had yet encountered Achilles on an equal footing; for like the great hero himself he was the son of a goddess, and possessed also, like Achilles, a suit of armour made for him by Hephæstus.

Before the heroes encountered each other in single combat, the two goddesses, Thetis and Eos, hastened to Olympus to intercede with its mighty ruler for the life of their sons. Resolved even in this instance not to act in opposition to the Moiræ, Zeus seized the golden scales in which he weighed the lot of mortals, and placed in it the respective fates of the two heroes, whereupon that of Memnon weighed down the balance, thus portending his death.

Eos abandoned Olympus in despair. Arrived on the battlefield she beheld the lifeless body of her son, who, after a long and brave defence, had at length succumbed to the all-conquering arm of Achilles. At her command her children, the Winds, flew down to the plain, and seizing the body of the slain hero conveyed it through the air safe from the desecration of the enemy.

The triumph of Achilles was not of long duration. Intoxicated with success he attempted, at the head of the Greek army, to storm the city of Troy, when Paris, by the aid of Phœbus-Apollo, aimed a well-directed dart at the hero, which pierced his vulnerable heel, and he fell to the ground fatally wounded before the Scæan gate. But though face to face with death, the intrepid hero, raising himself from the ground, still performed prodigies of valour, and not until his tottering limbs refused their office was the enemy aware that the wound was mortal.

By the combined efforts of Ajax and Odysseus the body of Achilles was wrested from the enemy after a long and terrible fight, and conveyed to the Greek camp. Weeping bitterly over the untimely fate of her gallant son, Thetis came to embrace him for the last time, and mingled her regrets and lamentations with those of the whole Greek army. The funeral pyre was then lighted, and the voices of the Muses were heard chanting his funeral dirge. When, according to the custom of the ancients, the body had been burned on the pyre, the bones of the hero were collected, inclosed in a golden urn, and deposited beside the remains of his beloved friend Patroclus.

In the funereal games celebrated in honour of the fallen hero, the property of her son was offered by Thetis as the prize of victory. But it was unanimously agreed that the beautiful suit of armour made by Hephæstus should be awarded to him who had contributed the most to the rescue of the body from the hands of the enemy. Popular opinion unanimously decided in favour of Odysseus, which verdict was confirmed by the Trojan prisoners who were present at the engagement. Unable to endure the slight, the unfortunate Ajax lost his reason, and in this condition put an end to his existence.

Final Measures.—Thus were the Greeks deprived at one and the same time of their bravest and most powerful leader, and of him also who approached the nearest to this distinction. For a time operations were at a standstill, until Odysseus at length, contrived by means of a cleverly-arranged ambush to capture Helenus, the son of Priam. Like his sister Cassandra, Helenus possessed the gift of prophecy, and the unfortunate youth was now coerced by Odysseus into using this gift against the welfare of his native city.

The Greeks learned from the Trojan prince that three conditions were indispensable to the conquest of Troy:—In the first place the son of Achilles must fight in their ranks; secondly, the arrows of Heracles must be used against the enemy; and thirdly, they must obtain possession of the wooden image of Pallas-Athene, the famous Palladium of Troy.

The first condition was easily fulfilled. Ever ready to serve the interests of the community, Odysseus repaired to the island of Scyros, where he found Neoptolemus, the son of Achilles. Having succeeded in arousing the ambition of the fiery youth, he generously resigned to him the magnificent armour of his father, and then conveyed him to the Greek camp, where he immediately distinguished himself in single combat with Eurypylus, the son of Telephus, who had come to the aid of the Trojans.

To procure the poison-dipped arrows of Heracles was a matter of greater difficulty. They were still in the possession of the much-aggrieved Philoctetes, who had remained in the island of Lemnos, his wound still unhealed, suffering the most abject misery. But the judicious zeal of the indefatigable and ever-active Odysseus, who was accompanied in this under-taking by Diomedes, at length gained the day, and he induced Philoctetes to accompany him to the camp, where the skilful leech Machaon, the son of Asclepias, healed him of his wound.

Philoctetes became reconciled to Agamemnon, and in an engagement which took place soon after, he mortally wounded Paris, the son of Priam. But though pierced by the fatal arrow of the demi-god, death did not immediately ensue; and Paris, calling to mind the prediction of an oracle, that his deserted wife Œnone could alone cure him if wounded, caused himself to be transported to her abode on Mount Ida, where he implored her by the memory of their past love to save his life. But mindful only of her wrongs, Œnone crushed out of her heart every womanly feeling of pity and compassion, and sternly bade him depart. Soon, however, all her former affection for her husband awoke within her. With frantic haste she followed him; but on her arrival in the city she found the dead body of Paris already laid on the lighted funeral pile, and, in her remorse and despair, Œnone threw herself on the lifeless form of her husband and perished in the flames.

The Trojans were now shut up within their walls and closely besieged; but the third and most difficult condition being still unfulfilled, all efforts to take the city were unavailing. In this emergency the wise and devoted Odysseus came once more to the aid of his comrades. Having disfigured himself with self-inflicted wounds, he assumed the disguise of a wretched old mendicant, and then crept stealthily into the city in order to discover where the Palladium was preserved. He succeeded in his object, and was recognized by no one save the fair Helen, who after the death of Paris had been given in marriage to his brother Deiphobus. But since death had robbed her of her lover, the heart of the Greek princess had turned yearningly towards her native country and her husband Menelaus, and Odysseus now found in her a most unlooked-for ally. On his return to the camp Odysseus called to his aid the valiant Diomedes, and with his assistance the perilous task of abstracting the Palladium from its sacred precincts was, after some difficulty, effected.

The conditions of conquest being now fulfilled, a council was called to decide on final proceedings. Epeios, a Greek sculptor, who had accompanied the expedition, was desired to construct a colossal wooden horse large enough to contain a number of able and distinguished heroes. On its completion a band of warriors concealed themselves within, whereupon the Greek army broke up their camp, and then set fire to it, as though, wearied of the long and tedious ten years' siege, they had abandoned the enterprise as hopeless.

Accompanied by Agamemnon and the sage Nestor, the fleet set sail for the island of Tenedos, where they cast anchor, anxiously awaiting the torch signal to hasten back to the Trojan coast.

Destruction of Troy.—When the Trojans saw the enemy depart, and the Greek camp in flames, they believed themselves safe at last, and streamed in great numbers out of the town in order to view the site where the Greeks had so long encamped. Here they found the gigantic wooden horse, which they examined with wondering curiosity, various opinions being expressed with regard to its utility. Some supposed it to be an engine of war, and were in favour of destroying it, others regarded it as a sacred idol, and proposed that it should be brought into the city. Two circumstances which now occurred induced the Trojans to incline towards the latter opinion.

Chief among those who suspected a treacherous design in this huge contrivance was Laocoon, a priest of Apollo, who, in company with his two young sons, had issued from the city with the Trojans in order to offer a sacrifice to the gods. With all the eloquence at his command he urged his countrymen not to place confidence in any gift of the Greeks, and even went so far as to pierce the side of the horse with a spear which he took from a warrior beside him, whereupon the arms of the heroes were heard to rattle. The hearts of the brave men concealed inside the horse quailed within them, and they had already given themselves up for lost, when Pallas-Athene, who ever watched over the cause of the Greeks, now came to their aid, and a miracle occurred in order to blind and deceive the devoted Trojans;—for the fall of Troy was decreed by the gods.

Whilst Laocoon with his two sons stood prepared to perform the sacrifice, two enormous serpents suddenly rose out of the sea, and made direct for the altar. They entwined themselves first round the tender limbs of the helpless youths, and then encircled their father who rushed to their assistance, and thus all three were destroyed in sight of the horrified multitude. The Trojans naturally interpreted the fate of Laocoon and his sons to be a punishment sent by Zeus for his sacrilege against the wooden horse, and were now fully convinced that it must be consecrated to the gods.

The crafty Odysseus had left behind his trusty friend Sinon with full instructions as to his course of action. Assuming the rôle assigned to him, he now approached king Priam with fettered hands and piteous entreaties, alleging that the Greeks, in obedience to the command of an oracle, had attempted to immolate him as a sacrifice; but that he had contrived to escape from their hands, and now sought protection from the king.

The kind-hearted monarch, believing his story, released his bonds, assured him of his favour, and then begged him to explain the true meaning of the wooden horse. Sinon willingly complied. He informed the king that Pallas-Athene, who had hitherto been the hope and stay of the Greeks throughout the war, was so deeply offended at the removal of her sacred image, the Palladium, from her temple in Troy, that she had withdrawn her protection from the Greeks, and refused all further aid till it was restored to its rightful place. Hence the Greeks had returned home in order to seek fresh instructions from an oracle. But before leaving, Calchas the seer had advised their building this gigantic wooden horse as a tribute to the offended goddess, hoping thereby to appease her just anger. He further explained that it had been constructed of such colossal proportions in order to prevent its being brought into the city, so that the favour of Pallas-Athene might not be transferred to the Trojans.

Hardly had the crafty Sinon ceased speaking when the Trojans, with one accord, urged that the wooden horse should be brought into their city without delay. The gates being too low to admit its entrance, a breach was made in the walls, and the horse was conveyed in triumph into the very heart of Troy; whereupon the Trojans, overjoyed at what they deemed the successful issue of the campaign, abandoned themselves to feasting and rioting.

Amidst the universal rejoicing the unhappy Cassandra, foreseeing the result of the admission of the wooden horse into the city, was seen rushing through the streets with wild gestures and dishevelled hair, warning her people against the dangers which awaited them. But her eloquent words fell on deaf ears; for it was ever the fate of the unfortunate prophetess that her predictions should find no credence.

When, after the day's excitement, the Trojans had retired to rest, and all was hushed and silent, Sinon, in the dead of night, released the heroes from their voluntary imprisonment. The signal was then given to the Greek fleet lying off Tenedos, and the whole army in unbroken silence once more landed on the Trojan coast.

To enter the city was now an easy matter, and a fearful slaughter ensued. Aroused from their slumbers, the Trojans, under the command of their bravest leaders, made a gallant defence, but were easily overcome. All their most valiant heroes fell in the fight, and soon the whole city was wrapt in flames.

Priam fell by the hand of Neoptolemus, who killed him as he lay prostrate before the altar of Zeus, praying for divine assistance in this awful hour of peril. The unfortunate Andromache with her young son Astyanax had taken refuge on the summit of a tower, where she was discovered by the victors, who, fearing lest the son of Hector might one day rise against them to avenge the death of his father, tore him from her arms and hurled him over the battlements.

Æneas alone, the son of Aphrodite, the beloved of gods and men, escaped the universal carnage with his son and his old father Anchises, whom he carried on his shoulders out of the city. He first sought refuge on Mount Ida, and afterwards fled to Italy, where he became the ancestral hero of the Roman people.

Menelaus now sought Helen in the royal palace, who, being immortal, still retained all her former beauty and fascination. A reconciliation took place, and she accompanied her husband on his homeward voyage. Andromache, the widow of the brave Hector, was given in marriage to Neoptolemus, Cassandra fell to the share of Agamemnon, and Hecuba, the gray-haired and widowed queen, was made prisoner by Odysseus.

The boundless treasures of the wealthy Trojan king fell into the hands of the Greek heroes, who, after having levelled the city of Troy to the ground, prepared for their homeward voyage.

RETURN OF THE GREEKS FROM TROY.

During the sacking of the city of Troy the Greeks, in the hour of victory, committed many acts of desecration and cruelty, which called down upon them the wrath of the gods, for which reason their homeward voyage was beset with manifold dangers and disasters, and many perished before they reached their native land.

Nestor, Diomedes, Philoctetes, and Neoptolemus were among those who arrived safely in Greece after a prosperous voyage. The vessel which carried Menelaus and Helen was driven by violent tempests to the coast of Egypt, and only after many years of weary wanderings and vicissitudes did they succeed in reaching their home at Sparta.

Ajax the Lesser having offended Pallas-Athene by desecrating her temple on the night of the destruction of Troy, was shipwrecked off Cape Caphareus. He succeeded, however, in clinging to a rock, and his life might have been spared but for his impious boast that he needed not the help of the gods. No sooner had he uttered the sacrilegious words than Poseidon, enraged at his audacity, split with his trident the rock to which the hero was clinging, and the unfortunate Ajax was overwhelmed by the waves.

Fate of Agamemnon.—The homeward voyage of Agamemnon was tolerably uneventful and prosperous; but on his arrival at Mycenæ misfortune and ruin awaited him.

His wife Clytemnestra, in revenge for the sacrifice of her beloved daughter Iphigenia, had formed a secret alliance during his absence with Ægisthus, the son of Thyestes, and on the return of Agamemnon they both conspired to compass his destruction. Clytemnestra feigned the greatest joy on beholding her husband, and in spite of the urgent warnings of Cassandra, who was now a captive in his train, he received her protestations of affection with the most trusting confidence. In her well-assumed anxiety for the comfort of the weary traveller, she prepared a warm bath for his refreshment, and at a given signal from the treacherous queen, Ægisthus, who was concealed in an adjoining chamber, rushed upon the defenceless hero and slew him.

During the massacre of the retainers of Agamemnon which followed, his daughter Electra, with great presence of mind, contrived to save her young brother Orestes. He fled for refuge to his uncle Strophius, king of Phocis, who educated him with his own son Pylades, and an ardent friendship sprung up between the youths, which, from its constancy and disinterestedness, has become proverbial.

As Orestes grew up to manhood, his one great all-absorbing desire was to avenge the death of his father. Accompanied by his faithful friend Pylades, he repaired in disguise to Mycenæ, where Ægisthus and Clytemnestra reigned conjointly over the kingdom of Argos. In order to disarm suspicion he had taken the precaution to despatch a messenger to Clytemnestra, purporting to be sent by king Strophius, to announce to her the untimely death of her son Orestes through an accident during a chariot-race at Delphi.

Arrived at Mycenæ, he found his sister Electra so overwhelmed with grief at the news of her brother's death that to her he revealed his identity. When he heard from her lips how cruelly she had been treated by her mother, and how joyfully the news of his demise had been received, his long pent-up passion completely overpowered him, and rushing into the presence of the king and queen, he first pierced Clytemnestra to the heart, and afterwards her guilty partner.

But the crime of murdering his own mother was not long unavenged by the gods. Hardly was the fatal act committed when the Furies appeared and unceasingly pursued the unfortunate Orestes wherever he went. In this wretched plight he sought refuge in the temple of Delphi, where he earnestly besought Apollo to release him from his cruel tormentors. The god commanded him, in expiation of his crime, to repair to Taurica-Chersonnesus and convey the statue of Artemis from thence to the kingdom of Attica, an expedition fraught with extreme peril. We have already seen in a former chapter how Orestes escaped the fate which befell all strangers who landed on the Taurian coast, and how, with the aid of his sister Iphigenia, the priestess of the temple, he succeeded in conveying the statue of the goddess to his native country.

But the Furies did not so easily relinquish their prey, and only by means of the interposition of the just and powerful goddess Pallas-Athene was Orestes finally liberated from their persecution. His peace of mind being at length restored, Orestes assumed the government of the kingdom of Argos, and became united to the beautiful Hermione, daughter of Helen and Menelaus. On his faithful friend Pylades he bestowed the hand of his beloved sister, the good and faithful Electra.

Homeward Voyage of Odysseus.—With his twelve ships laden with enormous treasures, captured during the sacking of Troy, Odysseus set sail with a light heart for his rocky island home of Ithaca. At length the happy hour had arrived which for ten long years the hero had so anxiously awaited, and he little dreamt that ten more must elapse before he would be permitted by the Fates to clasp to his heart his beloved wife and child.

During his homeward voyage his little fleet was driven by stress of weather to a land whose inhabitants subsisted entirely on a curious plant called the lotus, which was sweet as honey to the taste, but had the effect of causing utter oblivion of home and country, and of creating an irresistible longing to remain for ever in the land of the lotus-eaters. Odysseus and his companions were hospitably received by the inhabitants, who regaled them freely with their peculiar and very delicious food; after partaking of which, however, the comrades of the hero refused to leave the country, and it was only by sheer force that he at length succeeded in bringing them back to their ships.

Polyphemus.—Continuing their journey, they next arrived at the country of the Cyclops, a race of giants remarkable for having only one eye, which was placed in the centre of their foreheads. Here Odysseus, whose love of adventure overcame more prudent considerations, left his fleet safely anchored in the bay of a neighbouring island, and with twelve chosen companions set out to explore the country.

Near the shore they found a vast cave, into which they boldly entered. In the interior they saw to their surprise huge piles of cheese and great pails of milk ranged round the walls. After partaking freely of these provisions his companions endeavoured to persuade Odysseus to return to the ship; but the hero being curious to make the acquaintance of the owner of this extraordinary abode, ordered them to remain and await his pleasure.

Towards evening a fierce giant made his appearance, bearing an enormous load of wood upon his shoulders, and driving before him a large flock of sheep. This was Polyphemus, the son of Poseidon, the owner of the cave. After all his sheep had entered, the giant rolled before the entrance to the cave an enormous rock, which the combined strength of a hundred men would have been powerless to move.

Having kindled a fire of great logs of pine-wood he was about to prepare his supper when the flames revealed to him, in a corner of the cavern, its new occupants, who now came forward and informed him that they were shipwrecked mariners, and claimed his hospitality in the name of Zeus. But the fierce monster railed at the great ruler of Olympus—for the lawless Cyclops knew no fear of the gods—and hardly vouchsafed a reply to the demand of the hero. To the consternation of Odysseus the giant seized two of his companions, and, after dashing them to the ground, consumed their remains, washing down the ghastly meal with huge draughts of milk. He then stretched his gigantic limbs on the ground, and soon fell fast asleep beside the fire.

Thinking the opportunity a favourable one to rid himself and his companions of their terrible enemy, Odysseus drew his sword, and, creeping stealthily forward, was about to slay the giant when he suddenly remembered that the aperture of the cave was effectually closed by the immense rock, which rendered egress impossible. He therefore wisely determined to wait until the following day, and set his wits to work in the meantime to devise a scheme by which he and his companions might make their escape.

When, early next morning, the giant awoke, two more unfortunate companions of the hero were seized by him and devoured; after which Polyphemus leisurely drove out his flock, taking care to secure the entrance of the cave as before.

Next evening the giant devoured two more of his victims, and when he had finished his revolting meal Odysseus stepped forward and presented him with a large measure of wine which he had brought with him from his ship in a goat's skin. Delighted with the delicious beverage the giant inquired the name of the donor. Odysseus replied that his name was Noman, whereupon Polyphemus, graciously announced that he would evince his gratitude by eating him the last.

The monster, thoroughly overcome with the powerful old liquor, soon fell into a heavy sleep, and Odysseus lost no time in putting his plans into execution. He had cut during the day a large piece of the giant's own olive-staff, which he now heated in the fire, and, aided by his companions, thrust it into the eye-ball of Polyphemus, and in this manner effectually blinded him.

The giant made the cave resound with his howls of pain and rage. His cries being heard by his brother Cyclops, who lived in caves not far distant from his own, they soon came trooping over the hills from all sides, and assailed the door of the cave with inquiries concerning the cause of his cries and groans. But as his only reply was, "Noman has injured me," they concluded that he had been playing them a trick, and therefore abandoned him to his fate.

The blinded giant now groped vainly round his cave in hopes of laying hands on some of his tormentors; but wearied at length of these fruitless exertions he rolled away the rock which closed the aperture, thinking that his victims would rush out with the sheep, when it would be an easy matter to capture them. But in the meantime Odysseus had not been idle, and the subtlety of the hero was now brought into play, and proved more than a match for the giant's strength. The sheep were very large, and Odysseus, with bands of willow taken from the bed of Polyphemus, had cleverly linked them together three abreast, and under each centre one had secured one of his comrades. After providing for the safety of his companions, Odysseus himself selected the finest ram of the flock, and, by clinging to the wool of the animal, made his escape. As the sheep passed out of the cave the giant felt carefully among them for his victims, but not finding them on the backs of the animals he let them pass, and thus they all escaped.

They now hastened on board their vessel, and Odysseus, thinking himself at a safe distance, shouted out his real name and mockingly defied the giant; whereupon Polyphemus seized a huge rock, and, following the direction of the voice, hurled it towards the ship, which narrowly escaped destruction. He then called upon his father Poseidon to avenge him, entreating him to curse Odysseus with a long and tedious voyage, to destroy all his ships and all his companions, and to make his return as late, as unhappy, and as desolate as possible.

Further Adventures.—After sailing about over unknown seas for some time the hero and his followers cast anchor at the island of Æolus, king of the Winds, who welcomed them cordially, and sumptuously entertained them for a whole month.

When they took their leave he gave Odysseus the skin of an ox, into which he had placed all the contrary winds in order to insure to them a safe and speedy voyage, and then, having cautioned him on no account to open it, caused the gentle Zephyrus to blow so that he might waft them to the shores of Greece.

On the evening of the tenth day after their departure they arrived in sight of the watch-fires of Ithaca. But here, unfortunately, Odysseus, being completely wearied out, fell asleep, and his comrades, thinking Æolus had given him a treasure in the bag which he so sedulously guarded, seized this opportunity of opening it, whereupon all the adverse winds rushed out, and drove them back to the Æolian island. This time, however, Æolus did not welcome them as before, but dismissed them with bitter reproaches and upbraidings for their disregard of his injunctions.

After a six days' voyage they at length sighted land. Observing what appeared to be the smoke from a large town, Odysseus despatched a herald, accompanied by two of his comrades, in order to procure provisions. When they arrived in the city they discovered to their consternation that they had set foot in the land of the Læstrygones, a race of fierce and gigantic cannibals, governed by their king Antiphates. The unfortunate herald was seized and killed by the king; but his two companions, who took to flight, succeeded in reaching their ship in safety, and urgently entreated their chief to put to sea without delay.

But Antiphates and his fellow-giants pursued the fugitives to the sea-shore, where they now appeared in large numbers. They seized huge rocks, which they hurled upon the fleet, sinking eleven of the ships with all hands, on board; the vessel under the immediate command of Odysseus being the only one which escaped destruction. In this ship, with his few remaining followers, Odysseus now set sail, but was driven by adverse winds to an island called Æœa.

Circe.—The hero and his companions were in sore need of provisions, but, warned by previous disasters, Odysseus resolved that only a certain number of the ship's crew should be despatched to reconnoitre the country; and on lots being drawn by Odysseus and Eurylochus, it fell to the share of the latter to fill the office of conductor to the little band selected for this purpose.

They soon came to a magnificent marble palace, which was situated in a charming and fertile valley. Here dwelt a beautiful enchantress called Circe, daughter of the sun-god and the sea-nymph Perse. The entrance to her abode was guarded by wolves and lions, who, however, to the great surprise of the strangers, were tame and harmless as lambs. These were, in fact, human beings who, by the wicked arts of the sorceress, had been thus transformed. From within they heard the enchanting voice of the goddess, who was singing a sweet melody as she sat at her work, weaving a web such as immortals alone could produce. She graciously invited them to enter, and all save the prudent and cautious Eurylochus accepted the invitation.

As they trod the wide and spacious halls of tesselated marble objects of wealth and beauty met their view on all sides. The soft and luxuriant couches on which she bade them be seated were studded with silver, and the banquet which she provided for their refreshment was served in vessels of pure gold. But while her unsuspecting guests were abandoning themselves to the pleasures of the table the wicked enchantress was secretly working their ruin; for the wine-cup which was presented to them was drugged with a potent draught, after partaking of which the sorceress touched them with her magic wand, and they were immediately transformed into swine, still, however, retaining their human senses.

When Odysseus heard from Eurylochus of the terrible fate which had befallen his companions he set out, regardless of personal danger, resolved to make an effort to rescue them. On his way to the palace of the sorceress he met a fair youth bearing a wand of gold, who revealed himself to him as Hermes, the divine messenger of the gods. He gently reproached the hero for his temerity in venturing to enter the abode of Circe unprovided with an antidote against her spells, and presented him with a peculiar herb called Moly, assuring him that it would inevitably counteract the baneful arts of the fell enchantress. Hermes warned Odysseus that Circe would offer him a draught of drugged wine with the intention of transforming him as she had done his companions. He bade him drink the wine, the effect of which would be completely nullified by the herb which he had given him, and then rush boldly at the sorceress as though he would take her life, whereupon her power over him would cease, she would recognize her master, and grant him whatever he might desire.

Circe received the hero with all the grace and fascination at her command, and presented him with a draught of wine in a golden goblet. This he readily accepted, trusting to the efficacy of the antidote. Then, in obedience to the injunction of Hermes, he drew his sword from its scabbard and rushed upon the sorceress as though he would slay her.

When Circe found that her fell purpose was for the first time frustrated, and that a mortal had dared to attack her, she knew that it must be the great Odysseus who stood before her, whose visit to her abode had been foretold to her by Hermes. At his solicitation she restored to his companions their human form, promising at the same time that henceforth the hero and his comrades should be free from her enchantments.

But all warnings and past experience were forgotten by Odysseus when Circe commenced to exercise upon him her fascinations and blandishments. At her request his companions took up their abode in the island, and he himself became the guest and slave of the enchantress for a whole year; and it was only at the earnest admonition of his friends that he was at length induced to free himself from her toils.

Circe had become so attached to the gallant hero that it cost her a great effort to part with him, but having vowed not to exercise her magic spells against him she was powerless to detain him further. The goddess now warned him that his future would be beset with many dangers, and commanded him to consult the blind old seer Tiresias,[52] in the realm of Hades, concerning his future destiny. She then loaded his ship with provisions for the voyage, and reluctantly bade him farewell.

The Realm of Shades.—Though somewhat appalled at the prospect of seeking the weird and gloomy realms inhabited by the spirits of the dead, Odysseus nevertheless obeyed the command of the goddess, who gave him full directions with regard to his course, and also certain injunctions which it was important that he should carry out with strict attention to detail.

He accordingly set sail with his companions for the dark and gloomy land of the Cimmerians, which lay at the furthermost end of the world, beyond the great stream Oceanus. Favoured by gentle breezes they soon reached their destination in the far west. On arriving at the spot indicated by Circe, where the turbid waters of the rivers Acheron and Cocytus mingled at the entrance to the lower world, Odysseus landed, unattended by his companions.

Having dug a trench to receive the blood of the sacrifices he now offered a black ram and ewe to the powers of darkness, whereupon crowds of shades rose up from the yawning gulf, clustering round him, eager to quaff the blood of the sacrifice, which would restore to them for a time their mental vigour. But mindful of the injunction of Circe, Odysseus brandished his sword, and suffered none to approach until Tiresias had appeared. The great prophet now came slowly forward leaning on his golden staff, and after drinking of the sacrifice proceeded to impart to Odysseus the hidden secrets of his future fate. Tiresias also warned him of the numerous perils which would assail him, not only during his homeward voyage but also on his return to Ithaca, and then instructed him how to avoid them.

Meanwhile numbers of other shades had quaffed the sense-awakening draught of the sacrifice, among whom Odysseus recognized to his dismay his tenderly-loved mother Anticlea. From her he learned that she had died of grief at her son's protracted absence, and that his aged father Laertes was wearing his life away in vain and anxious longings for his return. He also conversed with the ill-fated Agamemnon, Patroclus, and Achilles. The latter bemoaned his shadowy and unreal existence, and plaintively assured his former companion-in-arms that rather would he be the poorest day-labourer on earth than reign supreme as king over the realm of shades. Ajax alone, who still brooded over his wrongs, held aloof, refusing to converse with Odysseus, and sullenly retired when the hero addressed him.

But at last so many shades came swarming round him that the courage of Odysseus failed him, and he fled in terror back to his ship. Having rejoined his companions they once more put to sea, and proceeded on their homeward voyage.

The Sirens.—After some days' sail their course led them past the island of the Sirens.

Now Circe had warned Odysseus on no account to listen to the seductive melodies of these treacherous nymphs; for that all who gave ear to their enticing strains felt an unconquerable desire to leap overboard and join them, when they either perished at their hands, or were engulfed by the waves.

In order that his crew should not hear the song of the Sirens, Odysseus had filled their ears with melted wax; but the hero himself so dearly loved adventure that he could not resist the temptation of braving this new danger. By his own desire, therefore, he was lashed to the mast, and his comrades had strict orders on no account to release him until they were out of sight of the island, no matter how he might implore them to set him free.

As they neared the fatal shore they beheld the Sirens seated side by side on the verdant slopes of their island; and as their sweet and alluring strains fell upon his ear the hero became so powerfully affected by them, that, forgetful of all danger, he entreated his comrades to release him; but the sailors, obedient to their orders, refused to unbind him until the enchanted island had disappeared from view. The danger past, the hero gratefully acknowledged the firmness of his followers, which had been the means of saving his life.

The Island of Helios.—They now approached the terrible dangers of Scylla and Charybdis, between which Circe had desired them to pass. As Odysseus steered the vessel beneath the great rock, Scylla swooped down and seized six of his crew from the deck, and the cries of her wretched victims long rang in his ears. At length they reached the island of Trinacria (Sicily), whereon the sun-god pastured his flocks and herds, and Odysseus, calling to mind the warning of Tiresias to avoid this sacred island, would fain have steered the vessel past and left the country unexplored. But his crew became mutinous, and insisted on landing. Odysseus was therefore obliged to yield, but before allowing them to set foot on shore he made them take an oath not to touch the sacred herds of Helios, and to be ready to sail again on the following morning.

It happened, unfortunately, however, that stress of weather compelled them to remain a whole month at Trinacria, and the store of wine and food given to them by Circe at parting being completely exhausted, they were obliged to subsist on what fish and birds the island afforded. Frequently there was not sufficient to satisfy their hunger, and one evening when Odysseus, worn out with anxiety and fatigue, had fallen asleep, Eurylochus persuaded the hungry men to break their vows and kill some of the sacred oxen.

Dreadful was the anger of Helios, who caused the hides of the slaughtered animals to creep and the joints on the spits to bellow like living cattle, and threatened that unless Zeus punished the impious crew he would withdraw his light from the heavens and shine only in Hades. Anxious to appease the enraged deity Zeus assured him that his cause should be avenged. When, therefore, after feasting for seven days Odysseus and his companions again set sail, the ruler of

Olympus caused a terrible storm to overtake them, during which the ship was struck with lightning and went to pieces. All the crew were drowned except Odysseus, who, clinging to a mast, floated about in the open sea for nine days, when, after once more escaping being sucked in by the whirlpool of Charybdis, he was cast ashore on the island of Ogygia.

Calypso.—Ogygia was an island covered with dense forests, where, in the midst of a grove of cypress and poplar, stood the charming grotto-palace of the nymph Calypso, daughter of the Titan Atlas. The entrance to the grotto was entwined with a leafy trellis-work of vine-branches, from which depended clusters of purple and golden grapes; the plashing of fountains gave a delicious sense of coolness to the air, which was filled with the songs of birds, and the ground was carpeted with violets and mosses.

Calypso cordially welcomed the forlorn and shipwrecked hero, and hospitably ministered to his wants. In the course of time she became so greatly attached to him that she offered him immortality and eternal youth if he would consent to remain with her for ever. But the heart of Odysseus turned yearningly towards his beloved wife Penelope and his young son. He therefore refused the boon, and earnestly entreated the gods to permit him to revisit his home. But the curse of Poseidon still followed the unfortunate hero, and for seven long years he was detained on the island by Calypso, sorely against his will.

At length Pallas-Athene interceded with her mighty father on his behalf, and Zeus, yielding to her request, forthwith despatched the fleet-footed Hermes to Calypso, commanding her to permit Odysseus to depart and to provide him with the means of transport.

The goddess, though loath to part with her guest, dared not disobey the commands of the mighty Zeus. She therefore instructed the hero how to construct a raft, for which she herself wove the sails. Odysseus now bade her farewell, and alone and unaided embarked on the frail little craft for his native land.

Nausicaa.—For seventeen days Odysseus contrived to pilot the raft skilfully through all the perils of the deep, directing his course according to the directions of Calypso, and guided by the stars of heaven. On the eighteenth day he joyfully hailed the distant outline of the Phæacian coast, and began to look forward hopefully to temporary rest and shelter. But Poseidon, still enraged with the hero who had blinded and insulted his son, caused an awful tempest to arise, during which the raft was swamped by the waves, and Odysseus only saved himself by clinging for bare life to a portion of the wreck.

For two days and nights he floated about, drifted hither and thither by the angry billows, till at last, after many a narrow escape of his life, the sea-goddess Leucothea came to his aid, and he was cast ashore on the coast of Scheria, the island of the luxurious Phæaces. Worn out with the hardships and dangers he had passed through he crept into a thicket for security, and, lying down on a bed of dried leaves, soon fell fast asleep.

It chanced that Nausicaa, the beautiful daughter of king Alcinous and his queen Arete, had come down to the shore, accompanied by her maidens, to wash the linen which was destined to form part of her marriage portion. When they had finished their task they bathed and sat down to a repast, after which they amused themselves with singing and playing at ball.

Their joyous shouts at last awoke Odysseus, who, rising from his hiding place, suddenly found himself in the midst of the happy group. Alarmed at his wild aspect the attendants of Nausicaa fled in terror; but the princess, pitying the forlorn condition of the stranger, addressed him with kind and sympathetic words. After hearing from him the account of his shipwreck and the terrible hardships he had undergone, Nausicaa called back her attendants, reproached them for their want of courtesy, and bade them supply the wanderer with food, drink, and suitable raiment. Odysseus then left the maidens to resume their games, whilst he bathed and clothed himself with the garments with which they had furnished him. Athene now appeared to the hero and endowed him with a commanding and magnificent stature, and with more than mortal beauty. When he reappeared, the young princess was struck with admiration, and requested the hero to visit the palace of her father. She then desired her attendants to yoke the mules to the wagons and prepare to return home.

Odysseus was cordially received by the king and queen, who entertained him with magnificent hospitality, and in return for their kindness the hero related to them the history of his long and eventful voyage, and the many extraordinary adventures and miraculous escapes which had befallen him since his departure from the coast of Ilion.

When he at last took leave of his royal entertainers Alcinous loaded him with rich gifts, and ordered him to be conveyed in one of his own ships to Ithaca.

Arrival at Ithaca.—The voyage was a short and prosperous one. By the direction of king Alcinous rich furs had been laid on deck for the comfort of his guest, on which the hero, leaving the guidance of the ship to the Phæacian sailors, soon fell into a deep sleep. When next morning the vessel arrived in the harbour of Ithaca the sailors, concluding that so unusually profound a slumber must be sent by the gods, conveyed him on shore without disturbing him, where they gently placed him beneath the cool shade of an olive-tree.

When Odysseus awoke he knew not where he was, for his ever-watchful protectress Pallas-Athene had enveloped him in a thick cloud in order to conceal him from view. She now appeared to him in the disguise of a shepherd, and informed him that he was in his native land; that his father Laertes, bent with sorrow and old age, had withdrawn from the court; that his son Telemachus had grown to manhood, and was gone to seek for tidings of his father; and that his wife Penelope was harassed by the importunities of numerous suitors, who had taken possession of his home and devoured his substance. In order to gain time Penelope had promised to marry one of her lovers as soon as she had finished weaving a robe for the aged Laertes; but by secretly undoing at night what she had done in the day she effectually retarded the completion of the work, and thus deferred her final reply. Just as Odysseus had set foot in Ithaca the angry suitors had discovered her stratagem, and had become in consequence more clamorous than ever. When the hero heard that this was indeed his native land, which, after an absence of twenty years, the gods had at length permitted him to behold once more, he threw himself on the ground, and kissed it in an ecstacy of joy.

The goddess, who had meanwhile revealed her identity to Odysseus, now assisted him to conceal in a neighbouring cave the valuable gifts of the Phæacian king. Then seating herself beside him she consulted with him as to the best means of ridding his palace of its shameless occupants.

In order to prevent his being recognized she caused him to assume the form of an aged mendicant. His limbs became decrepid, his brown locks vanished, his eyes grew dim and bleared, and the regal robes given to him by king Alcinous were replaced by a tattered garb of dingy hue, which hung loosely round his shrunken form. Athene then desired him to seek shelter in the hut of Eumæus his own swine-herd.

Eumæus received the old beggar hospitably, kindly ministered to his wants, and even confided to him his distress at the long continued absence of his beloved old master, and his regrets at being compelled by the unruly invaders of his house, to slaughter for their use all the finest and fattest of the herd.

It chanced that the following morning Telemachus returned from his long and fruitless search for his father, and going first to the hut of Eumæus, heard from him the story of the seeming beggar whom he promised to befriend. Athene now urged Odysseus to make himself known to his son; and at her touch his beggar's rags disappeared, and he stood before Telemachus arrayed in royal robes and in the full strength and vigour of manhood. So imposing was the appearance of the hero that at first the young prince thought he must be a god; but when he was convinced that it was indeed his beloved father, whose prolonged absence had caused him so much grief, he fell upon his neck and embraced him with every expression of dutiful affection.

Odysseus charged Telemachus to keep his return a secret, and concerted with him a plan whereby they might rid themselves of the detested suitors. In order to carry it into effect Telemachus was to induce his mother to promise her hand to the one who could conquer in shooting with the famous bow of Odysseus, which the hero had left behind when he went to Troy, deeming it too precious a treasure to be taken with him. Odysseus now resumed his beggar's dress and appearance and accompanied his son to the palace, before the door of which lay his faithful dog Argo, who, though worn and feeble with age and neglect, instantly recognized his master. In his delight the poor animal made a last effort to welcome him; but his strength was exhausted, and he expired at his feet.

When Odysseus entered his ancestral halls he was mocked and reviled by the riotous suitors, and Antinous, the most shameless of them all, ridiculed his abject appearance, and insolently bade him depart; but Penelope hearing of their cruel conduct, was touched with compassion, and desired her maidens to bring the poor mendicant into her presence. She spoke kindly to him, inquiring who he was and whence he came. He told her that he was the brother of the king of Crete, in whose palace he had seen Odysseus, who was about starting for Ithaca, and had declared his intention of arriving there before the year was out. The queen, overjoyed at the happy tidings, ordered her maidens to prepare a bed for the stranger, and to treat him as an honoured guest. She then desired the old nurse Euryclea to provide him with suitable raiment and to attend to all his wants.

As the old servant was bathing his feet her eyes fell upon a scar which Odysseus had received in his youth from the tusks of a wild boar; and instantly recognizing the beloved master whom she had nursed as a babe, she would have cried aloud in her joy, but the hero placing his hand upon her mouth, implored her not to betray him.

The next day was a festival of Apollo, and the suitors in honour of the occasion feasted with more than their accustomed revelry. After the banquet was over Penelope, taking down the great bow of Odysseus from its place, entered the hall and declared that whosoever of her lovers could bend it and send an arrow through twelve rings (a feat which she had often seen Odysseus perform) should be chosen by her as her husband.

All the suitors tried their skill, but in vain; not one possessed the strength required to draw the bow. Odysseus now stepped forward and asked permission to be allowed to try, but the haughty nobles mocked at his audacity, and would not have permitted it had not Telemachus interfered. The pretended beggar took up the bow, and with the greatest ease sent an arrow whizzing through the rings; then turning to Antinous, who was just raising a goblet of wine to his lips, he pierced him to the heart. At this the suitors sprang to their feet and looked round for their arms; but in obedience to the instructions of Odysseus Telemachus had previously removed them. He and his father now attacked the riotous revellers, and after a desperate encounter not one of the whole crew remained alive.

The joyful intelligence of the return of Odysseus being conveyed to Penelope she descended to the hall, but refused to recognize, in the aged beggar, her gallant husband; whereupon he retired to the bath, from which he emerged in all the vigour and beauty with which Athene had endowed him at the court of Alcinous. But Penelope, still incredulous, determined to put him to a sure test. She therefore commanded in his hearing that his own bed should be brought from his chamber. Now the foot of this bed had been fashioned by Odysseus himself out of the stem of an olive-tree which was still rooted in the ground, and round it he had built the walls of the chamber. Knowing therefore that the bed could not be moved, he exclaimed that the errand was useless, for that no mortal could stir it from its place. Then Penelope knew that it must be Odysseus himself who stood before her, and a most touching and affectionate meeting took place between the long-separated husband and wife.

The following day the hero set out to seek his old father Laertes, whom he found on one of his estates in the country engaged in digging up a young olive-tree. The poor old man, who was dressed in the humble garb of a labourer, bore the traces of deep grief on his furrowed countenance, and so shocked was his son at the change in his appearance that for a moment he turned aside to conceal his tears.

When Odysseus revealed himself to his father as the son whom he had so long mourned as lost, the joy of the poor old man was almost greater than he could bear. With loving care Odysseus led him into the house, where at length, for the first time since the departure of his son, Laertes once more resumed his regal robes, and piously thanked the gods for this great and unlooked-for happiness.

But not yet was the hero permitted to enjoy his well-earned repose, for the friends and relatives of the suitors now rose in rebellion against him and pursued him to the abode of his father. The struggle, however, was but a short one. After a brief contest negotiations of a peaceful nature were entered into between Odysseus and his subjects. Recognizing the justice of his cause, they became reconciled to their chief, who for many years continued to reign over them.

NOTES

[1]   The early Greeks supposed the earth to be a flat circle, in the centre of which was Greece. Oceanus, the ocean stream, encircled it; the Mediterranean being supposed to flow into this river on the one side, and the Euxine, or Black Sea, on the other.

[2]   Owing to the vagueness of the various accounts of creation, the origin of the primeval gods is variously accounted for. Thus, for instance, Oceanus, with some, becomes the younger brother of Uranus and Gæa.

[3]   The myth of Cronus swallowing his children is evidently intended by the poets to express the melancholy truth that time destroys all things.

[4]   Nectar was the drink, and ambrosia the food of the gods.

[5]   The Cyclops are generally mentioned as the sons of Uranus and Gæa, but Homer speaks of Polyphemus, the chief of the Cyclops, as the son of Poseidon, and states the Cyclops to be his brothers.

[6]   Possibly an image of him placed in readiness.

[7]   This age was contemporary with the commencement of the dynasty of Zeus.

[8]   Hesiod is said to have lived 850 years before the Christian era, consequently about 200 years after King David. He lived in Bœotia, where his tomb is still shown at Orchomenus. This ancient writer left behind him two great poems, one entitled "The Works and Days," in which he gives us some of the earliest Greek legends, and the other, "The Theogony," containing the genealogies of the gods; but, unfortunately, both these poems have been so interpolated by the

writers of the Alexandrian school that they have lost their value as reliable sources of information with regard to the early beliefs of the Greek nation.

[9] Epimetheus signifies after-thought, Prometheus fore-thought.

[10] There are various versions of this myth. According to some the jar or vase was full of all "the ills which flesh is heir to."

[11] From *Diaus*, the sky.

[12] A sacred shield made for Zeus by Hephæstus, which derived its name from being covered by the skin of the goat Amalthea, the word Ægis signifying goat's-skin.

[13] See Demeter.

[14] This frightful monster had sprung from the slimy and stagnant waters which remained on the surface of the earth after the deluge of Deucalion.

[15] Castor and Pollux were known by the name of the Dioscuri, from *dios*, gods, and *kuroi*, youths.

[16] The ancient Greeks attributed much of the subsequent character of an individual to early influences; hence Hera, the future queen and mistress of heaven, is represented as being brought up in a domesticated and orderly household, where home virtues are carefully inculcated.

[17] In the Homeric age peacocks were unknown; it is therefore the later poets who describe Hera surrounded with peacocks, which were brought to Greece from India.

[18] This circumstance has given rise to the erroneous conclusion that Juno presided over the finances of the state, but the word *moneta* is derived from the Latin *monere*, which means to warn or admonish.

[19] See Roman Festivals.

[20] The first large ship possessed by the Greeks fit for more than coast navigation.

[21] When Perseus, with the help of Athene, had cut off the head of the Medusa, the two sisters caused a sad dirge-like song to issue from the mouths of the many snakes of which their hair was composed, whereupon Athene, pleased with the sound, imitated the melody on a reed, and thus invented the flute.

[22] For details see Roman Festivals.

[23] See Legend of Troy.

[24] Some, with but little reason, make Demeter the daughter of Uranus and Gæa.

[25] Demeter transformed Ascalaphus into an owl for revealing the secret.

[26] The course which the sun ran was considered by the ancients to be a rising and descending curve, the centre of which was supposed to be reached by Helios at mid-day.

[27] The river Po.

[28] This great work of antiquity was destroyed by an earthquake fifty-six years after its erection, B.C. 256. The fragments remained on the ground for many centuries, until Rhodes was conquered by the Turks, and they were eventually sold by one of the generals of Caliph Othman IV to a merchant of Emesa for £36,000 in A.D. 672.

[29] According to some authorities, Strymon.

[30] This wonderful lyre, which had been given to Apollo by Hermes (Mercury) in exchange for the Caduceus or rod of wealth, is said to have possessed such extraordinary powers, that it caused a stone, upon which it was laid, to become so melodious, that ever afterwards, on being touched, it emitted a musical sound which resembled that produced by the lyre itself.

[31] Aristæus was worshipped as a rural divinity in various parts of Greece, and was supposed to have taught mankind how to catch bees, and to utilize honey and wax.

[32] Astræa was the daughter of the Titans Cœus and Phœbe. Perses was son of the Titans Crios and Eurybia.

[33] Called also Anaitis-Aphroditis.

[34] This occurred during the night Alexander the Great was born.

[35] Another version with regard to the origin of this defect, is that being born ugly and deformed, his mother Hera, disgusted at his unsightliness, herself threw him violently from her lap, and it was then that his leg was broken, producing the lameness from which he suffered ever after. On this occasion he fell into the sea, and was saved by the sea-nymphs Thetis and Eurynome, who kept him for nine years in a cavern beneath the ocean, where he made for them, in gratitude for their kindness, several beautiful ornaments, and trinkets of rare workmanship.

[36] According to some accounts Chares was the wife of Hephæstus.

[37] The trident resembled the arrow-headed pronged fork, used by the fishermen of the Mediterranean Sea in the eel-fishery.

[38] Scylla is a dangerous rock, much dreaded by mariners, in the Straits of Messina.

[39] The island of Rhodes owes its name to her.

[40] It is worthy of notice that the sons of Poseidon were, for the most part, distinguished by great force and turbulence of character, in

keeping with the element over which their father was the presiding deity. They were giants in power, and intractable, fiery, and impatient by nature, spurning all efforts to control them; in all respects, therefore, fitting representatives of their progenitor, the mighty ruler of the sea.

[41] A cubit is the length from the elbow to the extremity of the middle finger, and therefore an indefinite measure, but modern usage takes it as representing a length of seventeen to eighteen inches.

[42] On the Egyptian coast.

[43] See Legend of the Argonauts.

[44] His two sons Deimos and Phobos.

[45] Romulus was deified by the Romans after death, and was worshipped by them under the name of Quirinus, an appellation which he shared in common with his father Mars.

[46] Midas was the son of Cybele and Gordius, the king who tied the celebrated and intricate knot.

[47] The shades of those mortals whose lives had neither been distinguished by virtue nor vice, were condemned to a monotonous, joyless, existence in the Asphodel meadows of Hades.

[48] Echidna was a bloodthirsty monster, half maiden, half serpent.

[49] One of the horns of the goat Amalthea, broken off by Zeus, and supposed to possess the power of filling itself with whatsoever its owner desired.

[50] According to another account, Momus discovered that Aphrodite made a noise when she walked.

[51] The word Psyche signifies "butterfly," the emblem of the soul in ancient art.

[52] Tiresias alone, of all the shades, was in full possession of his mental vigour.

CLASSIC LITERATURE: WORDS AND PHRASES
adapted from the Collins English Dictionary

Accoucheur NOUN a male midwife or doctor ❑ *I think my sister must have had some general idea that I was a young offender whom an Accoucheur Policemen had taken up (on my birthday) and delivered over to her* (*Great Expectations* by Charles Dickens)

addled ADJ confused and unable to think properly ❑ *But she counted and counted till she got that addled* (*The Adventures of Huckleberry Finn* by Mark Twain)

admiration NOUN amazement or wonder ❑ *lifting up his hands and eyes by way of admiration* (*Gulliver's Travels* by Jonathan Swift)

afeard ADJ afeard means afraid ❑ *shake it—and don't be afeard* (*The Adventures of Huckleberry Finn* by Mark Twain)

affected VERB affected means to assume the appearance of ❑ *Hadst thou affected sweet divinity* (*Doctor Faustus 5.2* by Christopher Marlowe)

aground ADV when a boat runs aground, it touches the ground in a shallow part of the water and gets stuck ❑ *what kep' you?—boat get aground?* (*The Adventures of Huckleberry Finn* by Mark Twain)

ague NOUN a fever in which the patient has alternate hot and cold shivering fits ❑ *his exposure to the wet and cold had brought on fever and ague* (*Oliver Twist* by Charles Dickens)

alchemy ADJ false or worthless ❑ *all wealth alchemy* (*The Sun Rising* by John Donne)

all alike PHRASE the same all the time ❑ *Love, all alike* (*The Sun Rising* by John Donne)

alow and aloft PHRASE alow means in the lower part or bottom, and aloft means on the top, so alow and aloft means on the top and in the bottom or throughout ❑ *Someone's turned the chest out alow and aloft* (*Treasure Island* by Robert Louis Stevenson)

ambuscade NOUN ambuscade is not a proper word. Tom means an ambush, which is when a group of people attack their enemies, after hiding and waiting for them ❑ *and so we would lie in ambuscade, as he called it* (*The Adventures of Huckleberry Finn* by Mark Twain)

amiable ADJ likeable or pleasant ❑ *Such amiable qualities must speak for themselves* (*Pride and Prejudice* by Jane Austen)

amulet NOUN an amulet is a charm thought to drive away evil spirits. ❑ *uttered phrases at once occult and familiar, like the amulet worn on the heart* (*Silas Marner* by George Eliot)

amusement NOUN here amusement means a strange and disturbing puzzle ❑ *this was an amusement the other way* (*Robinson Crusoe* by Daniel Defoe)

ancient NOUN an ancient was the flag displayed on a ship to show which country it belongs to. It is also called the ensign ❑ *her ancient and pendants out* (*Robinson Crusoe* by Daniel Defoe)

antic ADJ here antic means horrible or grotesque ❑ *armed and dressed after a very antic manner* (*Gulliver's Travels* by Jonathan Swift)

antics NOUN antics is an old word meaning clowns, or people who do silly things to make other people laugh ❑ *And point like antics at his triple crown* (*Doctor Faustus 3.2* by Christopher Marlowe)

appanage NOUN an appanage is a living allowance ❑ *As if loveliness were not the special prerogative of woman–her legitimate appanage and heritage!* (*Jane Eyre* by Charlotte Brontë)

appended VERB appended means attached or added to ❑ *and these words appended* (*Treasure Island* by Robert Louis Stevenson)

approver NOUN an approver is someone who gives evidence against someone he used to work with ❑ *Mr. Noah Claypole: receiving a free pardon from the Crown in consequence of being admitted approver against Fagin* (*Oliver Twist* by Charles Dickens)

areas NOUN the areas is the space, below street level, in front of the basement of a house ❑ *The Dodger had a vicious propensity, too, of pulling the caps from the heads of small boys and tossing them down areas* (*Oliver Twist* by Charles Dickens)

argument NOUN theme or important idea or subject which runs through a piece of writing ❑ *Thrice needful to the argument which now* (*The Prelude* by William Wordsworth)

artificially ADV artfully or cleverly ❑ *and he with a sharp flint sharpened very artificially* (*Gulliver's Travels* by Jonathan Swift)

artist NOUN here artist means a skilled workman ❑ *This man was a most ingenious artist* (*Gulliver's Travels* by Jonathan Swift)

assizes NOUN assizes were regular court sessions which a visiting judge was in charge of ❑ *you shall hang at the next assizes* (*Treasure Island* by Robert Louis Stevenson)

attraction NOUN gravitation, or Newton's theory of gravitation ❑ *he predicted the same fate to attraction* (*Gulliver's Travels* by Jonathan Swift)

aver VERB to aver is to claim something strongly ❑ *for Jem Rodney, the mole catcher, averred that one evening as he was returning homeward* (*Silas Marner* by George Eliot)

baby NOUN here baby means doll, which is a child's toy that looks like a small person ❑ *and skilful dressing her baby* (*Gulliver's Travels* by Jonathan Swift)

bagatelle NOUN bagatelle is a game rather like billiards and pool ❑ *Breakfast had been ordered at a pleasant little tavern, a mile or so away upon the rising ground beyond the green; and there was a bagatelle board in the room, in case we should desire to unbend our minds after the solemnity.* (*Great Expectations* by Charles Dickens)

bah EXCLAM Bah is an exclamation of frustration or anger ❑ *"Bah," said Scrooge.* (*A Christmas Carol* by Charles Dickens)

bairn NOUN a northern word for child ❑ *Who has taught you those fine words, my bairn?* (*Wuthering Heights* by Emily Brontë)

bait VERB to bait means to stop on a journey to take refreshment ❑ *So, when they stopped to bait the horse, and ate and drank and enjoyed themselves, I could touch nothing that they touched, but kept my fast unbroken.* (*David Copperfield* by Charles Dickens)

balustrade NOUN a balustrade is a row of vertical columns that form railings ❑ *but I mean to say you might have got a hearse up that staircase, and taken it broadwise, with the splinter-bar towards the wall, and the door towards the balustrades: and done it easy* (*A Christmas Carol* by Charles Dickens)

bandbox NOUN a large lightweight box for carrying bonnets or hats ❑ *I am glad I bought my bonnet, if it is only for the fun of having another bandbox* (*Pride and Prejudice* by Jane Austen)

barren NOUN a barren here is a stretch or expanse of barren land ❑ *a line* *of upright stones, continued the length of the barren* (Wuthering Heights *by Emily Brontë*)

basin NOUN a basin was a cup without a handle ❏ *who is drinking his tea out of a basin* (Wuthering Heights *by Emily Brontë*)

battalia NOUN the order of battle ❏ *till I saw part of his army in battalia* (Gulliver's Travels *by Jonathan Swift*)

battery NOUN a Battery is a fort or a place where guns are positioned ❏ *You bring the lot to me, at that old Battery over yonder* (Great Expectations *by Charles Dickens*)

battledore and shuttlecock NOUN The game battledore and shuttlecock was an early version of the game now known as badminton. The aim of the early game was simply to keep the shuttlecock from hitting the ground. ❏ *Battledore and shuttlecock's a wery good game vhen you an't the shuttlecock and two lawyers the battledores, in which case it gets too excitin' to be pleasant* (Pickwick Papers *by Charles Dickens*)

beadle NOUN a beadle was a local official who had power over the poor ❏ *But these impertinences were speedily checked by the evidence of the surgeon, and the testimony of the beadle* (Oliver Twist *by Charles Dickens*)

bearings NOUN the bearings of a place are the measurements or directions that are used to find or locate it ❏ *the bearings of the island* (Treasure Island *by Robert Louis Stevenson*)

beaufet NOUN a beaufet was a sideboard ❏ *and sweet-cake from the beaufet* (Emma *by Jane Austen*)

beck NOUN a beck is a small stream ❏ *a beck which follows the bend of the glen* (Wuthering Heights *by Emily Brontë*)

bedight VERB decorated ❏ *and bedight with Christmas holly stuck into the*

top. (A Christmas Carol *by Charles Dickens*)

Bedlam NOUN Bedlam was a lunatic asylum in London which had statues carved by Caius Gabriel Cibber at its entrance ❏ *Bedlam, and those carved maniacs at the gates* (The Prelude *by William Wordsworth*)

beeves NOUN oxen or castrated bulls which are animals used for pulling vehicles or carrying things ❏ *to deliver in every morning six beeves* (Gulliver's Travels *by Jonathan Swift*)

begot VERB created or caused ❏ *Begot in thee* (On His Mistress *by John Donne*)

behoof NOUN behoof means benefit ❏ *"Yes, young man," said he, releasing the handle of the article in question, retiring a step or two from my table, and speaking for the behoof of the landlord and waiter at the door* (Great Expectations *by Charles Dickens*)

berth NOUN a berth is a bed on a boat ❏ *this is the berth for me* (Treasure Island *by Robert Louis Stevenson*)

bevers NOUN a bever was a snack, or small portion of food, eaten between main meals ❏ *that buys me thirty meals a day and ten bevers* (Doctor Faustus 2.1 *by Christopher Marlowe*)

bilge water NOUN the bilge is the widest part of a ship's bottom, and the bilge water is the dirty water that collects there ❏ *no gush of bilge-water had turned it to fetid puddle* (Jane Eyre *by Charlotte Brontë*)

bills NOUN bills is an old term meaning prescription. A prescription is the piece of paper on which your doctor writes an order for medicine and which you give to a chemist to get the medicine ❏ *Are not thy bills hung up as monuments* (Doctor Faustus 1.1 *by Christopher Marlowe*)

black cap NOUN a judge wore a black cap when he was about to sentence a prisoner to death ❏ *The judge assumed the black cap, and the prisoner still stood with the same air and gesture.* (*Oliver Twist* by Charles Dickens)

boot-jack NOUN a wooden device to help take boots off ❏ *The speaker appeared to throw a boot-jack, or some such article, at the person he addressed* (*Oliver Twist* by Charles Dickens)

booty NOUN booty means treasure or prizes ❏ *would be inclined to give up their booty in payment of the dead man's debts* (*Treasure Island* by Robert Louis Stevenson)

Bow Street runner PHRASE Bow Street runners were the first British police force, set up by the author Henry Fielding in the eighteenth century ❏ *as would have convinced a judge or a Bow Street runner* (*Treasure Island* by Robert Louis Stevenson)

brawn NOUN brawn is a dish of meat which is set in jelly ❏ *Heaped up upon the floor, to form a kind of throne, were turkeys, geese, game, poultry, brawn, great joints of meat, suckling-pigs* (*A Christmas Carol* by Charles Dickens)

bray VERB when a donkey brays, it makes a loud, harsh sound ❏ *and she doesn't bray like a jackass* (*The Adventures of Huckleberry Finn* by Mark Twain)

break VERB in order to train a horse you first have to break it ❏ *"If a high-mettled creature like this," said he, "can't be broken by fair means, she will never be good for anything"* (*Black Beauty* by Anna Sewell)

bullyragging VERB bullyragging is an old word which means bullying. To bullyrag someone is to threaten or force someone to do something they don't want to do ❏ *and a lot of loafers bullyragging him for sport* (*The Adventures of Huckleberry Finn* by Mark Twain)

but PREP except for (this) ❏ *but this, all pleasures fancies be* (*The Good-Morrow* by John Donne)

by hand PHRASE by hand was a common expression of the time meaning that baby had been fed either using a spoon or a bottle rather than by breast-feeding ❏ *My sister, Mrs. Joe Gargery, was more than twenty years older than I, and had established a great reputation with herself . . . because she had bought me up "by hand"* (*Great Expectations* by Charles Dickens)

bye-spots NOUN bye-spots are lonely places ❏ *and bye-spots of tales rich with indigenous produce* (*The Prelude* by William Wordsworth)

calico NOUN calico is plain white fabric made from cotton ❏ *There was two old dirty calico dresses* (*The Adventures of Huckleberry Finn* by Mark Twain)

camp-fever NOUN camp-fever was another word for the disease typhus ❏ *during a severe camp-fever* (*Emma* by Jane Austen)

cant NOUN cant is insincere or empty talk ❏ *"Man," said the Ghost, "if man you be in heart, not adamant, forbear that wicked cant until you have discovered What the surplus is, and Where it is."* (*A Christmas Carol* by Charles Dickens)

canty ADJ canty means lively, full of life ❏ *My mother lived til eighty, a canty dame to the last* (*Wuthering Heights* by Emily Brontë)

canvas VERB to canvas is to discuss ❏ *We think so very differently on this point Mr Knightley, that there can be no use in canvassing it* (*Emma* by Jane Austen)

capital ADJ capital means excellent or extremely good ❏ *for it's capital, so shady, light, and big* (*Little Women* by Louisa May Alcott)

capstan NOUN a capstan is a device used on a ship to lift sails and anchors ❑ *capstans going, ships going out to sea, and unintelligible sea creatures roaring curses over the bulwarks at respondent lightermen* (*Great Expectations* by Charles Dickens)

case-bottle NOUN a square bottle designed to fit with others into a case ❑ *The spirit being set before him in a huge case-bottle, which had originally come out of some ship's locker* (*The Old Curiosity Shop* by Charles Dickens)

casement NOUN casement is a word meaning window. The teacher in *Nicholas Nickleby* misspells window showing what a bad teacher he is ❑ *W-i-n, win, d-e-r, der, winder, a casement.* (*Nicholas Nickleby* by Charles Dickens)

cataleptic ADJ a cataleptic fit is one in which the victim goes into a trancelike state and remains still for a long time ❑ *It was at this point in their history that Silas's cataleptic fit occurred during the prayer-meeting* (*Silas Marner* by George Eliot)

cauldron NOUN a cauldron is a large cooking pot made of metal ❑ *stirring a large cauldron which seemed to be full of soup* (*Alice's Adventures in Wonderland* by Lewis Carroll)

cephalic ADJ cephalic means to do with the head ❑ *with ink composed of a cephalic tincture* (*Gulliver's Travels* by Jonathan Swift)

chaise and four NOUN a closed four-wheel carriage pulled by four horses ❑ *he came down on Monday in a chaise and four to see the place* (*Pride and Prejudice* by Jane Austen)

chamberlain NOUN the main servant in a household ❑ *In those times a bed was always to be got there at any hour of the night, and the chamberlain, letting me in at his ready wicket, lighted the candle next in order on his shelf* (*Great Expectations* by Charles Dickens)

characters NOUN distinguishing marks ❑ *Impressed upon all forms the characters* (*The Prelude* by William Wordsworth)

chary ADJ cautious ❑ *I should have been chary of discussing my guardian too freely even with her* (*Great Expectations* by Charles Dickens)

cherishes VERB here cherishes means cheers or brightens ❑ *some philosophic song of Truth that cherishes our daily life* (*The Prelude* by William Wordsworth)

chickens' meat PHRASE chickens' meat is an old term which means chickens' feed or food ❑ *I had shook a bag of chickens' meat out in that place* (*Robinson Crusoe* by Daniel Defoe)

chimeras NOUN a chimera is an unrealistic idea or a wish which is unlikely to be fulfilled ❑ *with many other wild impossible chimeras* (*Gulliver's Travels* by Jonathan Swift)

chines NOUN chine is a cut of meat that includes part or all of the backbone of the animal ❑ *and they found hams and chines uncut* (*Silas Marner* by George Eliot)

chits NOUN chits is a slang word which means girls ❑ *I hate affected, niminy-piminy chits!* (*Little Women* by Louisa May Alcott)

chopped VERB chopped means come suddenly or accidentally ❑ *if I had chopped upon them* (*Robinson Crusoe* by Daniel Defoe)

chute NOUN a narrow channel ❑ *One morning about day-break, I found a canoe and crossed over a chute to the main shore* (*The Adventures of Huckleberry Finn* by Mark Twain)

circumspection NOUN careful observation of events and circumstances; caution ❑ *I honour your circumspection* (*Pride and Prejudice* by Jane Austen)

clambered VERB clambered means to climb somewhere with difficulty, usually using your hands and your feet ❑ *he clambered up and down stairs* (*Treasure Island* by Robert Louis Stevenson)

clime NOUN climate ❑ *no season knows nor clime* (*The Sun Rising* by John Donne)

clinched VERB clenched ❑ *the tops whereof I could but just reach with my fist clinched* (*Gulliver's Travels* by Jonathan Swift)

close chair NOUN a close chair is a sedan chair, which is a covered chair which has room for one person. The sedan chair is carried on two poles by two men, one in front and one behind ❑ *persuaded even the Empress herself to let me hold her in her close chair* (*Gulliver's Travels* by Jonathan Swift)

clown NOUN clown here means peasant or person who lives off the land ❑ *In ancient days by emperor and clown* (*Ode on a Nightingale* by John Keats)

coalheaver NOUN a coalheaver loaded coal onto ships using a spade ❑ *Good, strong, wholesome medicine, as was given with great success to two Irish labourers and a coalheaver* (*Oliver Twist* by Charles Dickens)

coal-whippers NOUN men who worked at docks using machines to load coal onto ships ❑ *here, were colliers by the score and score, with the coal-whippers plunging off stages on deck* (*Great Expectations* by Charles Dickens)

cobweb NOUN a cobweb is the net which a spider makes for catching insects ❑ *the walls and ceilings were all hung round with cobwebs* (*Gulliver's Travels* by Jonathan Swift)

coddling VERB coddling means to treat someone too kindly or protect them too much ❑ *and I've been coddling the fellow as if I'd been his grandmother* (*Little Women* by Louisa May Alcott)

coil NOUN coil means noise or fuss or disturbance ❑ *What a coil is there?* (*Doctor Faustus 4.7* by Christopher Marlowe)

collared VERB to collar something is a slang term which means to capture. In this sentence, it means he stole it [the money] ❑ *he collared it* (*The Adventures of Huckleberry Finn* by Mark Twain)

colling VERB colling is an old word which means to embrace and kiss ❑ *and no clasping and colling at all* (*Tess of the D'Urbervilles* by Thomas Hardy)

colloquies NOUN colloquy is a formal conversation or dialogue ❑ *Such colloquies have occupied many a pair of pale-faced weavers* (*Silas Marner* by George Eliot)

comfit NOUN sugar-covered pieces of fruit or nut eaten as sweets ❑ *and pulled out a box of comfits* (*Alice's Adventures in Wonderland* by Lewis Carroll)

coming out VERB when a girl came out in society it meant she was of marriageable age. In order to "come out" girls were expecting to attend balls and other parties during a season ❑ *The younger girls formed hopes of coming out a year or two sooner than they might otherwise have done* (*Pride and Prejudice* by Jane Austen)

commit VERB commit means arrest or stop ❑ *Commit the rascals* (*Doctor Faustus 4.7* by Christopher Marlowe)

commodious ADJ commodious means convenient ❑ *the most commodious and effectual ways* (*Gulliver's Travels* by Jonathan Swift)

commons NOUN commons is an old term meaning food shared with others ❑ *his pauper assistants ranged themselves behind him; the gruel was served out; and a long grace was said over the short commons.* (*Oliver Twist* by Charles Dickens)

complacency NOUN here complacency means a desire to please others. To-day complacency means feeling pleased with oneself without good reason. ❑ *Twas thy power that raised the first complacency in me* (*The Prelude* by William Wordsworth)

complaisance NOUN complaisance was eagerness to please ❑ *we cannot wonder at his complaisance* (*Pride and Prejudice* by Jane Austen)

complaisant ADJ complaisant means polite ❑ *extremely cheerful and complaisant to their guest* (*Gulliver's Travels* by Jonathan Swift)

conning VERB conning means learning by heart ❑ *Or conning more* (*The Prelude* by William Wordsworth)

consequent NOUN consequence ❑ *as avarice is the necessary consequent of old age* (*Gulliver's Travels* by Jonathan Swift)

consorts NOUN concerts ❑ *The King, who delighted in music, had frequent consorts at Court* (*Gulliver's Travels* by Jonathan Swift)

conversible ADJ conversible meant easy to talk to, companionable ❑ *He can be a conversible companion* (*Pride and Prejudice* by Jane Austen)

copper NOUN a copper is a large pot that can be heated directly over a fire ❑ *He gazed in stupefied aston-ishment on the small rebel for some seconds, and then clung for support to the copper* (*Oliver Twist* by Charles Dickens)

copper-stick NOUN a copper-stick is the long piece of wood used to stir washing in the copper (or boiler) which was usually the biggest cooking pot in the house ❑ *It was Christmas Eve, and I had to stir the pudding for next day, with a copper-stick, from seven to eight by the Dutch clock* (*Great Expectations* by Charles Dickens)

counting-house NOUN a counting-house is a place where accountants work ❑ *Once upon a time–of all the good days in the year, on Christmas Eve–old Scrooge sat busy in his counting-house* (*A Christmas Carol* by Charles Dickens)

courtier NOUN a courtier is someone who attends the king or queen–a member of the court ❑ *next the ten courtiers;* (*Alice's Adventures in Wonderland* by Lewis Carroll)

covies NOUN covies were flocks of partridges ❑ *and will save all of the best covies for you* (*Pride and Prejudice* by Jane Austen)

cowed VERB cowed means frightened or intimidated ❑ *it cowed me more than the pain* (*Treasure Island* by Robert Louis Stevenson)

cozened VERB cozened means tricked or deceived ❑ *Do you remember, sir, how you cozened me* (*Doctor Faustus 4.7* by Christopher Marlowe)

cravats NOUN a cravat is a folded cloth that a man wears wrapped around his neck as a decorative item of clothing ❑ *we'd 'a' slept in our cravats to-night* (*The Adventures of Huckleberry Finn* by Mark Twain)

crock and dirt PHRASE crock and dirt is an old expression meaning soot and dirt ❑ *and the mare catching cold at the door, and the boy grimed with crock and dirt* (*Great Expectations* by Charles Dickens)

crockery NOUN here crockery means pottery ❑ *By one of the parrots was a cat made of crockery* (*The Adventures of Huckleberry Finn* by Mark Twain)

crooked sixpence PHRASE it was considered unlucky to have a bent sixpence ❑ *You've got the beauty, you see, and I've got the luck, so you must keep me by you for your crooked sixpence* (*Silas Marner* by George Eliot)

croquet NOUN croquet is a traditional English summer game in which players try to hit wooden balls through hoops ❑ *and once she remembered trying to box her own* *ears for having cheated herself in a game of croquet* (Alice's Adventures in Wonderland by Lewis Carroll)

cross PREP across ❏ *The two great streets, which run cross and divide it into four quarters* (Gulliver's Travels by Jonathan Swift)

culpable ADJ if you are culpable for something it means you are to blame ❏ *deep are the sorrows that spring from false ideas for which no man is culpable.* (Silas Marner by George Eliot)

cultured ADJ cultivated ❏ *Nor less when spring had warmed the cultured Vale* (The Prelude by William Wordsworth)

cupidity NOUN cupidity is greed ❏ *These people hated me with the hatred of cupidity and disappointment.* (Great Expectations by Charles Dickens)

curricle NOUN an open two-wheeled carriage with one seat for the driver and space for a single passenger ❏ *and they saw a lady and a gentleman in a curricle* (Pride and Prejudice by Jane Austen)

cynosure NOUN a cynosure is something that strongly attracts attention or admiration ❏ *Then I thought of Eliza and Georgiana; I beheld one the cynosure of a ballroom, the other the inmate of a convent cell* (Jane Eyre by Charlotte Brontë)

dalliance NOUN someone's dalliance with something is a brief involvement with it ❏ *nor sporting in the dalliance of love* (Doctor Faustus Chorus by Christopher Marlowe)

darkling ADV darkling is an archaic way of saying in the dark ❏ *Darkling I listen* (Ode on a Nightingale by John Keats)

delf-case NOUN a sideboard for holding dishes and crockery ❏ *at the pewter dishes and delf-case* (Wuthering Heights by Emily Brontë)

determined ■ VERB here determined means ended ❏ *and be out of vogue when that was determined* (Gulliver's Travels by Jonathan Swift) ■ VERB determined can mean to have been learned or found especially by investigation or experience ❏ *All the sensitive feelings it wounded so cruelly, all the shame and misery it kept alive within my breast, became more poignant as I thought of this; and I determined that the life was unendurable* (David Copperfield by Charles Dickens)

Deuce NOUN a slang term for the Devil ❏ *Ah, I dare say I did. Deuce take me, he added suddenly, I know I did. I find I am not quite unscrewed yet.* (Great Expectations by Charles Dickens)

diabolical ADJ diabolical means devilish or evil ❏ *and with a thousand diabolical expressions* (Treasure Island by Robert Louis Stevenson)

direction NOUN here direction means address ❏ *Elizabeth was not surprised at it, as Jane had written the direction remarkably ill* (Pride and Prejudice by Jane Austen)

discover VERB to make known or announce ❏ *the Emperor would discover the secret while I was out of his power* (Gulliver's Travels by Jonathan Swift)

dissemble VERB hide or conceal ❏ *Dissemble nothing* (On His Mistress by John Donne)

dissolve VERB dissolve here means to release from life, to die ❏ *Fade far away, dissolve, and quite forget* (Ode on a Nightingale by John Keats)

distrain VERB to distrain is to seize the property of someone who is in debt in compensation for the money owed ❏ *for he's threatening to distrain for it* (Silas Marner by George Eliot)

Divan NOUN a Divan was originally a Turkish council of state–the name was transferred to the couches they sat on and is used to mean this in English ❏ *Mr Brass applauded this picture very much, and the bed being soft and comfortable, Mr Quilp determined to use it, both as a sleeping place by night and as a kind of Divan by day.* (*The Old Curiosity Shop* by Charles Dickens)

divorcement NOUN separation ❏ *By all pains which want and divorcement hath* (*On His Mistress* by John Donne)

dog in the manger, PHRASE this phrase describes someone who prevents you from enjoying something that they themselves have no need for ❏ *You are a dog in the manger, Cathy, and desire no one to be loved but yourself* (*Wuthering Heights* by Emily Brontë)

dolorifuge NOUN dolorifuge is a word which Thomas Hardy invented. It means pain-killer or comfort ❏ *as a species of dolorifuge* (*Tess of the D'Urbervilles* by Thomas Hardy)

dome NOUN building ❏ *that river and that mouldering dome* (*The Prelude* by William Wordsworth)

domestic NOUN here domestic means a person's management of the house ❏ *to give some account of my domestic* (*Gulliver's Travels* by Jonathan Swift)

dunce NOUN a dunce is another word for idiot ❏ *Do you take me for a dunce? Go on?* (*Alice's Adventures in Wonderland* by Lewis Carroll)

Ecod EXCLAM a slang exclamation meaning "oh God!" ❏ *"Ecod," replied Wemmick, shaking his head, "that's not my trade."* (*Great Expectations* by Charles Dickens)

egg-hot NOUN an egg-hot (see also "flip" and "negus") was a hot drink made from beer and eggs, sweetened with nutmeg ❏ *She fainted when she saw me return, and made a little jug of egg-hot afterwards to console us while we talked it over.* (*David Copperfield* by Charles Dickens)

encores NOUN an encore is a short extra performance at the end of a longer one, which the entertainer gives because the audience has enthusiastically asked for it ❏ *we want a little something to answer encores with, anyway* (*The Adventures of Huckleberry Finn* by Mark Twain)

equipage NOUN an elegant and impressive carriage ❏ *and besides, the equipage did not answer to any of their neighbours* (*Pride and Prejudice* by Jane Austen)

exordium NOUN an exordium is the opening part of a speech ❏ *"Now, Handel," as if it were the grave beginning of a portentous business exordium, he had suddenly given up that tone* (*Great Expectations* by Charles Dickens)

expect VERB here expect means to wait for ❏ *to expect his farther commands* (*Gulliver's Travels* by Jonathan Swift)

familiars NOUN familiars means spirits or devils who come to someone when they are called ❏ *I'll turn all the lice about thee into familiars* (*Doctor Faustus* 1.4 by Christopher Marlowe)

fantods NOUN a fantod is a person who fidgets or can't stop moving nervously ❏ *It most give me the fantods* (*The Adventures of Huckleberry Finn* by Mark Twain)

farthing NOUN a farthing is an old unit of British currency which was worth a quarter of a penny ❏ *Not a farthing less. A great many back-payments are included in it, I assure you.* (*A Christmas Carol* by Charles Dickens)

farthingale NOUN a hoop worn under a skirt to extend it ❏ *A bell with an old voice–which I dare say in its time had often said to the house, Here is the green farthingale* (*Great Expectations* by Charles Dickens)

favours NOUN here favours is an old word which means ribbons ❏ *A* group of humble mourners entered the gate: wearing white favours (*Oliver Twist* by Charles Dickens)

feigned VERB pretend or pretending ❑ *not my feigned page* (*On His Mistress* by John Donne)

fence ■ NOUN a fence is someone who receives and sells stolen goods ❑ *What are you up to? Ill-treating the boys, you covetous, avaricious, in-sa-ti-a-ble old fence?* (*Oliver Twist* by Charles Dickens) ■ NOUN defence or protection ❑ *but honesty hath no fence against superior cunning* (*Gulliver's Travels* by Jonathan Swift)

fess ADJ fess is an old word which means pleased or proud ❑ *You'll be fess enough, my poppet* (*Tess of the D'Urbervilles* by Thomas Hardy)

fettered ADJ fettered means bound in chains or chained ❑ *"You are fettered," said Scrooge, trembling. "Tell me why?"* (*A Christmas Carol* by Charles Dickens)

fidges VERB fidges means fidgets, which is to keep moving your hands slightly because you are nervous or excited ❑ *Look, Jim, how my fingers fidges* (*Treasure Island* by Robert Louis Stevenson)

finger-post NOUN a finger-post is a sign-post showing the direction to different places ❑ *"The gallows," continued Fagin, "the gallows, my dear, is an ugly finger-post, which points out a very short and sharp turning that has stopped many a bold fellow's career on the broad highway."* (*Oliver Twist* by Charles Dickens)

fire-irons NOUN fire-irons are tools kept by the side of the fire to either cook with or look after the fire ❑ *the fire-irons came first* (*Alice's Adventures in Wonderland* by Lewis Carroll)

fire-plug NOUN a fire-plug is another word for a fire hydrant ❑ *The pony looked with great attention into a*

fire-plug, which was near him, and appeared to be quite absorbed in contemplating it (*The Old Curiosity Shop* by Charles Dickens)

flank NOUN flank is the side of an animal ❑ *And all her silken flanks with garlands dressed* (*Ode on a Grecian Urn* by John Keats)

flip NOUN a flip is a drink made from warmed ale, sugar, spice and beaten egg ❑ *The events of the day, in combination with the twins, if not with the flip, had made Mrs. Micawber hysterical, and she shed tears as she replied* (*David Copperfield* by Charles Dickens)

flit VERB flit means to move quickly ❑ *and if he had meant to flit to Thrushcross Grange* (*Wuthering Heights* by Emily Brontë)

floorcloth NOUN a floorcloth was a hard-wearing piece of canvas used instead of carpet ❑ *This avenging phantom was ordered to be on duty at eight on Tuesday morning in the hall (it was two feet square, as charged for floorcloth)* (*Great Expectations* by Charles Dickens)

fly-driver NOUN a fly-driver is a carriage drawn by a single horse ❑ *The fly-drivers, among whom I inquired next, were equally jocose and equally disrespectful* (*David Copperfield* by Charles Dickens)

fob NOUN a small pocket in which a watch is kept ❑ *"Certain," replied the man, drawing a gold watch from his fob* (*Oliver Twist* by Charles Dickens)

folly NOUN folly means foolishness or stupidity ❑ *the folly of beginning a work* (*Robinson Crusoe* by Daniel Defoe)

fond ADJ fond means foolish ❑ *Fond worldling* (*Doctor Faustus 5.2* by Christopher Marlowe)

fondness NOUN silly or foolish affection ❑ *They have no fondness for their colts or foals* (*Gulliver's Travels* by Jonathan Swift)

for his fancy PHRASE for his fancy means for his liking or as he wanted ❑ *and as I did not obey quick enough for his fancy* (*Treasure Island* by Robert Louis Stevenson)

forlorn ADJ lost or very upset ❑ *you are from that day forlorn* (*Gulliver's Travels* by Jonathan Swift)

foster-sister NOUN a foster-sister was someone brought up by the same nurse or in the same household ❑ *I had been his foster-sister* (*Wuthering Heights* by Emily Brontë)

fox-fire NOUN fox-fire is a weak glow that is given off by decaying, rotten wood ❑ *what we must have was a lot of them rotten chunks that's called fox-fire* (*The Adventures of Huckleberry Finn* by Mark Twain)

frozen sea PHRASE the Arctic Ocean ❑ *into the frozen sea* (*Gulliver's Travels* by Jonathan Swift)

gainsay VERB to gainsay something is to say it isn't true or to deny it ❑ *"So she had," cried Scrooge. "You're right. I'll not gainsay it, Spirit. God forbid!"* (*A Christmas Carol* by Charles Dickens)

gaiters NOUN gaiters were leggings made of a cloth or piece of leather which covered the leg from the knee to the ankle ❑ *Mr Knightley was hard at work upon the lower buttons of his thick leather gaiters* (*Emma* by Jane Austen)

galluses NOUN galluses is an old spelling of gallows, and here means suspenders. Suspenders are straps worn over someone's shoulders and fastened to their trousers to prevent the trousers falling down ❑ *and home-knit galluses* (*The Adventures of Huckleberry Finn* by Mark Twain)

galoot NOUN a sailor but also a clumsy person ❑ *and maybe a galoot on it chopping* (*The Adventures of Huckleberry Finn* by Mark Twain)

gayest ADJ gayest means the most lively and bright or merry ❑ *Beth played her gayest march* (*Little Women* by Louisa May Alcott)

gem NOUN here gem means jewellery ❑ *the mountain shook off turf and flower, had only heath for raiment and crag for gem* (*Jane Eyre* by Charlotte Brontë)

giddy ADJ giddy means dizzy ❑ *and I wish you wouldn't keep appearing and vanishing so suddenly; you make one quite giddy.* (*Alice's Adventures in Wonderland* by Lewis Carroll)

gig NOUN a light two-wheeled carriage ❑ *when a gig drove up to the garden gate: out of which there jumped a fat gentleman* (*Oliver Twist* by Charles Dickens)

gladsome ADJ gladsome is an old word meaning glad or happy ❑ *Nobody ever stopped him in the street to say, with gladsome looks* (*A Christmas Carol* by Charles Dickens)

glen NOUN a glen is a small valley; the word is used commonly in Scotland ❑ *a beck which follows the bend of the glen* (*Wuthering Heights* by Emily Brontë)

gravelled VERB gravelled is an old term which means to baffle or defeat someone ❑ *Gravelled the pastors of the German Church* (*Doctor Faustus 1.1* by Christopher Marlowe)

grinder NOUN a grinder was a private tutor ❑ *but that when he had had the happiness of marrying Mrs Pocket very early in his life, he had impaired his prospects and taken up the calling of a Grinder* (*Great Expectations* by Charles Dickens)

gruel NOUN gruel is a thin, watery cornmeal or oatmeal soup ❑ *and the little saucepan of gruel (Scrooge had a cold in his head) upon the hob.* (*A Christmas Carol* by Charles Dickens)

guinea, half a NOUN half a guinea was ten shillings and sixpence ❑ *but* *lay out half a guinea at Ford's* (*Emma* by Jane Austen)

gull VERB gull is an old term which means to fool or deceive someone ❑ *Hush, I'll gull him supernaturally* (*Doctor Faustus 3.4* by Christopher Marlowe)

gunnel NOUN the gunnel, or gunwale, is the upper edge of a boat's side ❑ *But he put his foot on the gunnel and rocked her* (*The Adventures of Huckleberry Finn* by Mark Twain)

gunwale NOUN the side of a ship ❑ *He dipped his hand in the water over the boat's gunwale* (*Great Expectations* by Charles Dickens)

Gytrash NOUN a Gytrash is an omen of misfortune to the superstitious, usually taking the form of a hound ❑ *I remembered certain of Bessie's tales, wherein figured a North-of-England spirit, called a "Gytrash"* (*Jane Eyre* by Charlotte Brontë)

hackney-cabriolet NOUN a two-wheeled carriage with four seats for hire and pulled by a horse ❑ *A hackney-cabriolet was in waiting; with the same vehemence which she had exhibited in addressing Oliver, the girl pulled him in with her, and drew the curtains close.* (*Oliver Twist* by Charles Dickens)

hackney-coach NOUN a four-wheeled horse-drawn vehicle for hire ❑ *The twilight was beginning to close in, when Mr. Brownlow alighted from a hackney-coach at his own door, and knocked softly.* (*Oliver Twist* by Charles Dickens)

haggler NOUN a haggler is someone who travels from place to place selling small goods and items ❑ *when I be plain Jack Durbeyfield, the haggler* (*Tess of the D'Urbervilles* by Thomas Hardy)

halter NOUN a halter is a rope or strap used to lead an animal or to tie it up ❑ *I had of course long been used to a halter and a headstall* (*Black Beauty* by Anna Sewell)

hamlet NOUN a hamlet is a small village or a group of houses in the countryside ❑ *down from the hamlet* (*Treasure Island* by Robert Louis Stevenson)

hand-barrow NOUN a hand-barrow is a device for carrying heavy objects. It is like a wheelbarrow except that it has handles, rather than wheels, for moving the barrow ❑ *his sea chest following behind him in a hand-barrow* (*Treasure Island* by Robert Louis Stevenson)

handspike NOUN a handspike was a stick which was used as a lever ❑ *a bit of stick like a handspike* (*Treasure Island* by Robert Louis Stevenson)

haply ADV haply means by chance or perhaps ❑ *And haply the Queen-Moon is on her throne* (*Ode on a Nightingale* by John Keats)

harem NOUN the harem was the part of the house where the women lived ❑ *mostly they hang round the harem* (*The Adventures of Huckleberry Finn* by Mark Twain)

hautboys NOUN hautboys are oboes ❑ *sausages and puddings resembling flutes and hautboys* (*Gulliver's Travels* by Jonathan Swift)

hawker NOUN a hawker is someone who sells goods to people as he travels rather than from a fixed place like a shop ❑ *to buy some stockings from a hawker* (*Treasure Island* by Robert Louis Stevenson)

hawser NOUN a hawser is a rope used to tie up or tow a ship or boat ❑ *Again among the tiers of shipping, in and out, avoiding rusty chain-cables, frayed hempen hawsers* (*Great Expectations* by Charles Dickens)

headstall NOUN the headstall is the part of the bridle or halter that goes around a horse's head ❑ *I had of course long been used to a halter and a headstall* (*Black Beauty* by Anna Sewell)

hearken VERB hearken means to listen ❑ *though we sometimes stopped to* lay hold of each other and hearken (*Treasure Island* by Robert Louis Stevenson)

heartless ADJ here heartless means without heart or dejected ❑ *I am not heartless* (*The Prelude* by William Wordsworth)

hebdomadal ADJ hebdomadal means weekly ❑ *It was the hebdomadal treat to which we all looked forward from Sabbath to Sabbath* (*Jane Eyre* by Charlotte Brontë)

highwaymen NOUN highwaymen were people who stopped travellers and robbed them ❑ *We are high-waymen* (*The Adventures of Huckleberry Finn* by Mark Twain)

hinds NOUN hinds means farm hands, or people who work on a farm ❑ *He called his hinds about him* (*Gulliver's Travels* by Jonathan Swift)

histrionic ADJ if you refer to some-one's behaviour as histrionic, you are being critical of it because it is dramatic and exaggerated ❑ *But the histrionic muse is the darling* (*The Adventures of Huckleberry Finn* by Mark Twain)

hogs NOUN hogs is another word for pigs ❑ *Tom called the hogs "ingots"* (*The Adventures of Huckleberry Finn* by Mark Twain)

horrors NOUN the horrors are a fit, called delirium tremens, which is caused by drinking too much alcohol ❑ *I'll have the horrors* (*Treasure Island* by Robert Louis Stevenson)

huffy ADJ huffy means to be obviously annoyed or offended about some-thing ❑ *They will feel that more than angry speeches or huffy actions* (*Little Women* by Louisa May Alcott)

hulks NOUN hulks were prison-ships ❑ *The miserable companion of thieves and ruffians, the fallen outcast of low haunts, the associate of the scourings of the jails and hulks* (*Oliver Twist* by Charles Dickens)

humbug NOUN humbug means nonsense or rubbish ❑ *"Bah," said Scrooge. "Humbug!"* (*A Christmas Carol* by Charles Dickens)

humours NOUN it was believed that there were four fluids in the body called humours which decided the temperament of a person depending on how much of each fluid was present ❑ *other peccant humours* (*Gulliver's Travels* by Jonathan Swift)

husbandry NOUN husbandry is farming animals ❑ *bad husbandry were plentifully anointing their wheels* (*Silas Marner* by George Eliot)

huswife NOUN a huswife was a small sewing kit ❑ *but I had put my huswife on it* (*Emma* by Jane Austen)

ideal ADJ ideal in this context means imaginary ❑ *I discovered the yell was not ideal* (*Wuthering Heights* by Emily Brontë)

If our two PHRASE if both our ❑ *If our two loves be one* (*The Good-Morrow* by John Donne)

ignis-fatuus NOUN ignis-fatuus is the light given out by burning marsh gases, which lead careless travellers into danger ❑ *it is madness in all women to let a secret love kindle within them, which, if unreturned and unknown, must devour the life that feeds it; and, if discovered and responded to, must lead ignis-fatuus-like, into miry wilds whence there is no extrication.* (*Jane Eyre* by Charlotte Brontë)

imaginations NOUN here imaginations means schemes or plans ❑ *soon drove out those imaginations* (*Gulliver's Travels* by Jonathan Swift)

impressible ADJ impressible means open or impressionable ❑ *for Marner had one of those impressible, self-doubting natures* (*Silas Marner* by George Eliot)

in good intelligence PHRASE friendly with each other ❑ *that these two persons were in good intelligence with each other* (*Gulliver's Travels* by Jonathan Swift)

inanity NOUN inanity is silliness or dull stupidity ❏ *Do we not wile away moments of inanity* (*Silas Marner* by George Eliot)

incivility NOUN incivility means rudeness or impoliteness ❏ *if it's only for a piece of incivility like to-night's* (*Treasure Island* by Robert Louis Stevenson)

indigenae NOUN indigenae means natives or people from that area ❏ *an exotic that the surly indigenae will not recognise for kin* (*Wuthering Heights* by Emily Brontë)

indocible ADJ unteachable ❏ *so they were the most restive and indocible* (*Gulliver's Travels* by Jonathan Swift)

ingenuity NOUN inventiveness ❏ *entreated me to give him something as an encouragement to ingenuity* (*Gulliver's Travels* by Jonathan Swift)

ingots NOUN an ingot is a lump of a valuable metal like gold, usually shaped like a brick ❏ *Tom called the hogs "ingots"* (*The Adventures of Huckleberry Finn* by Mark Twain)

inkstand NOUN an inkstand is a pot which was put on a desk to contain either ink or pencils and pens ❏ *throwing an inkstand at the Lizard as she spoke* (*Alice's Adventures in Wonderland* by Lewis Carroll)

inordinate ADJ without order. To-day inordinate means "excessive". ❏ *Though yet untutored and inordinate* (*The Prelude* by William Wordsworth)

intellectuals NOUN here intellectuals means the minds (of the workmen) ❏ *those instructions they give being too refined for the intellectuals of their workmen* (*Gulliver's Travels* by Jonathan Swift)

interview NOUN meeting ❏ *By our first strange and fatal interview* (*On His Mistress* by John Donne)

jacks NOUN jacks are rods for turning a spit over a fire ❏ *It was a small bit*

of pork suspended from the kettle hanger by a string passed through a large door key, in a way known to primitive housekeepers unpossessed of jacks (*Silas Marner* by George Eliot)

jews-harp NOUN a jews-harp is a small, metal, musical instrument that is played by the mouth ❏ *A jews-harp's plenty good enough for a rat* (*The Adventures of Huckleberry Finn* by Mark Twain)

jorum NOUN a large bowl ❏ *while Miss Skiffins brewed such a jorum of tea, that the pig in the back premises became strongly excited* (*Great Expectations* by Charles Dickens)

jostled VERB jostled means bumped or pushed by someone or some people ❏ *being jostled into the kennel* (*Gulliver's Travels* by Jonathan Swift)

keepsake NOUN a keepsake is a gift which reminds someone of an event or of the person who gave it to them. ❏ *books and ornaments they had in their boudoirs at home: keepsakes that different relations had presented to them* (*Jane Eyre* by Charlotte Brontë)

kenned VERB kenned means knew ❏ *though little kenned the lamplighter that he had any company but Christmas!* (*A Christmas Carol* by Charles Dickens)

kennel NOUN kennel means gutter, which is the edge of a road next to the pavement, where rain water collects and flows away ❏ *being jostled himself into the kennel* (*Gulliver's Travels* by Jonathan Swift)

knock-knee ADJ knock-knee means slanted, at an angle. ❏ *LOT 1 was marked in whitewashed knock-knee letters on the brewhouse* (*Great Expectations* by Charles Dickens)

ladylike ADJ to be ladylike is to behave in a polite, dignified and graceful way ❏ *No, winking isn't ladylike* (*Little Women* by Louisa May Alcott)

lapse NOUN flow ❑ *Stealing with silent lapse to join the brook* (*The Prelude* by William Wordsworth)

larry NOUN larry is an old word which means commotion or noisy celebration ❑ *That was all a part of the larry!* (*Tess of the D'Urbervilles* by Thomas Hardy)

laths NOUN laths are strips of wood ❑ *The panels shrunk, the windows cracked; fragments of plaster fell out of the ceiling, and the naked laths were shown instead* (*A Christmas Carol* by Charles Dickens)

leer NOUN a leer is an unpleasant smile ❑ *with a kind of leer* (*Treasure Island* by Robert Louis Stevenson)

lenitives NOUN these are different kinds of drugs or medicines: lenitives and palliatives were pain relievers; aperitives were laxatives; abstersives caused vomiting; corrosives destroyed human tissue; restringents caused constipation; cephalalgics stopped headaches; icterics were used as medicine for jaundice; apophlegmatics were cough medicine, and acoustics were cures for the loss of hearing ❑ *lenitives, aperitives, abstersives, corrosives, restringents, palliatives, laxatives, cephalalgics, icterics, apophlegmatics, acoustics* (*Gulliver's Travels* by Jonathan Swift)

lest CONJ in case. If you do something lest something (usually) unpleasant happens you do it to try to prevent it happening ❑ *She went in without knocking, and hurried upstairs, in great fear lest she should meet the real Mary Ann* (*Alice's Adventures in Wonderland* by Lewis Carroll)

levee NOUN a levee is an old term for a meeting held in the morning, shortly after the person holding the meeting has got out of bed ❑ *I used to attend the King's levee once or twice a week* (*Gulliver's Travels* by Jonathan Swift)

life-preserver NOUN a club which had lead inside it to make it heavier and therefore more dangerous ❑ *and with no more suspicious articles displayed to view than two or three heavy bludgeons which stood in a corner, and a "life-preserver" that hung over the chimney-piece.* (*Oliver Twist* by Charles Dickens)

lighterman NOUN a lighterman is another word for sailor ❑ *in and out, hammers going in ship-builders' yards, saws going at timber, clashing engines going at things unknown, pumps going in leaky ships, capstans going, ships going out to sea, and unintelligible sea creatures roaring curses over the bulwarks at respondent lightermen* (*Great Expectations* by Charles Dickens)

livery NOUN servants often wore a uniform known as a livery ❑ *suddenly a footman in livery came running out of the wood* (*Alice's Adventures in Wonderland* by Lewis Carroll)

livid ADJ livid means pale or ash coloured. Livid also means very angry ❑ *a dirty, livid white* (*Treasure Island* by Robert Louis Stevenson)

lottery-tickets NOUN a popular card game ❑ *and Mrs. Philips protested that they would have a nice comfortable noisy game of lottery tickets* (*Pride and Prejudice* by Jane Austen)

lower and upper world PHRASE the earth and the heavens are the lower and upper worlds ❑ *the changes in the lower and upper world* (*Gulliver's Travels* by Jonathan Swift)

lustres NOUN lustres are chandeliers. A chandelier is a large, decorative frame which holds light bulbs or candles and hangs from the ceiling ❑ *the lustres, lights, the carving and the guilding* (*The Prelude* by William Wordsworth)

lynched VERB killed without a criminal trial by a crowd of people ❑ *He'll never know how nigh he come to getting lynched* (*The Adventures* of *Huckleberry Finn* by Mark Twain)

malingering VERB if someone is malingering they are pretending to be ill to avoid working ❑ *And you stand there malingering* (*Treasure Island* by Robert Louis Stevenson)

managing PHRASE treating with consideration ❑ *to think the honour of my own kind not worth managing* (*Gulliver's Travels* by Jonathan Swift)

manhood PHRASE manhood means human nature ❑ *concerning the nature of manhood* (*Gulliver's Travels* by Jonathan Swift)

man-trap NOUN a man-trap is a set of steel jaws that snap shut when trodden on and trap a person's leg ❑ *"Don't go to him," I called out of the window, "he's an assassin! A man-trap!"* (*Oliver Twist* by Charles Dickens)

maps NOUN charts of the night sky ❑ *Let maps to others, worlds on worlds have shown* (*The Good-Morrow* by John Donne)

mark VERB look at or notice ❑ *Mark but this flea, and mark in this* (*The Flea* by John Donne)

maroons NOUN A maroon is someone who has been left in a place which it is difficult for them to escape from, like a small island ❑ *if schooners, islands, and maroons* (*Treasure Island* by Robert Louis Stevenson)

mast NOUN here mast means the fruit of forest trees ❑ *a quantity of acorns, dates, chestnuts, and other mast* (*Gulliver's Travels* by Jonathan Swift)

mate VERB defeat ❑ *Where Mars did mate the warlike Carthigens* (*Doctor Faustus Chorus* by Christopher Marlowe)

mealy ADJ Mealy when used to describe a face meant pallid, pale or colourless ❑ *I only know two sorts of boys. Mealy boys, and beef-faced boys* (*Oliver Twist* by Charles Dickens)

middling ADV fairly or moderately ❑ *she worked me middling hard for about an hour* (*The Adventures of Huckleberry Finn* by Mark Twain)

mill NOUN a mill, or treadmill, was a device for hard labour or punishment in prison ❑ *Was you never on the mill?* (*Oliver Twist* by Charles Dickens)

milliner's shop NOUN a milliner's sold fabrics, clothing, lace and accessories; as time went on they specialized more and more in hats ❑ *to pay their duty to their aunt and to a milliner's shop just over the way* (*Pride and Prejudice* by Jane Austen)

minching un' munching PHRASE how people in the north of England used to describe the way people from the south speak ❑ *Minching un' munching!* (*Wuthering Heights* by Emily Brontë)

mine NOUN gold ❑ *Whether both th'Indias of spice and mine* (*The Sun Rising* by John Donne)

mire NOUN mud ❑ *Tis my fate to be always ground into the mire under the iron heel of oppression* (*The Adventures of Huckleberry Finn* by Mark Twain)

miscellany NOUN a miscellany is a collection of many different kinds of things ❑ *under that, the miscellany began* (*Treasure Island* by Robert Louis Stevenson)

mistarshers NOUN mistarshers means moustache, which is the hair that grows on a man's upper lip ❑ *when he put his hand up to his mistarshers* (*Tess of the D'Urbervilles* by Thomas Hardy)

morrow NOUN here good-morrow means tomorrow and a new and better life ❑ *And now good-morrow to our waking souls* (*The Good-Morrow* by John Donne)

mortification NOUN mortification is an old word for gangrene which is when part of the body decays or "dies" because of disease ❑ *Yes, it was a mortification–that was it* (*The*

Adventures of Huckleberry Finn by Mark Twain)

mought VERB mought is an old spelling of might ❑ *what you mought call me? You mought call me captain* (*Treasure Island* by Robert Louis Stevenson)

move VERB move me not means do not make me angry ❑ *Move me not, Faustus* (*Doctor Faustus 2.1* by Christopher Marlowe)

muffin-cap NOUN a muffin-cap is a flat cap made from wool ❑ *the old one, remained stationary in the muffin-cap and leathers* (*Oliver Twist* by Charles Dickens)

mulatter NOUN a mulatter was another word for mulatto, which is a person with parents who are from different races ❑ *a mulatter, most as white as a white man* (*The Adventures of Huckleberry Finn* by Mark Twain)

mummery NOUN mummery is an old word that meant meaningless (or pretentious) ceremony ❑ *When they were all gone, and when Trabb and his men—but not his boy: I looked for him—had crammed their mummery into bags, and were gone too, the house felt wholesomer.* (*Great Expectations* by Charles Dickens)

nap NOUN the nap is the woolly surface on a new item of clothing. Here the surface has been worn away so it looks bare ❑ *like an old hat with the nap rubbed off* (*The Adventures of Huckleberry Finn* by Mark Twain)

natural ■ NOUN a natural is a person born with learning difficulties ❑ *though he had been left to his particular care by their deceased father, who thought him almost a natural.* (*David Copperfield* by Charles Dickens) ■ ADJ natural meant illegitimate ❑ *Harriet Smith was the natural daughter of some-body* (*Emma* by Jane Austen)

navigator NOUN a navigator was orig-inally someone employed to dig canals. It is the origin of the word

"navvy" meaning a labourer ❑ *She ascertained from me in a few words what it was all about, comforted Dora, and gradually convinced her that I was not a labourer—from my manner of stating the case I believe Dora concluded that I was a navi-gator, and went balancing myself up and down a plank all day with a wheelbarrow—and so brought us together in peace.* (*David Copperfield* by Charles Dickens)

necromancy NOUN necromancy means a kind of magic where the magician speaks to spirits or ghosts to find out what will happen in the future ❑ *He surfeits upon cursed necro-mancy* (*Doctor Faustus chorus* by Christopher Marlowe)

negus NOUN a negus is a hot drink made from sweetened wine and water ❑ *He sat placidly perusing the newspaper, with his little head on one side, and a glass of warm sherry negus at his elbow.* (*David Copperfield* by Charles Dickens)

nice ADJ discriminating. Able to make good judgements or choices ❑ *consequently a claim to be nice* (*Emma* by Jane Austen)

nigh ADV nigh means near ❑ *He'll never know how nigh he come to getting lynched* (*The Adventures of Huckleberry Finn* by Mark Twain)

nimbleness NOUN nimbleness means being able to move very quickly or skilfully ❑ *and with incredible accuracy and nimbleness* (*Treasure Island* by Robert Louis Stevenson)

noggin NOUN a noggin is a small mug or a wooden cup ❑ *you'll bring me one noggin of rum* (*Treasure Island* by Robert Louis Stevenson)

none ADJ neither ❑ *none can die* (*The Good-Morrow* by John Donne)

notices NOUN observations ❑ *Arch are his notices* (*The Prelude* by William Wordsworth)

occiput NOUN occiput means the back of the head ❑ *saw off the occiput of* *each couple* (Gulliver's Travels by Jonathan Swift)

officiously ADV kindly ❑ *the governess who attended Glumdalclitch very officiously lifted me up* (Gulliver's Travels by Jonathan Swift)

old salt PHRASE old salt is a slang term for an experienced sailor ❑ *a "true sea-dog", and a "real old salt"* (Treasure Island by Robert Louis Stevenson)

or ere PHRASE before ❑ *or ere the Hall was built* (The Prelude by William Wordsworth)

ostler NOUN one who looks after horses at an inn ❑ *The bill paid, and the waiter remembered, and the ostler not forgotten, and the chambermaid taken into consideration* (Great Expectations by Charles Dickens)

ostry NOUN an ostry is an old word for a pub or hotel ❑ *lest I send you into the ostry with a vengeance* (Doctor Faustus 2.2 by Christopher Marlowe)

outrunning the constable PHRASE outrunning the constable meant spending more than you earn ❑ *but I shall by this means be able to check your bills and to pull you up if I find you outrunning the constable.* (Great Expectations by Charles Dickens)

over ADV across ❑ *It is in length six yards, and in the thickest part at least three yards over* (Gulliver's Travels by Jonathan Swift)

over the broomstick PHRASE this is a phrase meaning "getting married without a formal ceremony" ❑ *They both led tramping lives, and this woman in Gerrard-street here, had been married very young, over the broomstick (as we say), to a tramping man, and was a perfect fury in point of jealousy.* (Great Expectations by Charles Dickens)

own VERB own means to admit or to acknowledge ❑ *It's my old girl that advises. She has the head. But I never own to it before her. Discipline must be maintained* (Bleak House by Charles Dickens)

page NOUN here page means a boy employed to run errands ❑ *not my feigned page* (On His Mistress by John Donne)

paid pretty dear PHRASE paid pretty dear means paid a high price or suffered quite a lot ❑ *I paid pretty dear for my monthly fourpenny piece* (Treasure Island by Robert Louis Stevenson)

pannikins NOUN pannikins were small tin cups ❑ *of lifting light glasses and cups to his lips, as if they were clumsy pannikins* (Great Expectations by Charles Dickens)

pards NOUN pards are leopards ❑ *Not charioted by Bacchus and his pards* (Ode on a Nightingale by John Keats)

parlour boarder NOUN a pupil who lived with the family ❑ *and somebody had lately raised her from the condition of scholar to parlour boarder* (Emma by Jane Austen)

particular, a London PHRASE London in Victorian times and up to the 1950s was famous for having very dense fog–which was a combination of real fog and the smog of pollution from factories ❑ *This is a London particular . . . A fog, miss* (Bleak House by Charles Dickens)

patten NOUN pattens were wooden soles which were fixed to shoes by straps to protect the shoes in wet weather ❑ *carrying a basket like the Great Seal of England in plaited straw, a pair of pattens, a spare shawl, and an umbrella, though it was a fine bright day* (Great Expectations by Charles Dickens)

paviour NOUN a paviour was a labourer who worked on the street pavement ❑ *the paviour his pickaxe* (Oliver Twist by Charles Dickens)

peccant ADJ peccant means unhealthy ❑ *other peccant humours* (Gulliver's Travels by Jonathan Swift)

penetralium NOUN penetralium is a word used to describe the inner rooms of the house ❑ *and I had no desire to aggravate his impatience previous to inspecting the penetralium* (*Wuthering Heights* by Emily Brontë)

pensive ADV pensive means deep in thought or thinking seriously about something ❑ *and she was leaning pensive on a tomb-stone on her right elbow* (*The Adventures of Huckleberry Finn* by Mark Twain)

penury NOUN penury is the state of being extremely poor ❑ *Distress, if not penury, loomed in the distance* (*Tess of the D'Urbervilles* by Thomas Hardy)

perspective NOUN telescope ❑ *a pocket perspective* (*Gulliver's Travels* by Jonathan Swift)

phaeton NOUN a phaeton was an open carriage for four people ❑ *often condescends to drive by my humble abode in her little phaeton and ponies* (*Pride and Prejudice* by Jane Austen)

phantasm NOUN a phantasm is an illusion, something that is not real. It is sometimes used to mean ghost ❑ *Experience had bred no fancies in him that could raise the phantasm of appetite* (*Silas Marner* by George Eliot)

physic NOUN here physic means medicine ❑ *there I studied physic two years and seven months* (*Gulliver's Travels* by Jonathan Swift)

pinioned VERB to pinion is to hold both arms so that a person cannot move them ❑ *But the relentless Ghost pinioned him in both his arms, and forced him to observe what happened next.* (*A Christmas Carol* by Charles Dickens)

piquet NOUN piquet was a popular card game in the C18th ❑ *Mr Hurst and Mr Bingley were at piquet* (*Pride and Prejudice* by Jane Austen)

plaister NOUN a plaister is a piece of cloth on which an apothecary (or pharmacist) would spread ointment. The cloth is then applied to wounds or bruises to treat them ❑ *Then, she gave the knife a final smart wipe on the edge of the plaister, and then sawed a very thick round off the loaf: which she finally, before separating from the loaf, hewed into two halves, of which Joe got one, and I the other.* (*Great Expectations* by Charles Dickens)

plantations NOUN here plantations means colonies, which are countries controlled by a more powerful country ❑ *besides our plantations in America* (*Gulliver's Travels* by Jonathan Swift)

plastic ADJ here plastic is an old term meaning shaping or a power that was forming ❑ *A plastic power abode with me* (*The Prelude* by William Wordsworth)

players NOUN actors ❑ *of players which upon the world's stage be* (*On His Mistress* by John Donne)

plump ADV all at once, suddenly ❑ *But it took a bit of time to get it well round, the change come so uncommon plump, didn't it?* (*Great Expectations* by Charles Dickens)

plundered VERB to plunder is to rob or steal from ❑ *These crosses stand for the names of ships or towns that they sank or plundered* (*Treasure Island* by Robert Louis Stevenson)

pommel ■ VERB to pommel someone is to hit them repeatedly with your fists ❑ *hug him round the neck, pommel his back, and kick his legs in irrepressible affection!* (*A Christmas Carol* by Charles Dickens) ■ NOUN a pommel is the part of a saddle that rises up at the front ❑ *He had his gun across his pommel* (*The Adventures of Huckleberry Finn* by Mark Twain)

poor's rates NOUN poor's rates were property taxes which were used to support the poor ❑ *"Oh!" replied the undertaker; "why, you know, Mr. Bumble, I pay a good deal towards the poor's rates."* (*Oliver Twist* by Charles Dickens)

popular ADJ popular means ruled by the people, or Republican, rather than ruled by a monarch ❑ *With those of Greece compared and popular Rome* (*The Prelude* by William Wordsworth)

porringer NOUN a porringer is a small bowl ❑ *Of this festive composition each boy had one porringer, and no more* (*Oliver Twist* by Charles Dickens)

postboy NOUN a postboy was the driver of a horse-drawn carriage ❑ *He spoke to a postboy who was dozing under the gateway* (*Oliver Twist* by Charles Dickens)

post-chaise NOUN a fast carriage for two or four passengers ❑ *Looking round, he saw that it was a post-chaise, driven at great speed* (*Oliver Twist* by Charles Dickens)

postern NOUN a small gate usually at the back of a building ❑ *The little servant happening to be entering the fortress with two hot rolls, I passed through the postern and crossed the drawbridge, in her company* (*Great Expectations* by Charles Dickens)

pottle NOUN a pottle was a small basket ❑ *He had a paper-bag under each arm and a pottle of strawberries in one hand . . .* (*Great Expectations* by Charles Dickens)

pounce NOUN pounce is a fine powder used to prevent ink spreading on untreated paper ❑ *in that grim atmosphere of pounce and parchment, red-tape, dusty wafers, ink-jars, brief and draft paper, law reports, writs, declarations, and bills of costs* (*David Copperfield* by Charles Dickens)

pox NOUN pox means sexually transmitted diseases like syphilis ❑ *how the pox in all its consequences and denominations* (*Gulliver's Travels* by Jonathan Swift)

prelibation NOUN prelibation means a foretaste of or an example of something to come ❑ *A prelibation to the mower's scythe* (*The Prelude* by William Wordsworth)

prentice NOUN an apprentice ❑ *and Joe, sitting on an old gun, had told me that when I was 'prentice to him regularly bound, we would have such Larks there!* (*Great Expectations* by Charles Dickens)

presently ADV immediately ❑ *I presently knew what they meant* (*Gulliver's Travels* by Jonathan Swift)

pumpion NOUN pumpkin ❑ *for it was almost as large as a small pumpion* (*Gulliver's Travels* by Jonathan Swift)

punctual ADJ kept in one place ❑ *was not a punctual presence, but a spirit* (*The Prelude* by William Wordsworth)

quadrille ■ NOUN a quadrille is a dance invented in France which is usually performed by four couples ❑ *However, Mr Swiveller had Miss Sophy's hand for the first quadrille (country-dances being low, were utterly proscribed)* (*The Old Curiosity Shop* by Charles Dickens) ■ NOUN quadrille was a card game for four people ❑ *to make up her pool of quadrille in the evening* (*Pride and Prejudice* by Jane Austen)

quality NOUN gentry or upper-class people ❑ *if you are with the quality* (*The Adventures of Huckleberry Finn* by Mark Twain)

quick parts PHRASE quick-witted ❑ *Mr Bennet was so odd a mixture of quick parts* (*Pride and Prejudice* by Jane Austen)

quid NOUN a quid is something chewed or kept in the mouth, like a piece of tobacco ❑ *rolling his quid* (*Treasure Island* by Robert Louis Stevenson)

quit VERB quit means to avenge or to make even ❑ *But Faustus's death shall quit my infamy* (*Doctor Faustus 4.3* by Christopher Marlowe)

rags NOUN divisions ❏ *Nor hours, days, months, which are the rags of time* (*The Sun Rising* by John Donne)

raiment NOUN raiment means clothing ❏ *the mountain shook off turf and flower, had only heath for raiment and crag for gem* (*Jane Eyre* by Charlotte Brontë)

rain cats and dogs PHRASE an expression meaning rain heavily. The origin of the expression is unclear ❏ *But it'll perhaps rain cats and dogs to-morrow* (*Silas Marner* by George Eliot)

raised Cain PHRASE raised Cain means caused a lot of trouble. Cain is a character in the Bible who killed his brother Abel ❏ *and every time he got drunk he raised Cain around town* (*The Adventures of Huckleberry Finn* by Mark Twain)

rambling ADJ rambling means confused and not very clear ❏ *my head began to be filled very early with rambling thoughts* (*Robinson Crusoe* by Daniel Defoe)

raree-show NOUN a raree-show is an old term for a peep-show or a fairground entertainment ❏ *A raree-show is here, with children gathered round* (*The Prelude* by William Wordsworth)

recusants NOUN people who resisted authority ❏ *hardy recusants* (*The Prelude* by William Wordsworth)

redounding VERB eddying. An eddy is a movement in water or air which goes round and round instead of flowing in one direction ❏ *mists and steam-like fogs redounding everywhere* (*The Prelude* by William Wordsworth)

redundant ADJ here redundant means overflowing but Wordsworth also uses it to mean excessively large or too big ❏ *A tempest, a redundant energy* (*The Prelude* by William Wordsworth)

reflex NOUN reflex is a shortened version of reflexion, which is an alternative spelling of reflection ❏ *To cut across the reflex of a star* (*The Prelude* by William Wordsworth)

Reformatory NOUN a prison for young offenders/criminals ❏ *Even when I was taken to have a new suit of clothes, the tailor had orders to make them like a kind of Reformatory, and on no account to let me have the free use of my limbs.* (*Great Expectations* by Charles Dickens)

remorse NOUN pity or compassion ❏ *by that remorse* (*On His Mistress* by John Donne)

render VERB in this context render means give. ❏ *and Sarah could render no reason that would be sanctioned by the feeling of the community.* (*Silas Marner* by George Eliot)

repeater NOUN a repeater was a watch that chimed the last hour when a button was pressed–as a result it was useful in the dark ❏ *And his watch is a gold repeater, and worth a hundred pound if it's worth a penny.* (*Great Expectations* by Charles Dickens)

repugnance NOUN repugnance means a strong dislike of something or someone ❏ *overcoming a strong repugnance* (*Treasure Island* by Robert Louis Stevenson)

reverence NOUN reverence means bow. When you bow to someone, you briefly bend your body towards them as a formal way of showing them respect ❏ *made my reverence* (*Gulliver's Travels* by Jonathan Swift)

reverie NOUN a reverie is a daydream ❏ *I can guess the subject of your reverie* (*Pride and Prejudice* by Jane Austen)

revival NOUN a religious meeting held in public ❏ *well I'd ben a-running' a little temperance revival thar' bout a week* (*The Adventures of Huckleberry Finn* by Mark Twain)

revolt VERB revolt means turn back or stop your present course of action and go back to what you were doing before ❑ *Revolt, or I'll in piecemeal tear thy flesh* (*Doctor Faustus* 5.1 by Christopher Marlowe)

rheumatics/rheumatism NOUN rheumatics [rheumatism] is an illness that makes your joints or muscles stiff and painful ❑ *a new cure for the rheumatics* (*Treasure Island* by Robert Louis Stevenson)

riddance NOUN riddance is usually used in the form good riddance which you say when you are pleased that something has gone or been left behind ❑ *I'd better go into the house, and die and be a riddance* (*David Copperfield* by Charles Dickens)

rimy ADJ rimy is an adjective which means covered in ice or frost ❑ *It was a rimy morning, and very damp* (*Great Expectations* by Charles Dickens)

riper ADJ riper means more mature or older ❑ *At riper years to Wittenberg he went* (*Doctor Faustus chorus* by Christopher Marlowe)

rubber NOUN a set of games in whist or backgammon ❑ *her father was sure of his rubber* (*Emma* by Jane Austen)

ruffian NOUN a ruffian is a person who behaves violently ❑ *and when the ruffian had told him* (*Treasure Island* by Robert Louis Stevenson)

sadness NOUN sadness is an old term meaning seriousness ❑ *But I prithee tell me, in good sadness* (*Doctor Faustus* 2.2 by Christopher Marlowe)

sailed before the mast PHRASE this phrase meant someone who did not look like a sailor ❑ *he had none of the appearance of a man that sailed before the mast* (*Treasure Island* by Robert Louis Stevenson)

scabbard NOUN a scabbard is the covering for a sword or dagger ❑ *Girded round its middle was an antique scabbard; but no sword was in it, and the ancient sheath was eaten up with rust* (*A Christmas Carol* by Charles Dickens)

schooners NOUN A schooner is a fast, medium-sized sailing ship ❑ *if schooners, islands, and maroons* (*Treasure Island* by Robert Louis Stevenson)

science NOUN learning or knowledge ❑ *Even Science, too, at hand* (*The Prelude* by William Wordsworth)

scrouge VERB to scrouge means to squeeze or to crowd ❑ *to scrouge in and get a sight* (*The Adventures of Huckleberry Finn* by Mark Twain)

scrutore NOUN a scrutore, or escritoire, was a writing table ❑ *set me gently on my feet upon the scrutore* (*Gulliver's Travels* by Jonathan Swift)

scutcheon/escutcheon NOUN an escutcheon is a shield with a coat of arms, or the symbols of a family name, engraved on it ❑ *On the scutcheon we'll have a bend* (*The Adventures of Huckleberry Finn* by Mark Twain)

sea-dog PHRASE sea-dog is a slang term for an experienced sailor or pirate ❑ *a "true sea-dog", and a "real old salt,"* (*Treasure Island* by Robert Louis Stevenson)

see the lions PHRASE to see the lions was to go and see the sights of London. Originally the phrase referred to the menagerie in the Tower of London and later in Regent's Park ❑ *We will go and see the lions for an hour or two—it's something to have a fresh fellow like you to show them to, Copperfield* (*David Copperfield* by Charles Dickens)

self-conceit NOUN self-conceit is an old term which means having too high an opinion of oneself, or deceiving yourself ❑ *Till swollen with cunning, of a self-conceit* (*Doctor Faustus chorus* by Christopher Marlowe)

seneschal NOUN a steward ❑ *where a grey-headed seneschal sings a funny chorus with a funnier body of vassals* (*Oliver Twist* by Charles Dickens)

sensible ADJ if you were sensible of something you are aware or conscious of something ❑ *If my children are silly I must hope to be always sensible of it* (*Pride and Prejudice* by Jane Austen)

sessions NOUN court cases were heard at specific times of the year called sessions ❑ *He lay in prison very ill, during the whole interval between his committal for trial, and the coming round of the Sessions.* (*Great Expectations* by Charles Dickens)

shabby ADJ shabby places look old and in bad condition ❑ *a little bit of a shabby village named Pikesville* (*The Adventures of Huckleberry Finn* by Mark Twain)

shay-cart NOUN a shay-cart was a small cart drawn by one horse ❑ *"I were at the Bargemen t'other night, Pip;" whenever he subsided into affection, he called me Pip, and whenever he relapsed into politeness he called me Sir; "when there come up in his shay-cart Pumblechook."* (*Great Expectations* by Charles Dickens)

shilling NOUN a shilling is an old unit of currency. There were twenty shillings in every British pound ❑ *"Ten shillings too much," said the gentleman in the white waistcoat.* (*Oliver Twist* by Charles Dickens)

shines NOUN tricks or games ❑ *well, it would make a cow laugh to see the shines that old idiot cut* (*The Adventures of Huckleberry Finn* by Mark Twain)

shirking VERB shirking means not doing what you are meant to be doing, or evading your duties ❑ *some of you shirking lubbers* (*Treasure Island* by Robert Louis Stevenson)

shiver my timbers PHRASE shiver my timbers is an expression which was used by sailors and pirates to express surprise ❑ *why, shiver my timbers, if I hadn't forgotten my score!* (*Treasure Island* by Robert Louis Stevenson)

shoe-roses NOUN shoe-roses were roses made from ribbons which were stuck on to shoes as decoration ❑ *the very shoe-roses for Netherfield were got by proxy* (*Pride and Prejudice* by Jane Austen)

singular ADJ singular means very great and remarkable or strange ❑ *"Singular dream," he says* (*The Adventures of Huckleberry Finn* by Mark Twain)

sire NOUN sire is an old word which means lord or master or elder ❑ *She also defied her sire* (*Little Women* by Louisa May Alcott)

sixpence NOUN a sixpence was half of a shilling ❑ *if she had only a shilling in the world, she would be very lilkely to give away sixpence of it* (*Emma* by Jane Austen)

slavey NOUN the word slavey was used when there was only one servant in a house or boarding-house–so she had to perform all the duties of a larger staff ❑ *Two distinct knocks, sir, will produce the slavey at any time* (*The Old Curiosity Shop* by Charles Dickens)

slender ADJ weak ❑ *In slender accents of sweet verse* (*The Prelude* by William Wordsworth)

slop-shops NOUN slop-shops were shops where cheap ready-made clothes were sold. They mainly sold clothes to sailors ❑ *Accordingly, I took the jacket off, that I might learn to do without it; and carrying it under my arm, began a tour of inspection of the various slop-shops.* (*David Copperfield* by Charles Dickens)

sluggard NOUN a lazy person ❑ *"Stand up and repeat 'Tis the voice of the sluggard,'" said the Gryphon.*

(*Alice's Adventures in Wonderland* by Lewis Carroll)

smallpox NOUN smallpox is a serious infectious disease ❏ *by telling the men we had smallpox aboard* (*The Adventures of Huckleberry Finn* by Mark Twain)

smalls NOUN smalls are short trousers ❏ *It is difficult for a large-headed, small-eyed youth, of lumbering make and heavy countenance, to look dignified under any circumstances; but it is more especially so, when superadded to these personal attractions are a red nose and yellow smalls* (*Oliver Twist* by Charles Dickens)

sneeze-box NOUN a box for snuff was called a sneeze-box because sniffing snuff makes the user sneeze ❏ *To think of Jack Dawkins—lummy Jack—the Dodger—the Artful Dodger—going abroad for a common twopenny-halfpenny sneeze-box!* (*Oliver Twist* by Charles Dickens)

snorted VERB slept ❏ *Or snorted we in the Seven Sleepers' den?* (*The Good-Morrow* by John Donne)

snuff NOUN snuff is tobacco in powder form which is taken by sniffing ❏ *as he thrust his thumb and forefinger into the proffered snuff-box of the undertaker: which was an ingenious little model of a patent coffin.* (*Oliver Twist* by Charles Dickens)

soliloquized VERB to soliloquize is when an actor in a play speaks to himself or herself rather than to another actor ❏ *"A new servitude! There is something in that," I soliloquized (mentally, be it understood; I did not talk aloud)* (*Jane Eyre* by Charlotte Brontë)

sough NOUN a sough is a drain or a ditch ❏ *as you may have noticed the sough that runs from the marshes* (*Wuthering Heights* by Emily Brontë)

spirits NOUN a spirit is the nonphysical part of a person which is believed to remain alive after their death ❏ *that I might raise up spirits when I please* (*Doctor Faustus* 1.5 by Christopher Marlowe)

spleen ◼ NOUN here spleen means a type of sadness or depression which was thought to only affect the wealthy ❏ *yet here I could plainly discover the true seeds of spleen* (*Gulliver's Travels* by Jonathan Swift) ◼ NOUN irritability and low spirits ❏ *Adieu to disappointment and spleen* (*Pride and Prejudice* by Jane Austen)

spondulicks NOUN spondulicks is a slang word which means money ❏ *not for all his spondulicks and as much more on top of it* (*The Adventures of Huckleberry Finn* by Mark Twain)

stalled of VERB to be stalled of something is to be bored with it ❏ *I'm stalled of doing naught* (*Wuthering Heights* by Emily Brontë)

stanchion NOUN a stanchion is a pole or bar that stands upright and is used as a building support ❏ *and slid down a stanchion* (*The Adventures of Huckleberry Finn* by Mark Twain)

stang NOUN stang is another word for pole which was an old measurement ❏ *These fields were intermingled with woods of half a stang* (*Gulliver's Travels* by Jonathan Swift)

starlings NOUN a starling is a wall built around the pillars that support a bridge to protect the pillars ❏ *There were states of the tide when, having been down the river, I could not get back through the eddy-chafed arches and starlings of old London Bridge* (*Great Expectations* by Charles Dickens)

startings NOUN twitching or nighttime movements of the body ❏ *with midnight's startings* (*On His Mistress* by John Donne)

stomacher NOUN a panel at the front of a dress ❏ *but send her aunt the pattern of a stomacher* (*Emma* by Jane Austen)

stoop VERB swoop ❑ *Once a kite hovering over the garden made a stoop at me* (Gulliver's Travels by Jonathan Swift)

succedaneum NOUN a succedaneum is a substitute ❑ *But as a succedaneum* (The Prelude by William Wordsworth)

suet NOUN a hard animal fat used in cooking ❑ *and your jaws are too weak For anything tougher than suet* (Alice's Adventures in Wonderland by Lewis Carroll)

sultry ADJ sultry weather is hot and damp. Here sultry means unpleasant or risky ❑ *for it was getting pretty sultry for us* (The Adventures of Huckleberry Finn by Mark Twain)

summerset NOUN summerset is an old spelling of somersault. If someone does a somersault, they turn over completely in the air ❑ *I have seen him do the summerset* (Gulliver's Travels by Jonathan Swift)

supper NOUN supper was a light meal taken late in the evening. The main meal was dinner which was eaten at four or five in the afternoon ❑ *and the supper table was all set out* (Emma by Jane Austen)

surfeits VERB to surfeit in something is to have far too much of it, or to overindulge in it to an unhealthy degree ❑ *He surfeits upon cursed necromancy* (Doctor Faustus chorus by Christopher Marlowe)

surtout NOUN a surtout is a long close-fitting overcoat ❑ *He wore a long black surtout reaching nearly to his ankles* (The Old Curiosity Shop by Charles Dickens)

swath NOUN swath is the width of corn cut by a scythe ❑ *while thy hook Spares the next swath* (Ode to Autumn by John Keats)

sylvan ADJ sylvan means belonging to the woods ❑ *Sylvan historian* (Ode on a Grecian Urn by John Keats)

taction NOUN taction means touch. This means that the people had to be touched on the mouth or the ears to get their attention ❑ *without being roused by some external taction upon the organs of speech and hearing* (Gulliver's Travels by Jonathan Swift)

Tag and Rag and Bobtail PHRASE the riff-raff, or lower classes. Used in an insulting way ❑ *"No," said he; "not till it got about that there was no protection on the premises, and it come to be considered dangerous, with convicts and Tag and Rag and Bobtail going up and down."* (Great Expectations by Charles Dickens)

tallow NOUN tallow is hard animal fat that is used to make candles and soap ❑ *and a lot of tallow candles* (The Adventures of Huckleberry Finn by Mark Twain)

tan VERB to tan means to beat or whip ❑ *and if I catch you about that school I'll tan you good* (The Adventures of Huckleberry Finn by Mark Twain)

tanyard NOUN the tanyard is part of a tannery, which is a place where leather is made from animal skins ❑ *hid in the old tanyard* (The Adventures of Huckleberry Finn by Mark Twain)

tarry ADJ tarry means the colour of tar or black ❑ *his tarry pig-tail* (Treasure Island by Robert Louis Stevenson)

thereof PHRASE from there ❑ *By all desires which thereof did ensue* (On His Mistress by John Donne)

thick with, be PHRASE if you are "thick with someone" you are very close, sharing secrets–it is often used to describe people who are planning something secret ❑ *Hasn't he been thick with Mr Heathcliff lately?* (Wuthering Heights by Emily Brontë)

thimble NOUN a thimble is a small cover used to protect the finger while sewing ❑ *The paper had been sealed in several places by a thimble*

(*Treasure Island* by Robert Louis Stevenson)

thirtover ADJ thirtover is an old word which means obstinate or that someone is very determined to do want they want and can not be persuaded to do something in another way ❑ *I have been living on in a thirtover, lackadaisical way* (*Tess of the D'Urbervilles* by Thomas Hardy)

timbrel NOUN timbrel is a tambourine ❑ *What pipes and timbrels?* (*Ode on a Grecian Urn* by John Keats)

tin NOUN tin is slang for money/cash ❑ *Then the plain question is, an't it a pity that this state of things should continue, and how much better would it be for the old gentleman to hand over a reasonable amount of tin, and make it all right and comfortable* (*The Old Curiosity Shop* by Charles Dickens)

tincture NOUN a tincture is a medicine made with alcohol and a small amount of a drug ❑ *with ink composed of a cephalic tincture* (*Gulliver's Travels* by Jonathan Swift)

tithe NOUN a tithe is a tax paid to the church ❑ *and held farms which, speaking from a spiritual point of view, paid highly-desirable tithes* (*Silas Marner* by George Eliot)

towardly ADJ a towardly child is dutiful or obedient ❑ *and a towardly child* (*Gulliver's Travels* by Jonathan Swift)

toys NOUN trifles are things which are considered to have little importance, value, or significance ❑ *purchase my life from them by some bracelets, glass rings, and other toys* (*Gulliver's Travels* by Jonathan Swift)

tract NOUN a tract is a religious pamphlet or leaflet ❑ *and Joe Harper got a hymn-book and a tract* (*The Adventures of Huckleberry Finn* by Mark Twain)

train-oil NOUN train-oil is oil from whale blubber ❑ *The train-oil and*

gunpowder were shoved out of sight in a minute (*Wuthering Heights* by Emily Brontë)

tribulation NOUN tribulation means the suffering or difficulty you experience in a particular situation ❑ *Amy was learning this distinction through much tribulation* (*Little Women* by Louisa May Alcott)

trivet NOUN a trivet is a three-legged stand for resting a pot or kettle ❑ *a pocket-knife in his right; and a pewter pot on the trivet* (*Oliver Twist* by Charles Dickens)

trot line NOUN a trot line is a fishing line to which a row of smaller fishing lines are attached ❑ *when he got along I was hard at it taking up a trot line* (*The Adventures of Huckleberry Finn* by Mark Twain)

troth NOUN oath or pledge ❑ *I wonder, by my troth* (*The Good-Morrow* by John Donne)

truckle NOUN a truckle bedstead is a bed that is on wheels and can be slid under another bed to save space ❑ *It rose under my hand, and the door yielded. Looking in, I saw a lighted candle on a table, a bench, and a mattress on a truckle bedstead.* (*Great Expectations* by Charles Dickens)

trump NOUN a trump is a good, reliable person who can be trusted ❑ *This lad Hawkins is a trump, I perceive* (*Treasure Island* by Robert Louis Stevenson)

tucker NOUN a tucker is a frilly lace collar which is worn around the neck ❑ *Whereat Scrooge's niece's sister—the plump one with the lace tucker: not the one with the roses—blushed.* (*A Christmas Carol* by Charles Dickens)

tureen NOUN a large bowl with a lid from which soup or vegetables are served ❑ *Waiting in a hot tureen!* (*Alice's Adventures in Wonderland* by Lewis Carroll)

turnkey NOUN a prison officer; jailer ❑ *As we came out of the prison* *through the lodge, I found that the great importance of my guardian was appreciated by the turnkeys, no less than by those whom they held in charge.* (Great Expectations by Charles Dickens)

turnpike NOUN the upkeep of many roads of the time was paid for by tolls (fees) collected at posts along the road. There was a gate to prevent people travelling further along the road until the toll had been paid. ❑ *Traddles, whom I have taken up by appointment at the turnpike, presents a dazzling combination of cream colour and light blue; and both he and Mr. Dick have a general effect about them of being all gloves.* (David Copperfield by Charles Dickens)

twas PHRASE it was ❑ *twas but a dream of thee* (The Good-Morrow by John Donne)

tyrannized VERB tyrannized means bullied or forced to do things against their will ❑ *for people would soon cease coming there to be tyrannized over and put down* (Treasure Island by Robert Louis Stevenson)

'un NOUN 'un is a slang term for one– usually used to refer to a person ❑ *She's been thinking the old 'un* (David Copperfield by Charles Dickens)

undistinguished ADJ undiscriminating or incapable of making a distinction between good and bad things ❑ *their undistinguished appetite to devour everything* (Gulliver's Travels by Jonathan Swift)

use NOUN habit ❑ *Though use make you apt to kill me* (The Flea by John Donne)

vacant ADJ vacant usually means empty, but here Wordsworth uses it to mean carefree ❑ *To vacant musing, unreproved neglect* (The Prelude by William Wordsworth)

valetudinarian NOUN one too concerned with his or her own health. ❑ *for having been a valetudinarian all his life* (Emma by Jane Austen)

vamp VERB vamp means to walk or tramp to somewhere ❑ *Well, vamp on to Marlott, will 'ee* (Tess of the D'Urbervilles by Thomas Hardy)

vapours NOUN the vapours is an old term which means unpleasant and strange thoughts, which make the person feel nervous and unhappy ❑ *and my head was full of vapours* (Robinson Crusoe by Daniel Defoe)

vegetables NOUN here vegetables means plants ❑ *the other vegetables are in the same proportion* (Gulliver's Travels by Jonathan Swift)

venturesome ADJ if you are venturesome you are willing to take risks ❑ *he must be either hopelessly stupid or a venturesome fool* (Wuthering Heights by Emily Brontë)

verily ADV verily means really or truly ❑ *though I believe verily* (Robinson Crusoe by Daniel Defoe)

vicinage NOUN vicinage is an area or the residents of an area ❑ *and to his thought the whole vicinage was haunted by her.* (Silas Marner by George Eliot)

victuals NOUN victuals means food ❑ *grumble a little over the victuals* (The Adventures of Huckleberry Finn by Mark Twain)

vintage NOUN vintage in this context means wine ❑ *Oh, for a draught of vintage!* (Ode on a Nightingale by John Keats)

virtual ADJ here virtual means powerful or strong ❑ *had virtual faith* (The Prelude by William Wordsworth)

vittles NOUN vittles is a slang word which means food ❑ *There never was such a woman for givin' away vittles and drink* (Little Women by Louisa May Alcott)

voided straight PHRASE voided straight is an old expression which means emptied immediately ❑ *see the rooms be voided straight* (Doctor Faustus 4.1 by Christopher Marlowe)

wainscot NOUN wainscot is wood panel lining in a room so wainscoted means a room lined with wooden panels ❏ *in the dark wainscoted parlor* (*Silas Marner* by George Eliot)

walking the plank PHRASE walking the plank was a punishment in which a prisoner would be made to walk along a plank on the side of the ship and fall into the sea, where they would be abandoned ❏ *about hanging, and walking the plank* (*Treasure Island* by Robert Louis Stevenson)

want VERB want means to be lacking or short of ❏ *The next thing wanted was to get the picture framed* (*Emma* by Jane Austen)

wanting ADJ wanting means lacking or missing ❏ *wanting two fingers of the left hand* (*Treasure Island* by Robert Louis Stevenson)

wanting, I was not PHRASE I was not wanting means I did not fail ❏ *I was not wanting to lay a foundation of religious knowledge in his mind* (*Robinson Crusoe* by Daniel Defoe)

ward NOUN a ward is, usually, a child who has been put under the protection of the court or a guardian for his or her protection ❏ *I call the Wards in Jarndcye. They are caged up with all the others.* (*Bleak House* by Charles Dickens)

waylay VERB to waylay someone is to lie in wait for them or to intercept them ❏ *I must go up the road and waylay him* (*The Adventures of Huckleberry Finn* by Mark Twain)

weazen NOUN weazen is a slang word for throat. It actually means shrivelled ❏ *You with a uncle too! Why, I knowed you at Gargery's when you was so small a wolf that I could have took your weazen betwixt this finger and thumb and chucked you away dead* (*Great Expectations* by Charles Dickens)

wery ■ ADV very ❏ *Be wery careful o' vidders all your life* (*Pickwick Papers* by Charles Dickens) ■ *See* wibrated

wherry NOUN wherry is a small swift rowing boat for one person ❏ *It was flood tide when Daniel Quilp sat himself down in the wherry to cross to the opposite shore.* (*The Old Curiosity Shop* by Charles Dickens)

whether PREP whether means which of the two in this example ❏ *we came in full view of a great island or continent (for we knew not whether)* (*Gulliver's Travels* by Jonathan Swift)

whetstone NOUN a whetstone is a stone used to sharpen knives and other tools ❏ *I dropped pap's whetstone there too* (*The Adventures of Huckleberry Finn* by Mark Twain)

wibrated VERB in Dickens's use of the English language "w" often replaces "v" when he is reporting speech. So here "wibrated" means "vibrated". In *Pickwick Papers* a judge asks Sam Weller (who constantly confuses the two letters) "Do you spell it with a 'v' or a 'w'?" to which Weller replies "That depends upon the taste and fancy of the speller, my Lord" ❏ *There are strings . . . in the human heart that had better not be wibrated* (*Barnaby Rudge* by Charles Dickens)

wicket NOUN a wicket is a little door in a larger entrance ❏ *Having rested here, for a minute or so, to collect a good burst of sobs and an imposing show of tears and terror, he knocked loudly at the wicket* (*Oliver Twist* by Charles Dickens)

without CONJ without means unless ❏ *You don't know about me, without you have read a book by the name of The Adventures of Tom Sawyer* (*The Adventures of Huckleberry Finn* by Mark Twain)

wittles ■ NOUN wittles is a slang word which means food ❏ *I live on broken wittles—and I sleep on the* coals (*David Copperfield* by Charles Dickens) ■ *See* wibrated

woo VERB courts or forms a proper relationship with ❏ *before it woo* (*The Flea* by John Donne)

words, to have PHRASE if you have words with someone you have a disagreement or an argument ❏ *I do not want to have words with a young thing like you.* (*Black Beauty* by Anna Sewell)

workhouse NOUN workhouses were places where the homeless were given food and a place to live in return for doing very hard work ❏ *And the Union workhouses? demanded Scrooge. Are they still in operation?* (*A Christmas Carol* by Charles Dickens)

yawl NOUN a yawl is a small boat kept on a bigger boat for short trips. Yawl is also the name for a small fishing boat ❏ *She sent out her yawl, and we went aboard* (*The Adventures of Huckleberry Finn* by Mark Twain)

yeomanry NOUN the yeomanry was a collective term for the middle classes involved in agriculture ❏ *The yeomanry are precisely the order of people with whom I feel I can have nothing to do* (*Emma* by Jane Austen)

yonder ADV yonder means over there ❏ *all in the same second we seem to hear low voices in yonder!* (*The Adventures of Huckleberry Finn* by Mark Twain)